A morsel of genuine history
is a thing so rare as to be
always valuable.

Thomas Jefferson

Commodore Thomas Macdonough
from the painting by Thomas Sully (1815)
now hanging in the Governor's Suite
Legislative Hall, Dover, Delaware
Courtesy Delaware State Archives

The
Proudest Day

MACDONOUGH ON LAKE CHAMPLAIN

Charles G. Muller

The John Day Company
New York

For Marian

PROLOGUE

The War of 1812 renewed America's national feeling, which had lessened since the Revolution, and it won for the new country an equal position among the world's free nations.

While land campaigns bogged down under weight of staff ineptitude, naval genius achieved dramatic sea victories. James Madison foresaw that these would decide our fate. He told Captains Charles Stewart and William Bainbridge: "It is victories we want; if you give us them and lose your ships afterwards, they can be replaced by others."

Backed to the limit by an aggressive Secretary of the Navy, William Jones, young men eventually won the day on the ocean and on the lakes. Trained by such greats as Bainbridge, Stewart, Decatur, Hull, and Preble in a war with France and a campaign against the pirates of Tripoli, they had nourished their talents in merchant service when Congress cut the Navy to little more than a fleet of gunboats.

One of these young men, Lieutenant Thomas Macdonough, hammered out the decisive British defeat. More than any other single American action on land or sea, his Battle of Lake Champlain, echoing in Ghent, fully and finally severed Great Britain's ruthless sway.

Epitomizing the patriotic inner power that made it possible for our young country to reach its present world leadership, Thomas Macdonough coped with political disunity, hostile climate, human frailties, and endless disappointment to build and fight a fleet with ships as large as ocean-going *Bonhomme Richard* and *Constellation* and helped us become truly a United States in our "Second War of Independence." His light has burned long enough under a bushel—nearly 150 years.

WHAT HISTORIANS SAY

More nearly than any other incident of the War of 1812, the Battle of Lake Champlain merits the epithet "decisive."

> Admiral Alfred Thayer Mahan
> *Sea Power in Its Relations to the War of 1812*

[The British] were turned out of the United States, evicted one might say, by a few small ships manned by several hundred American sailors.

> Ralph D. Paine
> *The Fight for a Free Sea*

This is a proud day for America—the proudest day she ever saw.

> Lieut. Col. John Murray,
> British Army, Sept. 11, 1814.

[Commodore Thomas Macdonough's victory] is not surpassed by any naval victory on record ... it is, perhaps, one of the most important events in the history of our country.

> William Jones
> Secretary of the Navy, 1814

... the most decisive engagement of the war.

> Winston S. Churchill
> *A History of the English-Speaking People*

Macdonough alone among all American commanders is distinguished in having commanded the only smaller fleet that ever defeated a larger one.

> Charles H. Darling
> Assistant Secretary of the Navy,
> 1904

Captain Perry's name is more widely known than that of any other commander. Every schoolboy reads about him, if of no other sea captain; yet he certainly stands on a lower grade than Macdonough. . . . It will always be a source of surprise that the American public should have so glorified Perry's victory over an inferior force, and have paid comparatively little attention to Macdonough's victory which really won against decided odds in ships, men and metal. . . . Down to the time of the Civil War, he was the greatest figure in our naval history.

> Theodore Roosevelt
> *The Naval War of 1812*

CONTENTS

PART ONE

THE LAKE

After remaining a few months at Portland I was ordered by Mr. Madison to take the command of the vessels on Lake Champlain. Proceeded thither across the country through the notch of the White Mountains, partly on horseback, carrying my bundle with a valise on behind and a country lad only in company to return with my horses. I arrived fatigued at Burlington on the lake in about four days and took command of the vessels after waiting on the commanding general, Bloomfield.

Autobiography

1

Wednesday, October 7th of the year 1812, closed raining in western Vermont. Twenty-four miles from Lake Champlain, the downpour pelted the stable roof of Argalus Cobb's tavern in the post town of Waterbury as Lieutenant Thomas Macdonough of the United States Navy dismounted from his roan mare.

His bottom ached, and he groaned. He had had four days of riding, part on a hard leather seat in a shay, much in a harder saddle on his horse, across the autumn-red countryside of the White and Green Mountains of New Hampshire and Vermont from Portland, Maine; they had rested his mind but racked his body.

Unstrapping his oilskin-wrapped bundle from behind the wet saddle, he gave the apprehensive boy getting down off the gray horse a reassuring smile.

"I sound worse than I feel, Aze, but not much. After today's fifty-odd miles, we both need a hot bath, which I hope we can get here."

"I'll go ask, Captain." Grasping a valise still tied up in the cover that had kept it dry behind his own saddle, and putting the bundle under his arm, the boy shoved out into the rain for the inn's beckoning kitchen lights.

In the dim glow of a single sperm-oil lantern hung from an iron nail near the stable door, Lieutenant Macdonough turned. He faced the thick-necked stableman's malevolent stare, under black brows that joined heavily over a bulbous nose. For several seconds the stableman's gaze held steady.

What was this all about? Vermonters had a reputation for taciturnity, often mistaken for suspicion. This countryman had been taciturn, certainly. Hadn't said a word when the two rain-driven travelers clomped soggily into the barn. He had stood sullenly by the door. But why this animosity for two strangers he had never seen before? At Tripoli the pirates, cutlasses in hand, had stared from their decks with fierce, piercing eyes like this black and angry farmer's.

Maintaining a long-schooled self-control, the Lieutenant kept his emotions from his face. He nodded to the horses. "Take care of them well," he said. "They've had a hard day." His back to the man, he opened the door and strode through the courtyard's mud to the tavern.

In the well-lit, warm and aromatic kitchen a deep voice greeted him. "Come in and welcome, Captain!"

Argalus Cobb's long arms and strong hands held the Lieutenant's duffle. "I'll get you settled upstairs while the missus"—the innkeeper nodded his graying head toward a plump woman of forty whose white apron and cap looked freshly ironed—"fills the pains with hot water." He twisted his head on his stringy neck with a motion to Aze. "Follow me, son."

Aze shouldered a round, wooden tub and went up the stairs after the landlord.

Though he had scraped his black half-boots outside the door, the Lieutenant found he had tracked mud into the kitchen. "I'm sorry to dirty your floor, ma'am," he said, almost shyly.

The woman's laugh rang deep-toned, like her husband's speaking voice. She took his oilskins, and with practiced fingers strung them out to dry on a row of wooden pegs along the side wall.

On a three-legged maple stool, the Lieutenant pulled off his boots, wriggled his toes, and stretched his long legs. He wore tight, blue nankeen trousers that served well for riding, and a square-cut blue coat with a single row of plain brass buttons. Now he opened the coat and loosened the black stock around his neck.

"Good, Captain! Draw up and warm yourself a mite." The inn's mistress continued to bale water from a huge pot hung over blazing logs in the great fireplace that almost filled the kitchen's south end. "I'm Mercy Cobb, Mercy Dening that was." She looked up, caught sight of three young faces in a bedroom whose white door the children had surreptitiously pushed open. "Those are our youngest. Counting down, they're Enoch, Sally, and Dexter." The door quickly closed, to excited tittering.

The Lieutenant held his hands out to the fire. Between the friendly flames and this friendly housewife, he began to feel human again.

"I'm planning to marry a Denning. Her people came from New York."

"Spell her name with one *n* or two?"

"It's her grandfather's name. Hers is Shaler. Two *n*'s."

"Not our branch. We use but one *n*. And *my* grandfather started out in New Hampshire. We've been here in Vermont about fifteen years. We—"

"Where's that water, woman!" The landlord's bass tones rolled down the stairs. "Stop chewing off the young man's ear. It isn't often we get a guest that wants a bath, so let's show him how to provide a good one."

Mercy Cobb's face lighted. "Yes, dear," she called, "we're coming." She picked up two pails of water. "He always gets special pleasure when somebody stops with us that's from a distance."

Lifting the remaining pails, the Lieutenant smilingly answered her unasked question; so hearty herself, she seemed to warrant an equal neighborliness.

"I'm from Delaware, ma'am, via India and Portland in Maine. I'm going to Lake Champlain." After a moment's hesitation, he added: "To take charge of some boats."

Mercy Cobb saw the pails in his hands. "Put those down," she said. "Argalus'll fetch them."

"Lead the way, ma'am. I can carry these. I'm only tired where I sit down."

Two flights up, under the eaves, the Lieutenant found a bright and cozy bedroom with pineapple four-poster bed and gaily painted tin basin and pitcher on a polished cherry-wood commode. The landlord folded the oilskin covering of the Lieutenant's valise, to drop it in a corner. The boy already had laid out dry clothes from the opened bundle.

"This is Azariah Bellamy, from Portland, Mrs. Cobb. And Mr. Cobb. He came along to ride the horses back. I didn't figure he'd take care of me as well."

The boy beamed at the compliment. "I like to do it, Captain."

"And I appreciate it, Aze. But now get yourself settled and dried out." He looked toward the landlord. "Have you a place for him?"

"A room in the barn—if he doesn't mind running to it in the rain."

"Good. Besides a bath, make sure he gets all he wants to eat. He's still a growing boy."

Aze protested. "I'm nearly sixteen, Captain."

"You've told me that twice every day for the past week. Off you go—and get yourself a long sleep."

"Yes, sir."

Mercy Cobb had filled the wooden tub and tested the water with a chubby finger. She pulled up a maple ladder-back chair, placed a towel and washcloth on the cane seat, and on those laid a long-handled brush and a ball of soap.

"I hope you like my soap," she said as she followed her husband to the door. "It's something I make from the garden flowers during the summer."

The Lieutenant lifted the ball, and let his eyes tell her how much its rich-distilled bouquet pleased him.

"We'll serve his supper in the common room. He'll enjoy

talking with the neighbors," she said to her husband, and closed the door behind them.

In the tub, lathered and scrubbing with the soft brush, the Lieutenant relaxed with a sailor's skill. He had had twelve years of naval service since President John Adams had signed his midshipman's warrant. Well, here he was—warm, comfortable, with kind people, about to be well fed and tended, and on the edge of a new command—Lake Champlain.

His orders dated September 28th from the Secretary of the Navy, Paul Hamilton, had read:

> Six vessels have been purchased by the War Department, and there are two gunboats built by the Navy Department on the Lake, the whole of which is to be under your direction and command.

A welcome change ... active naval duty ... after almost two years' furlough commanding merchant ships. In the three months since the United States had declared war against Great Britain June 18th, he had gone as first lieutenant to frigate *Constellation,* Captain William Bainbridge, July 17th, then taken command of the gunboat division at Portland, August 14th, and now this.

Obtaining the Secretary's permission to leave the frigate for the Portland Station had been a good move; she was still fitting out in Washington, months away from possible action. Commodore Bainbridge had regretted *Constellation*'s loss, but, as he had written the Lieutenant a week later, "if love and the Gods have decreed it otherwise, I must be satisfied, and wherever you go you carry my best wishes for your happiness."

Bless the Commodore's tough old gentle heart for appreciating his need for Ann. Ann had waited for him six years— well, not waited exactly. He had met her when he helped Captain Isaac Hull construct those four gunboats at Middletown, Connecticut, with Bill Van Dusen, the contractor; Bill had introduced him to the Nathaniel Shalers and their six-teen-year-old daughter. But at twenty-one, what man could seriously concern himself with such a shy child?—though she did have the loveliest eyes and happiest smile. That was six years ago, however.

To the Lieutenant at twenty-eight—twenty-nine two days before next Christmas—it was time to take her out of circulation. At Champlain, not too far from Connecticut by passable roads, he would be in a position to act. If all went well with the new command, he could take time during the lake's winter freeze-up to drive (not ride!) to Middletown and marry her.

Now that he could expect to stay ashore for an indeterminate period, he wanted her close. They both wanted to start the family they had planned since his return last year from India as captain of brig *Gulliver* of Boston. His finances would reasonably take care of a wife. He had fifty dollars a month Navy pay, plus four rations a day at twenty cents each. And though the nonintercourse law that laid a ninety-day embargo on American trade with foreign ports had cut short his Lisbon voyage as captain of ship *Jeannette Snow* last April, he would eventually get his quarter share of her profits.

What, incidentally, had gone on in the Navy Department when his letter arrived demanding a furlough to command *Snow* on that voyage and offering to resign if he didn't get it? He knew the Secretary had endorsed the letter "resignation to be accepted." Who had had that rescinded? Bainbridge, Decatur, Hull? He could thank one of those three for not being dropped from the Navy.[1]

". . . the whole of which is to be under your direction and command." To keep the British off the American lake, to keep them up the Sorel River in Canada—no, down the Sorel, since Champlain emptied that way into the St. Lawrence between Montreal and Quebec.

What did the British have for an opposing fleet? Gunboats?

[1] This and other notes appear at the end of the narrative.

Sloops? Brigs? A ship, perhaps? Well, he would know when he reached Burlington tomorrow and went over to Plattsburg to wait on the commanding general of the Army.

Reaching for the towel, the Lieutenant stood up in the tub and rubbed himself dry. Some of the soreness had gone from his seat, and his well-knit, slender body felt good. In long wool underwear, he stood with spread legs, feet in white stockings that covered his knees, and low-cut black shoes, to brush his hair in the glass over the commode.

His hair glinted red in the flickering candle light, and refused to lie entirely ordered despite persistent brushing. A recalcitrant curling over his forehead gave him a gay and youthful look that brought a quick frown. He scowled. Every time it rains that wave would come back! The scowl vanished. "I wish my hair waved like yours," Ann used to tease him. He wished she were here to say it now.

He put on a clean white shirt, slipped momentarily out of his shoes and into a pair of white pantaloons, and tied a fresh white stock around his neck. With its wide lapels and tails, his coat for the evening's meal gave considerable dignity to his youth. The people of Waterbury who came to the inn tonight to drink or play cards or talk politics might mistake Thomas Macdonough for a business man from Boston or New York. No one would be likely to take him for a sailor. He could indulge in a pleasant evening observing and listening.

Among these people he would spend the next years of his life. He wanted to know them.

2

Like its kitchen, the inn's common room on the second floor held out a warm and cozy welcome to Lieutenant Macdonough.

A good-sized rectangle, with shuttered windows nearly touching the ceiling on two sides, it had plastered walls that displayed the landlady's decorative touch. Fishing and hunting prints (doubtless come to Vermont from England via sporting Dening antecedents) combined with engraved portraits of General George Washington and the Marquis de Lafayette to suggest an acquaintance with a world wider than Waterbury, Vermont. But wrought-iron candelabra and sconces of local origin helped retain the room's native New England character.

Along one wall stood a bench with carved spindles, long enough to seat four; beside it, open shelves of a matching walnut dresser held pewter plates, porringers, spoons, and tankards for the needs of the evening visitors. Tables for two —round, square, butterfly—with black-painted Windsor armchairs, ranged along the other walls.

Wet capes, umbrellas, caps and tricorn hats lay piled on the bench, and at two big center tables a dozen men smoked clay pipes. They played cards, quaffed beer, and talked quietly to the irregular clink of coins thrown on the battered top of the octagonal table; at the round table they just talked.

From the bar below, Mercy Cobb reached the landing in time to lead the Lieutenant to his seat at one of the small tables.

10

"You don't look like a man that's been in the saddle all day," she said. But as he eased gingerly into his chair, she told him, "You do now. But we'll fix that with a good meal. Would you like a veal and bacon pie?"

"If it's part of those wonderful kitchen smells, I would indeed like it," he said. "To start with, however, will you have Mr. Cobb mull me a serving of rum, please?"

In a moment the landlady returned with a covered pewter tankard. "Argalus had it waiting. Said he never heard of a sailor didn't want rum on a wet voyage."

Sipping the hot drink, the Lieutenant lost his aches. "My compliments to your good husband," he said, and the woman went below to the kitchen.

He studied the men around him, for the most part absorbed in card-playing and conversation. One or two read a four-page newspaper, the *Centinel*. Printed nearby? Burlington perhaps? They looked to be farmers, mostly, with an occasional individual whose softer hands pointed him out as a shopkeeper, a banker, a lawyer, or a doctor. Amazing how these towns sprang from a settlement in so few years!

Mercy Cobb came up the stairs again, with a laden tray.

"When was Waterbury settled?" he asked. "Forty years ago?"

"Less than thirty." She set the meal out. "James Marsh, his wife and their eight children came over from Bath, in New Hampshire, in the summer of 'eighty-four. As I told you, we've been here fifteen years ourselves. The Marshes paid forty dollars for two hundred acres, and lived in a surveyor's cabin near the Winooski River. They'd had a promise of some other settlers, but for two years their nearest neighbors lived eight miles away in Bolton. How's my pie?"

As with the soap earlier, he answered with a glance and with a gesture of excellence made with his fingers. She beamed gratefully and fussed with the dishes, apparently wanting to stay to watch him enjoy her food. He asked: "Did you take over the inn when you came?" and learned how naïve he was about the wilderness of Vermont.

"Heavens, no, Captain!" she said. "We built this place, starting some three years ago. Up to then we did just what every other family does that comes here. We had maybe a hundred dollars. With some of it we bought a hundred and fifty acres, paying only a part of the price in ready money. Argalus brought along a cow, some pigs, and two sort-of horses. As a bride, I brought flour and cider."

"What kind of house did you come to?"

"None at all! We built our first cabin in two days, of logs. Then I took care of the animals and got some garden foods started while Argalus felled the smaller trees and fenced in the first field he wished to clear. The big oaks and pines he circled or stripped, and the next spring he burned them and cleared the field.

"We had pasturage for the cattle the first year, the grass grew so fast. Our wheat, corn, potatoes, garden and meadow came on real good. Our first harvest gave us eleven hundred fifty bushels of wheat. And with wild artichokes, peas, sweet potatoes, and onions, and all kinds of nuts—hickory, hazel, chestnuts, black walnuts—we got along fine."

The Lieutenant wiped his mouth. "This veal pie tastes as though it had some wild condiments in it."

"It has thyme, marjoram, savory, and parsley, along with salt and pepper. I'll have Argalus write out the way I make it and you can give it to your young lady when she starts house-keeping."

"What happened with your farm?"

"Nothing, except it got bigger. We paid for it in about four years and built a good-sized house, with the help of all the neighbors who'd come to these parts—and the help of my cider, which I always kept plenty of for when the neighbors got together to help us raise the roof and so on. Argalus and I worked hard, but no harder than most. When the children

THE LAKE • 13

started to grow up, we decided to come live nearer the center of things. So we built the inn."

Mercy Cobb helped the Lieutenant to more of the main dish. "Why do you look so surprised?" she asked. "Everybody goes through the same things when they start, don't they?"

He nodded. Of course! He remembered the observations he had read in a book by a Frenchman named de Chastellux about his travels during the early 1780's. Astounded at America's spread over "a vast forest" in the previous hundred years to a nation with three million inhabitants, the traveler praised the bountiful land but reserved his best encomiums for the people.

"In America," de Chastellux wrote, after seeing a hundred settlements taking shape, "a man is never alone, never an isolated being. The neighbours, for they are everywhere to be found, make it a point of hospitality to aid the new farmer. A cask of cider drunk in common, and with gaiety, or a gallon of rum, are the only recompense for these services. . . ."

As a boy he had never ceased to marvel at the fortitude of the country's early settlers. His own grandfather, James McDonough, had crossed the Atlantic from County Kildare to prosper in The Trap, Delaware. And although the old gentleman had died before his grandson reached nine, he had so pictured the first days of his life in the Colonies that they flashed vividly across the Lieutenant's mind at this very moment. From his grandfather's lips he had also learned about his father and his Uncle James in the Revolution—his father a major. So much happened so fast in America!

He looked up at Mercy Cobb. "Waterbury and I started about the same time," he said.

"Well, both of you seem to have done all right," she said. "And I'm glad you've done all right, too, with my buns." Again she beamed, at his hearty relish of her cooking.

Good people lived in Vermont, if the Cobbs represented them, which seemed likely. But thus far not a mention of the war. So close to Canada, they must have strong feelings. Like the people of New York on Lake Champlain, they must always have done much of their trading over the border.

How had President Jefferson's embargo affected their trade in previous years? Or had people up here, so far from Washington, paid no heed to the embargo? Coming over the mountains in New Hampshire he had heard mention of Smuggler's Notch. He had paid no particular attention to it at the time, being too concerned with arranging for an extra horse to replace the shay he had abandoned because of the road's impassability. But now—what did Vermonters do about laws against trading with the enemy? Would chasing smugglers be one of his chief duties? Would he have to wet-nurse the local customs officials, as well as the Army?

When Argalus Cobb brought beer for himself, along with his guest's after-dinner rum, the Lieutenant waved his host to a seat beside him. Momentarily he debated whether to beat around the bush, in deference to New England custom, or ask his host direct questions. Argalus had given every evidence of an open nature, like his wife's. The Lieutenant decided to go toward his objectives with reasonable dispatch.

"Your good wife told me about your farm. She said you did pretty well from the start with wheat for a cash crop."

The innkeeper nodded. "Along with potash. Canada took all the wood ash we could get from burning the trees when we cleared our land. Canadian cash kept us solvent, and of course we bought some of the potash back in the form of medicines and baking soda."

"I suppose potash still commands a good price?"

"Seventy and eighty dollars a ton at times, I hear."

As if he had answered too fast, the landlord glanced quickly toward the nearby tables and back to his guest.

"Look, Captain, you said you're going to Burlington to take care of some boats. You wouldn't mean St. Albans now, would you?" He eyed the Lieutenant squarely.

"St. Albans? Where's that?"

The landlord looked much relieved. "You'll find out sooner or later, so I may as well give you the straight of it. Laws or no laws, people need cash. They still get it by shipping potash across the border, in sloops out of Lake towns. That's why I wondered about you and the boats. I don't rightly hold with trading with the enemy, but there's many around here that do. One sloop, the *Black Snake* out of St. Albans, carries a fortune every time she slips down the Sorel River, which is frequent."

"Sounds like the Maine and Massachusetts coasts," the Lieutenant said. "Small boats running to Canada and back, through fog and at night, as though they'd never heard of the war—or cared."

Nearby voices began to rise in tone and in volume. Leaning across the table, Argalus motioned with his shining eyes. He said: "These are some of our chief citizens getting warmed up. About this time they start on politics. Like to join them?"

"If they won't mind."

With no apparent concern for the others, the landlord kept the Lieutenant engaged in unobtrusive small talk until he had edged his chair close to the large round table. A few moments later he had inserted himself—and, by an easy presumption, the Lieutenant—into the general conversation.

In due course he told the group, "Captain Macdonough's from Maine. Going to the Lake."

The Lieutenant nodded inclusively to acknowledge the introduction. "Gentlemen," he said. The discussion, momentarily held back, immediately washed over the table like an enveloping wave.

"Now, Doctor," one voice cut clearly over the others, "just what is the political standing of an inhabitant of Waterbury, in the state of Vermont?"

Round-faced, with a small black mustache and mild brown eyes behind gold-rimmed glasses, the doctor held up a small hand for quiet. When he had the floor, he faced his questioner.

"Mr. Rich," he said, "I wish you'd leave your law court manner at home instead of lugging it up here every night. Since you insist on being formal, however, here goes."

From his pocket he took a well-worn paper which, unfolded, looked to the Lieutenant like much amended rough notes for a speech. "An inhabitant of Waterbury is a *citizen* of the United States," he read, "and a *subject* of the state of Vermont."

"And to what power," demanded the lawyer, "does he owe his allegiance?"

The doctor referred to his paper. "To the power that governs and protects him in his just rights. When he is absent from the United States, he then looks to the United States for protection. When in Waterbury or in any other part of the state, he expects protection from the state of Vermont."

"And why," the lawyer asked, "does he owe allegiance to the United States?"

"Because," the doctor read, "owing allegiance to his own state, he is bound by any compacts made by his own state; and as this state, with others, has yielded for a certain time certain portions of its sovereignty to the United States, so every inhabitant of the State, when paying due obeisance to the laws of the United States, is strictly and truly obeying the sovereign authority of the State of Vermont."

The lawyer waved a dramatic hand. "I rest my case."

With exaggerated deliberation, the doctor took off his glasses and laid them on the table on top of the paper. "I'm not saying, Brother Rich, that I don't hold with what your uncle's trying to get the legislature at Montpelier to agree to, but I don't say that I do hold with it either. These notes you wrote for him make out a good case for you Republicans. Pay due obeisance to the United States laws." His voice rose. "Sure! But if we all starve obeying them, they're no good to us."

"Look who's starving!" A huge, balding, quiet-voiced man beside the lawyer peered over his tankard. "What would you know, Doc, about going hungry—with a practice that cuts across two counties?"

"That's how I *do* know, Jesse. I don't sit on my fat butt all day in a prosperous tin factory figuring out the profits like all you Federalists. I get out amongst people that work for a living." The doctor lighted a long clay pipe from a candle flame, puffed for a moment as he outstared the mill owner, and went on. "Half the farm families I treat send cattle and potash over the border. You know it's what keeps them going. The other half haven't either cows or trees to trade with."

"Seems to me," Jesse said, "you don't like anybody—Federalists or Republicans. Or maybe you don't know which is which."

The doctor took the stem of his churchwarden out of his mouth. "Who does? No matter which is in office, they act the same—all for the Federal constitution and free trade."

"That's what it looks like over in Montpelier these days," the lawyer agreed, and took the floor by virtue of bringing authentic news. "You can't tell one from the other even with a crystal ball. Used to be that any red-faced storekeeper with a big British belly was a Federalist and every skinny farmer in ragged pants or Revolution jacket voted Republican. Now Governor Galusha's got the legislature so confused that Federalists and Republicans are saying good morning to each other and tipping their hats. They wouldn't even eat at the same table last year."

"If it weren't for the war," the doctor said, "they'd still be at it hammer and tongs."

"What war?" demanded a fractious voice.

The Lieutenant caught a glimpse of the stableman's face at the turn of the stairs above the bar. As he looked, the face disappeared.

Argalus Cobb leaned over his shoulder. He said: "That's Jacob Dibble. Always agin' the government, no matter who's running it. He tends my stable—you must have seen him. Has a farm just outside of town that his missus and half a dozen sons keep from going to rack and ruin. Hands are hard to find, so I keep him on."

The doctor continued, as if long accustomed to heckling. "Because everybody realizes we have to win this war just like the last one, most of us are willing to wear shackles we wouldn't let anybody put on us in peacetime." As the lawyer started to interrupt, the doctor quickly added, "I know the two parties sound bitter on the legislature floor, as always. But you'll see—they'll second the national government's actions the way Governor Galusha wants."

"For how long?" the lawyer demanded. "If the farmers you're telling about are so hard put to get cash anywhere but from across the border, what's going to happen when the legislature passes a bill to fine 'em a thousand dollars, with seven years' hard labor, for intercourse with Canada?"

The doctor looked shocked. "You believe they'll pass a bill like that?"

"Sure as shooting," the lawyer said. "It's drawn up. I saw it. It'll go through before the end of the month." He paused. "Which means, as I see it, we'll have to send a whole new batch of men to Montpelier next year to rescind the measure. What else can we do?"

"What do you mean by that question?" the doctor asked.

"Well, this legislature's also going to pass some taxes to pay the militia with."

"Yes?"

"Which puts us all in a box! Because we'll have to let our farmers go over the border for Canadian money to pay taxes for American soldiers to keep the British from invading Vermont and New York. If the farmers get caught, it'll cost them a thousand dollars and prison." He paused, to impress his audience. "If they don't go to Canada for the money to pay the militia, then us poor defenseless Yankees'll all get shot when the British army comes marching down!" he guffawed. "Doc, you've sure got us running around in a vicious circle!"

The Lieutenant laughed with the others at the lawyer's specious argument. He saw, however, that it had made an impression on the men, having given verbal shape to an awkward dilemma.

The doctor moved his head up and down very slowly, as if reluctantly agreeing. "That's about how it is, Brother Rich. They're damned if they do, and they're damned if they don't," he said. "And I'm damned with them if I know where the right of it lies."

Having had his fun, the lawyer slapped the big table top. "Well, I know what we should do here and now—have a final round. I've got to get home. Argalus, serve my bemused friends."

3

Lieutenant Macdonough waked slowly next morning, with the sun streaming through the open window at the foot of his bed and with some small hope that the night's rest on the soft down mattress had eased his muscles. He tentatively stretched his legs under the bright wool blankets. But his bottom ached almost as much as the evening before. What good had his early country training done if a few years at sea could so soften him? Horses!

A knock on the door and the edge of a large, painted tin tray preceded the entrance of Mistress Cobb with hot water for shaving.

"It's a lovely day, Captain," she said. "Indian summer, like. You'll have a fine ride into Burlington."

"I plan to walk!" He laughed in spite of his soreness. "What makes you think I have the strength of character to sit that mare for twenty-five miles more?"

"Because it's only twenty-four miles," she said. She reached outside the door. "And because your boy's cleaned your boots so they shine." She closed the window, felt the traveling clothes he had hung in the walnut clothespress the night before, found them dry, and turned to leave. "And because I've got bacon and eggs, and buns, and butter, and potatoes, and some of last night's pie, and tea for breakfast. What would you like?" Her plump hand on the doorknob and a quizzical expression on her scrubbed face, she said, "I know. You want them all! Just as Aze did. All right! Breakfast in the kitchen, if you don't mind. No hurry. It'll be waiting whenever you get down." She smiled and went out.

He got up slowly, stretched his arms, bent gingerly to touch his toes, and winced. Long accustomed to sleeping at sea without night clothes, he slipped into his long johns against the room's early morning chill. Too bad to leave this pleasant inn with its friendly proprietors. Tonight he would be where? In Burlington, no doubt, unless he could get transportation across Lake Champlain to Army headquarters at Plattsburg before nightfall.

He cleaned his teeth with an English-made brush and a combination of fine salt, alum, gum myrrh, and casteel soap —a prescription he had found in a Boston magazine article by a Dr. Jennings. Shaving, he decided to stay this side of the Lake no matter when he reached Burlington. He needed another good night's sleep before presenting himself to the commanding general. The best part of a week on a horse's bony back had lamed him more than he wanted to admit. He could use another hot bath and another quiet evening. He should write Ann, too. And he needed to prepare himself properly for the meeting with the Army.

If past experience could guide, the commanding general wouldn't like Paul Hamilton's orders for him (Lieutenant Thomas Macdonough, United States Navy, sir!) to assume command of the vessels the Army had bought. He'd need his full strength—physical as well as mental—to bring off the first meeting with due military respect (What, sir, makes the Navy think they can take over *our* boats?) for the naval function on Lake Champlain.

Before descending to the kitchen, the Lieutenant tied his bundle and packed his valise; the oilskins drying downstairs could be strapped on the horses unpacked. At the bedroom's small pigeonhole desk, he found paper, ink in a pewter stand, pen points and a holder, and for several minutes he wrote rapidly. Sanding the brief note, he slipped it into an envelope, addressed the envelope, put it into his riding-coat pocket, put the coat on, and went down to breakfast.

Aze awaited him, face aglow. But the Lieutenant caught a disturbed expression on the boy's face before it lighted. Intuitively he felt there had been trouble for Aze not long since. He decided to bide his time about finding out.

As he sat down to breakfast, Mercy Cobb took a black water kettle off the long iron arm that extended over blazing logs in the fireplace and made fresh tea. She seemed to want to stretch his stay to its utmost limit.

He knew he should be pleased, and he told her so when Aze brought down his gear and they prepared to go out to the barn. Paying for the night, he said: "You and your husband have been most hospitable, ma'am. I don't know when I've felt so well looked after."

Mercy Cobb put a hand over his. "I think you're a Navy officer, Captain," she said. "If I'm right, God bless you on the Lake and take good care of you!" She brushed her eyes. Later, from the doorway, she called across the sun-shafted stable yard. "Bring your young lady to see us, when you can."

He followed Aze to the barn. The boy shook as if cold. From inside tumbled shouts and the stomping of frightened horses. At the door, he saw Argalus Cobb, back on the manure-covered floor, trying to ward off the red swollen fists of Jacob Dibble.

On top of the prostrate landlord, Dibble—his face a horrible contorted mask in the barn's shadow, the veins of his bulbous nose red and blue—viciously kneed Argalus. "Don't you tell me what I can't do to any kid whether he's mine or not!" he screamed. His fist crashed into the landlord's face with a sickening smash and rose for another blow.

Reaching from behind and above, with a hammerlock the Lieutenant hoisted the stableman to his feet, shoved him against a stall partition, and swung him around. As Dibble's astonished eyes saw his opponent, the Lieutenant's fist smashed into the bridge of his nose, and when the stableman frantically raised his hands to ward off the fury of the attack, the Lieutenant smashed him twice more—a left to the bleeding nose again and a right to the jaw. Dibble sank to the stall's urine-soaked straw, and the Lieutenant helped Aze lift Argalus Cobb.

"He's just no good," the landlord said through bloody lips. "He was abusive to Aze when the boy tried to saddle the horses before you arrived down to breakfast. When I came out to finish the saddling, he started berating me for harboring spies. He got so profane I told him to get off the place and stay off. He came at me then."

The three dragged Dibble to the side of the highway, at the edge of the inn grounds. The Lieutenant and Aze mounted their horses, and the Lieutenant reached down to shake farewell with the landlord.

He said: "You can tell Dibble I'm not a spy; but if ever I catch him on the Lake trying to run the line to Canada, he'll find out soon enough who I am. You can also tell him, if he thinks any of suing me for assault and battery, that there's a bigger and better man—a blacksmith [1] in the Brooklyn Navy Yard on Long Island—who's still trying to collect for the damage I did to *his* face when he maliciously walloped one of my midshipmen."

The Lieutenant's eyes lighted. "Say, Argalus, my behind doesn't hurt any more! That exercise took the kinks out. Good-by."

The road to Burlington followed north of the shimmering Winooski River, snaking through a mountain-channeled valley. Against the bright sun, the Lieutenant caught a distant glimpse of Mansfield Mount. Red and golden leaves on hillside trees held the myriad-color shadings of a summer sunrise on the Atlantic Ocean, a sight he'd never expected to find equaled ashore. These New England autumns, like many New England women, had great and unexpected variety.

The first few miles passed in silence. Obviously Aze wanted to talk, but the Lieutenant wanted their emotions to simmer down awhile. Politely they saluted an occasional carriage driven by bundled-up men who nodded their heads briefly above wool scarves wound round their necks against the wind. When the Burlington-Montpelier stage rattled by, they saw its passengers clinging to the window posts as they jounced over the rutted road. The coach's heavy leather springs cushioned only the worst jolts. Aze turned to watch its four galloping horses. He shook his head, fascinated. "Captain, there's real speed!"

The Lieutenant nodded. "If you wanted to go faster, I guess you'd have to be shot out of a cannon." He added: "It couldn't be much more uncomfortable!"

Realizing that the boy had overcome his earlier shakes, he let him see that if he wanted to talk he could.

Aze came to the point explosively. "I'd like to be a midshipman, Captain—with you," he burst out.

The Lieutenant's face hid the depth of his feeling. Had he flushed so excitedly when he entered his first ship, *Ganges*? When he joined *Enterprise* had he looked so . . . so appealingly boyish to Stephen Decatur? Could Decatur possibly have looked at him as he now studied Aze, enjoying the youthful enthusiasm, wanting to do anything in his power to keep it fresh, as if the boy were his own flesh and blood? Aze was waiting. He must tell him something.

When he spoke, he sounded to his own ears like an old man trying to hide worldly wisdom behind a bantering front. He said: "You're not old enough to be a sailor, son. You—"

"I've fished salt water with my father since I was twelve, sir. I've been off the Banks with him."

The Lieutenant acknowledged the experience. "But manning a war vessel's different, Aze. It's rough work. You have to—" He stopped short. Words come hard when you try to tell a boy that you love your country. He decided he did not dare try . . . he would sound pompous, or trite. He wished he could remember a few of the phrases his father had used to describe the reasons men in his command had given for fighting—and dying—in the Revolution.

With an understanding completely unpredictable to the Lieutenant, Aze said, "I'm as old as you were when you got your midshipman's warrant, sir. I guess I must feel about the same way you did then, Captain."

The Lieutenant let his features relax. Relieved, he said: "You look a lot younger than I did." Realizing that this served only to fool himself, not the boy, he grinned almost sheepishly. "All right, Aze."

From his pocket he took the letter he had written in his room before breakfast and handed it to the boy. "When you ask one of your state senators to sponsor you, give him this letter to send along with his."

Aze let his eyes fall on the superscription: "The Honorable Paul Hamilton, Secretary of the Navy, Washington." He looked up quickly.

"Go ahead; read it," the Lieutenant said.

Aze opened the envelope. The short note recommended him to the President and the Secretary for a midshipman's warrant and asked for his assignment to the Champlain station.

The boy glanced up from the letter, but looked quickly down again, trying to hide tears of joy, brushing at his eyes with his sleeve, fumbling to replace the letter in the envelope. "Thank you very much, Captain," he said.

"When you get back to Portland," the Lieutenant said, to ease the boy's embarrassment, "tell our mutual friend Ludlow Dashwood that if he gives my right age away again, I won't pay his accounts—especially for this mare."

Aze laughed self-consciously. "I will, sir."

"And don't ride so fast going home that you run over the Montpelier stage."

"I won't, sir. But if it's all right with you," he said, unable to cloak his eagerness, "I *would* like to start back as soon as we reach Burlington this afternoon."

Burlington, when they arrived after a wayside lunch, paid them little attention. Near the University of Vermont's four-story stone building on the hill above Burlington Bay, the Lieutenant caught his first sight of Lake Champlain. In the town, he came on soldiers in blue winter uniforms with brilliant yellow artillery trimmings and white infantry detail. At the tavern, near the courthouse, he turned the horses over to Aze, gave him money for the return journey to Portland, and bade the boy Godspeed.

That afternoon he soaked in hot suds, had his best uniform pressed, and wrote to Lucy Ann Shaler in Middletown. After which he practiced standing up against the outraged Army blast he'd inevitably encounter when he called tomorrow on Brigadier General Joseph Bloomfield—former governor of New Jersey, now commanding at Plattsburg—and showed him the Secretary's billet-doux of September 28th.

That evening, after a long and refreshing walk along the waterfront, he arranged with an Army captain to sail the twenty-two miles northwest across the Lake to Plattsburg next morning in a nondescript sloop with uncommonly clean sails. He also ferreted out the Navy's whereabouts; under Lieutenant Sidney Smith, it lay in Shelburne Bay, three miles south of Burlington.

The Lieutenant retired early. The bed seemed shorter and harder than Argalus Cobb's. Curling his legs a little, he closed his eyes and slept—fatigued, but ready to take up his new command.

4

Lieutenant Macdonough had anticipated an on-shore storm when he waited on General Bloomfield, but not in such a calm and quiet haven—a lovely old clapboard house near the center of Plattsburg. Located north of the Saranac River where it empties into the northwest corner of a bight of the Lake—Plattsburg Bay—Army headquarters proved lavish by the Lieutenant's standards of the last week.

Up two broad stone slabs that served for steps from a rose-garden path, he entered the house through a wistaria-vine-covered doorway. While a frozen-faced aide-de-camp left him in a small parlor and went with Paul Hamilton's letter to announce the Lieutenant's arrival, his eyes roved over the room's India cotton curtains, crystal chandelier, and highly polished mahogany furniture. For several moments they rested on the easy chair. Its red-printed cotton, made in England for sale in America, showed Washington driving a triumphal chariot and Franklin walking with the Goddess of Liberty.

Anteroom to the General's offices, this small parlor had quiet charm. Over the pine-paneled fireplace hung a "Kentucky rifle" and powder horn—Revolution relics—and over that a framed Sarat-Menier print of West Point with the *Clermont* steaming up the Hudson.

The General's "office" parlor, when the aide ushered the Lieutenant into it, seemed twice as large and, in the few seconds he looked in silence at General Bloomfield and the General surveyed him, twice as quiet as the anteroom.

General Bloomfield sat at a large oval table under a round

Colonial mirror whose eagle's gold wings seemed poised to lift the huge looking glass into the air. To a man under thirty, the General in his sixties looked old, as all Army officers seemed ancient to the comparative youngsters who commanded in the Navy. But the Lieutenant knew he faced a brave soldier and a capable executive. Bloomfield's reputation in the Revolution and as governor of New Jersey for more than ten years proved these characteristics beyond question.

Acknowledging the aide's presentation, the General rose and took his visitor's hand in a solid grip.

The Lieutenant saw before him a well-fed man of average height whose round face featured a firm jaw and lips overshadowed by imperious eyes. His broad forehead sloped steeply back in a continuance of the line of his long, curved nose. He wore a wig, and a white stock with black band at his neck. The shoulders of his high-collared, white-lapeled coat, in the old tradition, carried one-star epaulets. This could be a difficult man to do business with, if you didn't choose to do it his way.

"Welcome to Lake Champlain, Lieutenant," the General said in a pleasant voice. When he had reseated himself stolidly under the eagle mirror, militarily erect as if to set an example to the tall visitor who sat easily, not stiffly, in a straight-backed chair opposite, he added: "General Dearborn, who as you know is in command of the ninth district which includes the Lake, had a letter under date of September twelfth from the Secretary of War saying a naval officer by the name of Macdonough had been ordered here."

The Lieutenant nodded. "The Secretary of the Navy's orders to me, which I see in front of you, sir, bear that out."

"You may also know then, Lieutenant, that Henry Dearborn as senior General has had all government vessels on the Lake under his command."

Storm warnings up! He'd better get sail in and put an extra hand at the wheel.

"Where does General Dearborn command from?" he asked.

"From Albany, of course!" But the moment he said it, General Bloomfield looked as though it had only then dawned on him that Albany, on the Hudson River, was a poor place from which to run a Lake Champlain flotilla. "Through me, of course, here," he hurried to add.

The Lieutenant nodded blandly. "I see," he said.

The General tried to read behind his placid expression, paused, went on conversationally. "We're glad you've come to help us." He smiled expansively. "Even though you're such a surprisingly young man."

"Thank you, General."

Bloomfield looked sharply across the desk and the churning seas that lay between them. "Well, that's settled, then," he said. "We'll find quarters for you in town, and later you and Quartermaster General Lewis can sit down and work out details for getting the fleet into the shape General Dearborn wants."

The Lieutenant smiled pleasantly and waited for the General to come to a dead stop. Now to keep firm hold on the wheel. "Thank you very much, sir. That's very kind of you," he said. "I'd prefer, however, your giving the Quartermaster General instructions to turn the boats over to me to inspect with the naval personnel. In due course I'll notify you of their condition and"—he smiled pleasantly again—"you can communicate to General Dearborn what measures I propose to take."

General Bloomfield stiffened. He blinked several times, trying to get himself in hand. When he spoke, his eyes let their fire blaze unchecked. "I assume you have no wish to be insubordinate, Lieutenant Macdonough," he said. "But your manner impresses me as overassured for one in your position."

The Lieutenant pointed to Paul Hamilton's letter, lying in front of General Bloomfield. "I have no wish to impress you, sir, with anything other than the fact that I've been ordered by the Secretary of the Navy to take command of the vessels on this Lake."

General Bloomfield's full lips tightened. "I shall be glad to put the Army's facilities at your disposal. But you must appreciate," he said, with great restraint, "that there can be only one commander on the Lake and that he should be under the War Department."

To ride out the storm, the Lieutenant again let the General come to a full stop before he spoke. Keeping his voice low and gracious, he said: "That's a point of view, of course, with much to be said for it. And I do indeed sympathize with it. But my instructions, from Mr. Madison himself, are the same as from Mr. Hamilton. I don't consider myself in a position to debate the pros and cons of a single command, General. I can only try to carry out what I've been instructed to do." The Lieutenant braced himself.

But General Bloomfield let his lips curl in amusement while he banked the fires in his eyes. His voice came across the desk piercingly cold. "Perhaps you'd like to state your position to General Dearborn in person."

The Lieutenant guffawed, an unrestrained guffaw. He remembered reading that Washington frequently burst into immoderate laughter, astounding oaths, Olympian anger. He didn't compare himself with Washington, but he understood well enough what must have made Washington hilarious and irate by turns—the generals he had to win a war with.

"With no disrespect, sir," he said quickly to the shocked Bloomfield, "I just recalled how amazed the captain of a British man-of-war looked when I hauled an impressed American seaman out of his boat at Gibraltar and took the man aboard our brig *Syren*. The captain threatened to turn his frigate's guns on us, and I suppose he could have sunk our brig." He paused, and looked gravely at Bloomfield. "But we kept the man, sir." [1]

The General gazed back evenly, without comment. He apparently refused to be drawn further at this time into what began to look like a pretty even engagement, despite rank, with this naval newcomer to the Lake.

"I'll write General Dearborn," said Bloomfield, "and tell him"—he put his tongue over his lips while he debated his phrasing—"and tell him you've arrived, ready to put the fleet into fighting shape. We've got plans for a campaign next month that needs the best possible support." He paused a moment. Then: "I don't know what he'll do about your . . . insistence on taking responsibility for the boats."

The Lieutenant could feel the iron under Bloomfield's velvet tones.

"Thank you, General," he said. As a final stroke to secure his stand, he added: "I'm sure that General Dearborn can always reach the President's ear if he thinks the Navy is incompetent."

General Bloomfield flushed. But the Lieutenant gave no indication that his suggestion reflected on the running of the Northern Army, that it related in the slightest to growing public sentiment against military losses to the British on Lake Erie and Lake Ontario's borders. Nor did he mention Isaac Hull's capture of *Guerriere* and David Porter's capture of *Alert* in August—"great victories for America's young Navy," as the newspapers had acclaimed—which had come at the same time as General William Hull's ignominious surrender of the American forces at Detroit to Sir Isaac Brock.

Having always trusted his intuition to recognize the critical moment and to act, the Lieutenant smiled at General Bloomfield before the other could determine whether to take umbrage.

"With your permission, sir," he said, "I'll go with Lieutenant Sidney Smith, my predecessor, to look over the Navy's old gunboats and the sloops the Army's bought." As if both acknowledged that, whatever Dearborn might think about a single command, they would make a good military-naval team, he added: "You and I can get together again as soon as I see what's needed to be done."

In the silence that followed, like the calm in the center of a hurricane, the Lieutenant waited for the wind to roar again. You could be sure an old Army codger like Bloomfield, brought up in conservative, hoary tradition, would let no minutest portion of prescriptive Army command go without a battle. No more would Dearborn. To them he represented the new and presumptuous naval establishment. Emotionally, he knew, they could not have much less love for the British.

Bloomfield closed his eyes and puffed his lips two or three times. The flush gradually left his face. His proud eyes, open, gave him a slightly baronial, beneficent look as they rested on the Lieutenant's unrevealing countenance. He rose from his big armchair.

"I'm having a few neighbors in for dinner," he said. "Peter Sailly; he's Collector of Customs. General Mooers, who's living on Cumberland Point, around the bay. Won't you join us? I know they'd like to meet the young man who's going to keep the enemy off Lake Champlain." He smiled. "That gives you several hours to look over our military layout. I'll order an escort to show you whatever you want to see."

"Thank you, sir." The Lieutenant felt he had won the General's respect, and showed his pleasure. "I know I'll enjoy meeting your friends and neighbors."

This was a gracious old man, and shrewd. He knew when to pull in his horns, to wait out his time. A man to be respected, in turn. Angry, hurt, as Bloomfield undoubtedly had felt at the Secretary of the Navy's giving to a young lieutenant command equal to that of a sixty-year-old Army veteran, the man had well hidden his feelings, controlled his emotions.

What if General Bloomfield hadn't kept such control? The Lieutenant chuckled to himself. That situation would have been interesting to handle, too!

Lieutenant Macdonough came honestly by his ability to handle himself, via a capable family.

Great-grandfather Thomas MacDonough lived in Ireland's

County Kildare. From there, about 1730, went Grandfather James McDonough (the family changed the form of its name at will from generation to generation) to settle at The Trap, St. George's Hundred, New Castle County, Delaware.

Grandfather McDonough, a physician of considerable means according to family tradition, saw youngest son Micah off to fight the Indians in 1791. Middle son James died in the Revolution. The eldest son, Dr. Thomas, the Lieutenant's father, "threw away the lancet and buckled on the sword" to fight in that war as a major; he also served in Delaware's Privy Council and its General Assembly, and ended up a justice of the Court of Common Pleas.

Dr. Thomas McDonough had married Mary Vance, of English stock and an "engaging and accomplished woman who inspired with respect all who approached her." To them, on the day that General George Washington resigned his military commission into the custody of Congress—December 23, 1783—Thomas Macdonough was born in their one-and-a-half-story log house. Sixth of their ten children, he moved next year to a house built of bricks brought from England and still standing on the "Trap farm."

In 1799 his older brother, Midshipman James, lost a leg when wounded in the tops of frigate *Constellation* when she took *L'Insurgente*.

Thus the Lieutenant learned something from uncles, father, and brother of how to cope practically with the Army, politics, and the Navy.

And from family and the farm on which he grew up in an atmosphere of independence, he absorbed a love of country and a sense of responsibility for its welfare. When, at sixteen, he received from President John Adams his warrant as midshipman in the Navy, he had had a basic orientation for the arduous, precarious, and often frustrating career ahead.

Ordered to ship *Ganges*, Captain John Mullowney, 15 May 1800, Midshipman Macdonough plunged into the war with France in the West Indies, took part in capturing two Guineamen and a French privateer, caught yellow fever, and was sent ashore to a Havana hospital where "nearly all the men and officers died and were taken out in carts as so many hogs would have been." * A year later he joined frigate *Constellation*, Commodore Alexander Murray, and "had a brush with the gunboats off Tripoli." *

In 1803, bound for Mediterranean war with the Tripolitan pirates, frigate *Philadelphia*, Captain William Bainbridge, captured a Moorish vessel of thirty guns, and Midshipman Macdonough "was put on board to assist in taking her to Gibraltar." * Here he was left aboard the prize while Bainbridge sailed on, to ground *Philadelphia* on a reef off Tripoli and spend nineteen months as prisoner.

As a passenger aboard frigate *Constitution*, Captain Edward Preble ("a daring and vigilant officer" *), Midshipman Macdonough went to rejoin *Philadelphia*. But news of that frigate's disaster sent him from *Old Ironsides* to schooner *Enterprise*, Lieutenant Stephen Decatur, in the harbor of Syracuse. There developed one of the American Navy's greatest exploits, beginning with a communication from prisoner Bainbridge to squadron commander Preble advising that a small vessel might enter Tripoli harbor and destroy captured *Philadelphia*. This needed doing before the enemy refitted her for their use (under protection of shore batteries mounting 115 pieces of heavy cannon and under further protection of nineteen gunboats, two galleys, two schooners, a brig, and a long range of rocks and shoals!).

Decatur volunteered for, and got, the assignment. He selected from *Enterprise* three lieutenants, his surgeon, his favorite midshipman Thomas Macdonough, and some sixty crew—together with midshipmen from two other vessels. On a previously captured ketch, renamed *Intrepid* and loaded with combustibles, they slipped into Tripoli harbor the night of February 16, 1804, ghosted under the shore batteries,

* *Autobiography.*

and with deck crew disguised as Maltese made fast to the captured American frigate. Within five minutes Decatur held full possession; in less than twenty, he set fires (in the forward storeroom, under Midshipman Macdonough's direction), and the party regained *Intrepid*. *Philadelphia* burned, blew up, sank.

Midshipman Macdonough also accompanied Decatur "when he captured, by boarding, the gunboats in one of the actions with the enemy's vessels and batteries. Here I consider was the school where our Navy received its first lessons, and its influence has remained to this day and will continue as long as the Navy exists." *

Remaining in the squadron during all its operations against Tripoli, Midshipman Macdonough "presented the flags of the captured boats to Commodore Preble at the request of Captain Decatur, and was in 1805 or 6 appointed a lieutenant of the schooner *Enterprise*." * He passed the winter in Venice, prepared four small vessels for gunboats, and—peace having been made with Tripoli—joined brig *Syren*, Captain John Smith, as first lieutenant. He visited Naples, Rome, Pompeii, Herculanaeum, Mount Aetna, Malta, and the towns of the Barbary Powers; and returned home.

In 1806 he joined Captain Isaac Hull in superintending construction of four gunboats at Middletown, Connecticut; in 1807 went to ship *Wasp*, Captain Smith, carrying dispatches to England, France, and the Mediterranean; then home to cruise the American coast from Boston to Charleston in 1808, enforcing the embargo laws. From *Wasp* he went in 1809 to ship *John Adams* and, shortly, to frigate *Essex*, Captain Smith.

"At this time the Navy was unpopular and many officers quitted it." * He procured a furlough, captained brig *Gulliver* to Liverpool, Calcutta, St. Helena, and home to New

* *Autobiography.*

York—fifteen months. Then the interrupted *Jeannette Snow* voyage—and war with Great Britain.

Yes, Lieutenant Macdonough had the seasoning to stand up to Generals Bloomfield and Dearborn. He had the brine-soaked toughness of a prize fighter's fists. He had boarded pirate warships and helped destroy a frigate. He had built war vessels and captained merchant ships. He had commanded men in war and peace, and won their respect. He knew his naval job.

As he left Bloomfield's headquarters, Lieutenant Macdonough also knew he had his work cut out to accomplish, in this Army-dominated area, the Navy Secretary's objectives on Lake Champlain.

5

The Plattsburg garrison sprawled over endless acreage. Seemingly erected on random sites, the numerous barracks, stables, and blockhouses focused great individual confusion.

"Things still haven't got shaken down," said the artillery colonel detailed to accompany Lieutenant Macdonough on his inspection.

The Lieutenant smiled to himself at the officer's understatement. "I can see you have a big job on your hands," he said.

"Indeed we have," said the Colonel, and diligently proceeded to detail most of the Army's growing pains.

From him the Lieutenant learned that General Bloomfield had marched some 8,000 regulars and militia from lower New York State only two months ago; that the militia, composed mostly of volunteers, made military affairs difficult for their officers; that their independent disregard for rules and regulations amounted in practice almost to individual action or, at best, to action taken by group decision rather than orders from a superior; that, inexperienced as soldiers, they knew how to shoot a musket.

He learned, too, that the hospital did a rushing business with dysentery and influenza; that the guardhouse had more guests than Plattsburg's United States Hotel—mostly affected by injudicious mixing of beer with gin, or rum with gin; that small advance parties had been thrown forward toward the border as far as Chazy (14 miles) and Champlain (21 miles); that upward of a hundred and fifty boats, to carry fifty men each, had been chiefly finished under the Quartermaster General's aegis.

Most pertinent, he learned that Lake Champlain stretched 100 miles north from Whitehall to Rouses Point on the American side of the Canadian border; that from Whitehall (which lay 78 miles above Albany where General Dearborn kept his wary eye on the fleet!), the Lake flowed little wider than a river to Ticonderoga; that it had a 10-mile average width north of Burlington; and that, mostly, the wind blew directly up or down this narrow inland sea.

Interestingly, he learned that the citizens of New York, like Vermonters, would welcome an American army on the Canadian frontier; because, then, they could run pork and potash over the border for profit at night and chase after the enemy for plunder next day, each gain equally acceptable.

As he drew the Colonel out, he looked forward to dinner at General Bloomfield's. Over good food and drink, the General and his guests should, among them, paint a background picture that would place the miscellaneous data he'd picked up in a clearer perspective.

The Army must have broad plans, clear-cut objectives; the shambles he had observed today must be just a stage in pulling together a combat force from bare elements, as he had often heard his father say about the manner in which the Revolutionary Army had been created out of volunteers with squirrel guns. The cost of fighting without a standing army (with which, God knew, no one in his right mind wanted to saddle the country) came high. Waste, inefficiency, compounded confusion! No wonder the press facetiously predicted that the British would be beaten (eventually) by sheer weight of military stupidity—our own.

Say what you would about the Navy's youth, presumptuousness, brashness, it made out of its midshipmen officers equal to any in the world—and made them responsible early. A laborious and dangerous apprenticeship. (How had he got

LAKE CHAMPLAIN

North Portion   South Portion

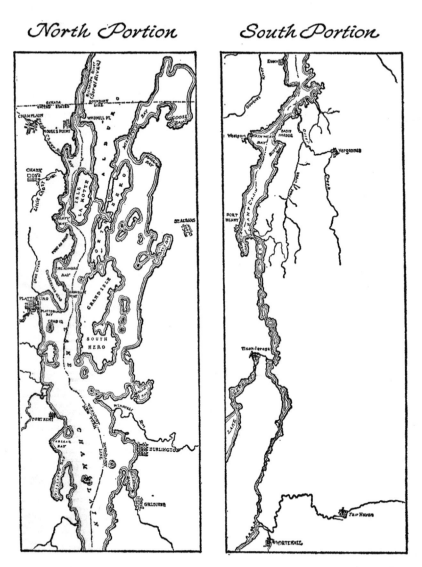

NOTE: *Up the lake = toward its source, or south*
Down the lake = toward its outlet, or north

through the burning of *Philadelphia* without a scratch; and that night in Syracuse, again with Decatur, when they'd fought their way through the streets with their swords?) [1] "Wards and children of the public," they called themselves as a huge joke.

Left to pick up as best they could the technical education needed to fit them for their profession, they looked on ship schoolmasters, conspicuous by their absence, as fictional characters existing only in the minds of idealistic Congressmen. While they learned no exacting etiquette or rigid courtesy, they learned discipline at the end of an intemperate tongue or an even more incisive length of rope.

The unceasing strain, the intense exactions on a boy's nervous system, pitilessly weeded out all but the determined and the rugged. Maybe they had had to find berths in the merchant service while Washington made up its legislative mind to build ships for a Navy worthy of the name; but that extracurricular experience had only sharpened their skills, increased their resourcefulness and self-reliance.

America could be proud of her sailors as well as her officers. Patriots a country could boast of, many of her sailors even now stood alone against the enemy. "One American seaman," he'd read in the Portland newspaper as reported two weeks ago by an American in Bermuda, "has been flogged through the British fleet for refusing to do duty, determined to die rather than serve them any longer." Six thousand more like him had been impressed, enslaved over the past fifteen years.

Impressed! He knew how that felt. [2]

How could any citizen of the United States, even so far from the Atlantic as Vermont and upper New York, doubt the need to fight an arrogant oppressor that had blockaded his country's shores, had captured and condemned a thousand vessels? What kept people from seeing clearly that the British sought inexorably to annihilate America's Navy, to destroy her hard-won commercial prosperity?

At the United States Hotel, to which the Lieutenant had sent his bag earlier, Thomas Green, the proprietor, handed him a message from General Bloomfield—a succinct note making him an overnight guest at the General's headquarters.

"Your bag's already gone," said Green.

The "few neighbors for dinner" turned out to be a company of nearly twenty when, at early dusk, the guests sat down at a damask-covered table that stretched diagonally across a white-wainscoted dining room. A fire blazed in a marble-faced fireplace on whose mantel stood porcelain figurines from Europe. With his first glance, the Lieutenant recognized that the man who turned this house over to the General had ample means. He also quickly appreciated that, if the meal reasonably sampled the domestic setup, Bloomfield spared himself nothing in food and drink.

Served by four amiable Negro patriarchs dressed in black satin knee breeches, the repast (what else could you call it?) consisted of eight or ten large platters (silver, not pewter) of meat and poultry, with white potatoes, sweet potatoes, and a variety of vegetables on delicate chinaware the likes of which the Lieutenant had not seen since Venice.

The second course, of pastry, comprised pie and puddings in abundance.

For the toasts, formal, which continuously reminded the group that each guest formed part of the company, the General's aides kept glasses filled under the supervision of one aide who sat at the bottom of the table to distribute the bottles of claret and Madeira.

What with the bustle of butlers and sommeliers, the lifting of glasses to toast the President of the United States, the Secretary of War, General Henry Dearborn, the Governor of New York, and the individual guests—winding up with the lone naval representative who, in turn, brought the Secretary of the Navy to the fore—the dinner left little opportunity for intimate conversation.

But with the cloth taken off and the serving of apples and

a great quantity of nuts, toasting waned and talking waxed. Picking at half-opened hickory nuts made for agreeable relaxation.

"I've always thought," said the man at the Lieutenant's right, "that Stephen Decatur's burning of the *Philadelphia* ranks as one of the most brilliant achievements in the history of the Navy."

The Lieutenant stiffened protectively as Peter Sailly, in his late fifties, portly, looked out of clear blue eyes. His dark hair, brushed forward, held a slight wave, his long nose curved upward, and his lips framed a large and smiling mouth. All combined (but the clear look in his eyes contributed most) to give the Customs Collector an easy, likable appearance. Relaxing, the Lieutenant nodded.

"You and Nelson," he said. "Nelson called it the boldest act of the age."

Continuing to pick at hickory nuts, the pair finally laughed together.

"I just used that as an opening gambit," Peter Sailly said as the tension snapped. "I'd like to get to know you, Mr. Macdonough. I've heard much about you from Dr. Bullus."

Already attracted to this stranger, the Lieutenant felt warmed by mention of the long-time good friend of Ann's grandparents in New York. "I suppose you know he's Navy Agent there now," he said.

Peter Sailly nodded. "As one of his competitors for available military supplies, I know very well indeed!"

The ice broken, Peter Sailly told about himself—born in France but now, as he showed in his conversation, one of the most deeply patriotic Americans the Lieutenant had met in months.

"I came back to Lake Champlain in the spring of 1786," Sailly related, "after exploring it and the Mohawk Valley two years earlier when I was thirty. I settled here in Plattsburg with Mrs. Sailly. We've been very happy. I like the people; they seem to like me. I've been a justice, a member of the state assembly, and for the past four years Collector of Customs—appointed by Mr. Jefferson and continued by Mr. Madison."

The more the man talked, the more the Lieutenant felt drawn to him. Intelligent, precise in speech, he appeared to have quality of a high order. The Lieutenant said:

"From what I could discover coming through Vermont, Mr. Sailly, the people on the other side of the Lake have mixed feelings about the war. Seems as though they'd like to win it just so long as winning it doesn't interrupt their business with Canada."

Peter Sailly agreed. "It's the same on both sides of the Lake, Lieutenant," he said. "I don't think anyone in New York has an iota of political friendship for Britain, but trade with Canada has produced every effect of political friendship."

He paused to nibble on a nut. Then: "Feeling is quite different on the Lake, I think you'll find, from what you must have encountered in eastern New England. There, self-righteousness and the assumption of superior wisdom—combined with such facility of the pen that their writers make more noise than those of the rest of the states—have arrayed people against their country, openly and defiantly."

The Lieutenant's expression showed his accord. Sailly went on.

"I don't think our people on the Lake feel that way. They're confused, certainly, torn between business and patriotism. And the greatest danger in any hour of peril for any nation is lack of patriotism."

He sipped at his wine. Then he said: "A nation's fundamental need is patriotism, Lieutenant. History shows that. History also shows that the greatest inspiration to patriotism is the example of those who have served their country with honor, with their lives. The Revolution's still close, with all its examples. Young men like you have since demonstrated, abroad, our country's basic strength. I think that when the time comes our people will make the right decision." Peter Sailly lifted his glass.

Touched, the Lieutenant raised his. This man had truly embraced his adopted country, to find in his heart such deepfelt belief in the integrity of America's people. No less could he, Thomas Macdonough, keep his faith in their basic love of country.

General Bloomfield's plump hand on his arm shook him out of his distraction. "What did you think of the garrison?"

He sought to put the best face he could on his afternoon's observations.

"You cover a good deal of territory, General," he said, groping for something he could praise or, at least, speak about with sincerity. "Your guards struck me as well-disciplined and efficient." He smiled at General Bloomfield, who beamed appreciatively. "The variety of uniforms also impressed me," he added. "I must have seen everything from homespun to— well, I thought I saw a couple of British uniforms, but I must not have seen clearly."

"You saw the militia," the General said with a disgruntled snort. "They'll be the death of me yet. They wear everything they can lay hands on that doesn't cost them any money."

"Now, Joseph, don't malign the militia." On Bloomfield's left, General Benjamin Mooers—high forehead and long nose set off by white hair and bushy sideburns—marched serenely to the foot soldier's defense.

Into the Lieutenant's ear Peter Sailly whispered, "If you don't heap praise on the militia in Ben Mooers' presence, he thinks you're a renegade. They love him for it."

"Remember Bennington, Joseph," said the old Revolutionary War hero. "An undisciplined militia fought that battle. They weren't any different from the men you've got here today—except these are their sons." General Mooers lifted his glass.

"To the militia!" he toasted. "Warmed by patriotism and animated by individual hatred of oppression—the bulwark of our country's defense. Bless their independent hearts!"

General Bloomfield shook his head in mock despair. "You're an incorrigible optimist, Ben," he said.

Bloomfield turned to the Lieutenant. "We've got the regulars, infantry and artillery, into the new short blue 'coatees,' as they call them. How did those appeal to you?" he asked.

The Lieutenant looked down at his own coat. "General," he said, "we've been wearing jackets in the Navy for some time. Naturally we're delighted that the Army likes the new style, too." He raised his glass. "To short coats and long pants—"

General Bloomfield broke in, rising with a burst of laughter to the occasion: "—for you men-of-the-line. But to long coats for us desk warriors who need padded coattails to keep our rumps from getting calloused."

Warmed by his own wine, by the fire that burned at his back, and by the candles that heated as well as lighted the table, General Bloomfield appeared to have reached a stage of geniality much different from his earlier antagonism toward his naval colleague-to-be. He said:

"Dearborn tells me your Captain Isaac Chauncey has gone up to Lake Ontario to superintend the building and commissioning of a fleet. Have you heard details?"

The Lieutenant shook his head. "Only that a considerable number of ships' carpenters left New York last month for Ontario as well as for Erie, which Commodore Chauncey also commands. He's a good man. I wonder who'll command under him on Erie?"

The Lieutenant had picked up what little he knew of grand military strategy wherever he could find a clue—newspapers, letters from fellow officers and friends, general gossip. As in midshipman days, no schoolmaster presented himself with basic knowledge to dispense; what you needed, you dug out. His digging, he knew, scratched only the surface. Thus far, however, the pieces seemed to fit into a sensible pattern.

Blockading America's ports to prevent trade and to bring about dissolution of the country's mercantile prosperity, England aimed now to invade through Canada, to encircle and strangle the hard core of the United States.

The American Army could counter in two ways. It could invade Canada before the British massed an attack. But Hull's unsuccessful July trek into Canada, and back, had shown the impracticability, at this time, of the first alternative—invasion. Canadians cherished their British allegiance; without Canadian support, the Americans could not feed and support a large army.

The second way to negate British strategy lay in building a strong defense along the northern New York border. With American fleets dominating Lakes Ontario and Erie, preventing passage by water of munitions and food, Britain could not mount an effective invasion west of Montreal.

With the northern border closed to the west, the British had only one line of attack left—Lake Champlain, a natural invasion path for troops aimed at New York City. From Montreal as mobilization center, up the St. Lawrence to Lake Champlain, up Lake Champlain to the Hudson River, then down the Hudson to New York—an almost straight line. Most important, this path lay through terrain abundant with food. Here a large British force could live as it marched.

If the American Army, with the Navy's help, could block the northern border from Montreal to Detroit—keep the British from skirting the Army's western flank—then Britain must throw her full force of arms at Lake Champlain. Breaking through there, her troops would descend on New York; and America would be conquered!

"Lieutenant Macdonough!" General Bloomfield's voice came through to his consciousness. "I don't want you to get the wrong impression of the Army, either here at Plattsburg or in the west." The General seemed not about to offer apologies so much as to make explanations of fact to a man he deemed capable of appreciating the difference. He said: "No need to tell you there's distrust and jealousy among officers. That's evident from the breakdown in discipline and, on occasion, insubordination among the militia and volunteers."

General Bloomfield gave no indication that he remembered the morning's impasse, putting no stress on the word insubordination.

The Lieutenant accepted the confidence. By way of showing his understanding, he said: "Some of our states have taken a defiant attitude toward the national government itself, I believe, General. They don't seem to realize this war is between England and all the states united."

The General sat up sharply. "That's the crux of the matter, young man—United States!" he said. "When? When will they unite? How can the administration carry on a successful war without their united support?" He banged the table with a heavy fist. "Lieutenant, I've been in politics a long time. I know the difference between politics and sedition in high places. With what's going on in Washington and some of our state capitals, it astounds me, by God, that our soldiers have any morale whatever!"

The table quieted. The General's eyes sparkled with honest ire.

"The states either supply only a part of the militia they're called on for, or they send none at all," he said. "Committed to supply certain munitions and equipment, they neglect to supply them. On top of that, they oppose national loans and taxes; so the Federal government itself lacks funds to buy what the states fail to provide.

"In spite of all this, and almost without any military training whatever, our soldiers"—he bowed to the Lieutenant—"yes, and your sailors, fight mighty well!"

General Bloomfield took a deep breath. His eyes continued to blaze. He lifted his glass, freshly filled, and motioned his guests to rise with him.

"To unity of action, gentlemen," he said. "To a United States united in fact!"

6

As the dinner guests departed two servants shortened the table, converting it into a round shape. While the Lieutenant watched, curious, they laid a cloth. "For supper," Peter Sailly informed him.

The plain gold watch at the end of his fob showed only 7:30 but, to leave General Bloomfield free for whatever business he planned for the evening, the Lieutenant retired to his bedroom.

In shirtsleeves, stock open to help him recover from the effects of almost continuous toasting, he plumped down into a huge wing chair and toyed with the idea of getting a quick note off to Ann before taking a good night's sleep in preparation for next day's visit to Shelburne Bay.... His eyes drooped, and he dozed.

A knock on the door, at first timid, then insistent, waked him.

"Lieutenant Macdonough, sir," called a soft Negro voice, "General Bloomfield's expectin' you to supper, sir."

Eat again? It could not be an hour since he had left the dinner table. He groaned inwardly. "All right," he answered through the door. "My respects to the General. I'll be with him in a few minutes."

He returned to the dining room where General Bloomfield explained that, himself accustomed to take something in the evening, he thought the Lieutenant would perhaps nibble on a little fruit and assist in the conversation. Peter Sailly still was there, and a tall bearded civilian. General Bloomfield introduced the newcomer.

"Lieutenant Macdonough of the Navy—Mr. Eleazer Williams."

To more claret and Madeira toasts, the Lieutenant puzzled over the stranger. In his middle or late twenties, Eleazer Williams looked Indian, large-framed, strong and muscular, features heavily molded, coppery skin of peculiar Indian texture. His hair, including eyebrows and eyelashes, could only be called inky, raven black. His hazel eyes, dark and bright, were separated by a small nose and surmounted by an ample and intellectual but receding forehead. A scar that marred his left eyebrow, a mole on the left cheek near his mouth, and a long Austrian upper lip invested him with an intriguing, mysterious air.

His most surprising feature lay in his hands—small, delicate, facile (picking out nut kernels) as a woman's. And though unable to see beneath the table, the Lieutenant felt certain that Eleazer Williams' feet—small as his hands, no doubt—inevitably toed in. Unquestionably, this man had much, if not all, Indian blood.

His head, forward on his shoulders as he bent over his plate of fruit and nuts, was set proudly on a graceful, well-formed neck. He looked genial, and fond of good living.

"Let me bring Mr. Macdonough up to date, Lazare," said General Bloomfield as Williams cleared his throat to continue a discussion that, apparently, the Lieutenant had interrupted.

Williams shrugged expressively. "As you will, General. I'm a modest man, however. Please don't exaggerate my services."

General Bloomfield blinked. "Exaggeration I leave to you, my friend, as an expert," he riposted, winking at Peter Sailly whose straight face gave back no response. He turned toward the Lieutenant.

"Mr. Williams comes from Albany where General Dearborn and others feted him—"

"A brilliant entertainment," Williams interrupted.

"—celebrating his return from Sault St. Louis—"

"Four leagues above Montreal on the south side of the St. Lawrence." Williams again. Did he do this in order not to lose the floor for himself?

"—where he prevailed on the Iroquois Indians—"

"Largely Mohawks, with a few Oneidas."

"—to remain neutral." General Bloomfield stopped to sip his Madeira.

"Lazare did the same for us with the St. Regis Indians," Peter Sailly picked up. "With the Indians to the north refusing to fight for the British—"

"—we Americans can fight better."

Peter Sailly caught the Lieutenant's eye. "He's referring to Hull's surrender—"

"And to the fact that in the first battle of the war on American soil, at Brownstown, August fifth, the only British troops in actual combat were Indians under Tecumseh."

"He also refers—" Sailly managed to interpose before he lost the floor.

"—to the fact that the first American soldier to fall in the war, Captain McCullough, fell in this battle—shot from ambush and scalped before he died!"

General Bloomfield looked toward the Lieutenant. "We seem to have a certain dislike for letting Indians loose on either soldiers or civilians. Tell him, Lazare, what you were telling Peter Sailly and me before he joined us—about Hull. This, Mr. Macdonough, may help you understand the Army better."

Williams drained his glass. His expression became grave, almost melancholy. He wiped his mouth with a napkin and refilled his glass from the claret bottle.

"Two considerations caused General Hull to give Detroit up—one real, one imagined. The second, the lesser, was a letter smuggled to him, intercepted on its way to General Brock. It told of British forces marching to Brock's support, enough to overwhelm the Detroit garrison. We discovered, later, that the letter was faked. At the time, to Hull, however, it had every appearance of authenticity."

Williams put away more wine, seemingly able to absorb it in quantity with no outward effect on his big body. "It was Brock's concrete threat—on top of this letter—to turn his Indians loose on the fort and the town, on women, and on children, that swayed Hull into capitulating."

General Bloomfield took a slip of paper from his pocket. "Dearborn sent me Brock's exact message to Hull." He read:

> "It is far from my inclination to join in a war of elimination, but you must be aware that the numerous body of Indians who have attached themselves to my troops will be beyond my control the moment the contest commences."

In the silence that followed, the Lieutenant felt something of Hull's agony in deciding whether to fight against overwhelming odds, certain to lose, with a promised massacre for climax.

"Who can say he made the wrong decision?" murmured Peter Sailly.

General Bloomfield's hand, the Lieutenant saw, guided the Madeira bottle quite steadily to his glass. "God help the rest of us, facing that!"

The Lieutenant turned. "Mr. Williams—" he said.

"Lazare, if you will, Mr. Macdonough," Williams requested.

The Lieutenant started over. "Lazare," he said, "if you know the Indians to the north so well—"

"I was born in the Caughnawaga tribe."

"—would it be possible for you to keep me apprised of British naval movements on the other side of the border?"

"With ease, sir," said Williams.

The Lieutenant noticed that General Bloomfield, and Peter Sailly too, seemed about to laugh. Disconcerted by this

—rather than by Williams' interjections which, now that the Lieutenant himself had weathered a couple, seemed to provide a melodic counterpoint to the conversation—he stopped short.

The General slapped him on the back. "My apologies, Lieutenant. Please forgive me," he said. "I omitted to tell you that Lazare commands our secret corps of Army rangers and scouts. They are—"

"—the most daring, reckless, unscrupulous men in the Army. I call them 'the terrible corps.'"

"Yes, Lieutenant, he can and will keep us informed. His men—"

"—spread themselves everywhere. They freely pass in and out of the enemy's camp."

"Lazare operates," finished Bloomfield, "under General Dearborn."

The Lieutenant sought to reappraise Williams as a soldier instead of a civilian, sought to adjust to the idea of this strange (it certainly isn't usual to interrupt *every* conversation!) type being privy to all military secrets and contributing, in fact, the background material for high-level strategy decisions.

Peter Sailly broke the silence. He said: "Lazare has an interesting background, Lieutenant. His grandmother was Eunice Williams, daughter of the Reverend John Williams, whom the Indians carried captive to Canada after the Deerfield massacre. He was born on the shores of Lake George while his Caughnawaga father hunted, after the Revolution. He—"

"—educated himself at Dartmouth College." Williams showed great pride in this.

"Last year he taught for the Jesuits among the people of the tribe he was born into," said Peter Sailly. He finished with: "A man of many sides."

Williams shone in the spotlight, glowed in the warmth of the description. But he looked questioningly toward Sailly. "Some of those sides said to be seamy, Peter?"

Sailly nodded. "I've heard you called a few things."

"Like cunning, crafty, quick to invent, apt to exaggerate, utterly untruthful, a damned liar?"

"To that effect."

"Indolent and shiftless—a typical half-breed Indian?"

Sailly confirmed the self-appraisal. "Some even say you'd just as soon be notorious as celebrated." He paused. "You can't be both, you know, Lazare."

An infectious, cheerful expression replaced the gravity with which Williams had detailed his popularly held shortcomings.

"Peter, wouldn't you think I'd be afraid to trust myself if I believed everything my friends and enemies say about me?"

"I know I'd be—for the nation's good."

General Bloomfield's gaze fell lightly on his swarthy guest. He said:

"If I thought for a moment, Lazare, that you and your secret corps misled me by as much as one miscount of troops, or one false statement regarding British movements—I'd have both your ears so fast you wouldn't know where they went!"

The Lieutenant sensed that Bloomfield and Sailly sought, under cover of their jests, to put the fear of God into the man they had to rely on for the major part of their intelligence. He also sensed that Williams, so sure of himself on the surface, wanted—needed—the good will and spoken admiration of these men. He felt, too, that Williams wanted his, the Lieutenant's, confidence as well. Giving that, he told himself, would depend; would depend on whether Williams brought him more and better information on British activities than he could uncover for himself.

"What with trading over the border," he said casually, "I suppose the farmers on the Lake, as well as the captains and crews of smuggling vessels, pick up pretty solid information."

"Not much useful information is just *picked up*, sir," said Williams. "I train my men to ferret out what we need. We evaluate our sources before we go to them, and we assay their information thoroughly after we get it." [1]

Well, decided the Lieutenant, that seems straightforward enough!

Peter Sailly tugged from a pocket of his sateen vest a large gold-embossed watch that could have come from nowhere but France and, likely, from his grandfather or his grandfather's grandfather. He pretended shock on discovering the hour.

"I must be off, General."

"I, too," said Williams.

"So a last toast of the evening," Peter Sailly proposed, "a sentiment to a lady."

The four raised their glasses.

"To the lovely bride-to-be of Lieutenant Thomas Macdonough," said Peter Sailly. The Lieutenant smiled appreciatively. "To the beautiful Miss Lucy Ann Shaler of Middletown, Connecticut, whom I now know only by distant report but whom we shall soon know in her own charming person."

Navigating with great caution to the haven of his bedroom, the Lieutenant wondered how General Joseph Bloomfield possibly could negotiate his evening's cargo of rare wines to rest. And he fervently hoped that Peter Sailly, good, new friend, and Eleazer Williams, chief of those terrible rangers, would eventually wander safely home and into bed—not into Plattsburg Bay.

7

When Lieutenant Thomas Macdonough sailed back across Lake Champlain from Plattsburg to Shelburne Bay to take over his command, he stood at the sloop's rail with mixed emotions.

Saturday, October 10th, had opened clear and cold. In the early dawn, waked by one of General Bloomfield's gentle Negro servants who brought a breakfast tray to his room, he had risen, shaved, dressed, eaten, and departed Army headquarters. Carrying his bag, he had boarded the waiting sloop, whose captain and one-man crew (both barely in their twenties) sleepily had hoisted the oddly clean jib and mainsail. Into the strong head wind that blew down the Lake, the sloop had begun a long series of short tacks.

Recovered resiliently from the previous night's dining and wining, the Lieutenant felt the need for getting down to the business that had brought him to the Lake. For generals like Bloomfield, graduated from the Revolutionary War with its comparatively leisurely pace, such elaborate eating and drinking might fit into a campaign schedule. But for him this war called for a different attitude. You would not win it sitting at a dinner table indoors; you would have to go outside and fight it.

From Eleazer Williams, he'd learned that the British had "two or three gunboats in the Sorel River." The secret corps must have merely picked up this information, like smugglers;

or hadn't had time to assay the exact number! Keeping Britain's gunboats bottled up in the Sorel, which some Canadians and some Americans called the Richelieu River, should not prove too difficult. What with two United States Navy gunboats in commission and six Army sloops ready to fit out for fighting, his fleet should have ascendancy on the Lake from the start.

He found himself, nonetheless, bothered by a feeling that the military establishment's growing pains and Bloomfield's adamant resistance to the idea of separate naval operations indicated that he might encounter unexpected obstacles to keeping the British off Lake Champlain. Just a hunch, but a strong one.

As the sloop zigzagged toward Shelburne Point, the wind bit at his face. It lacked a tang which he finally realized he must learn to do without—the salt sting of the ocean. For a few seconds his heart sank. Had he made a mistake leaving Commodore Bainbridge and *Constellation?* Would they, as the Old Man had written, run away from the coast and do something clever? Would he lose an opportunity for acquiring fame and making his fortune?

The mood passed quickly. Naturally buoyant, he smiled. He told himself: You made up your own mind about leaving *Constellation;* you figured the chances you took. Now, which do you prefer—salt water under Bainbridge or fresh water under Macdonough? He laughed. "Sir," he told himself, "I like it here with Macdonough."

When the sloop slipped under the protection of Shelburne Point as the sun stood overhead at noon, the wind came off the Lake and over the bay's long, wooded arm at an angle that sent the vessel on an easy starboard-tack reach along the western shore. In the lee of 400-foot hills rising gently off the beach, the water went suddenly quiet after its noisy outside chop. The Lieutenant realized that he'd failed to ask General Bloomfield what his command included besides the two gunboats and the six sailing vessels—how many men, how many buildings, how many guns, how much in munitions and supplies.

Aside from the numerical size of his fleet, all he knew was the name of the Navy lieutenant now in charge—Sidney Smith. Why hadn't Paul Hamilton given him a few basic facts? You couldn't keep personal track of every individual among the Navy's five hundred officers.

The youth at the wheel pointed toward the inner rim of the bay. "There's your boats, Captain," he said.

A hundred yards ahead the Lieutenant picked out the hulls of the two scows on the beach and the masts of five weather-battered sloops anchored just off the shore. His ships? Those derelicts!

He took the joke without batting an eye.

"They're only five," he parried. "My fleet has six."

The man at the wheel nodded. "Yes, sir, I know. This one we're on's the sixth—the *President*. Best of the lot, she is."

For the first time, the Lieutenant studied the boat's skipper. A local man, seemingly. About twenty-two, average size, capable, neatly dressed in faded blues, he appeared to be laughing grimly to himself.

"When I put you ashore, sir," the man said, "she's all yours and welcome. I hope you do better with her than I have."

Lieutenant Macdonough held his peace.

"The things that go on," the skipper said, "I'm almost sick and ashamed of the Army officers in this part of the country. When Colonel Isaac Clark and Lieutenant Rufus Hatch, assistant deputy quartermaster, bought these six sloops, I belonged to the gunboat department—the Navy department. But Lieutenant Smith advised me to go aboard this sloop because Lieutenant Hatch could pay me more." He trimmed the main sheet and cleated it. "So I've been transporting troops and provisions from place to place—and haven't had a cent! Nothing but fair promises. I reckon I may whistle for my money!"

Coming into the wind and anchoring alongside the other boats, *President*'s skipper helped his crew drop and furl the sloop's jib and huge mainsail. Tossing two duffle bags and the Lieutenant's bag into the lowered skiff alongside, he and his crew dropped into the skiff.

The Lieutenant followed. "What did you do for the Navy?" he asked.

"Sailing master and pilot."

"Would you work for me?"

"Yes, sir," said the skipper. "The Navy always paid me punctually."

The bow grounded. The Lieutenant lent a hand pulling the skiff up the beach. "What's your name?" he asked.

"I'm Joseph Barron—junior. I live with my wife and our children in Burlington." [1]

"I'll get in touch with you." He scanned the shore. "Where will I find the naval quarters?"

Joseph Barron shrugged. "Nowheres," he said. "But you'll probably find Lieutenant Smith in Shelburne, at the tavern along with some of the Army officers. Here, let me carry your bag, sir."

No naval quarters! What goes on? His mind raced over the implications of the sorry-looking fleet. Why were the gunboats hauled out? Where were their guns? What had been done about arming the sloops? Why weren't Lieutenant Smith and all his men at work?

The Lieutenant pulled himself together. His first outrage, dying down, left a hot indignation at being so abruptly flung from the roseate clouds of his imagined command to its drab reality. Tight-lipped, he resolved to get the facts before he allowed himself further anger.

When Joseph Barron left him at the inn's front steps, he had himself in hand. By way of good-by, he said: "I hope you get your pay from the Army."

"I better had," Barron said dourly, "or my wife'll think I don't amount to bug dust."

The Lieutenant found Sidney Smith at a round table in the common room. With him sat a rosy-cheeked midshipman. The Lieutenant went to the table.

"May I join you gentlemen? I'm Macdonough."

The pair jumped to their feet.

"Mr. Macdonough, are we glad to see you!" Pumping the Lieutenant's hand, Sidney Smith beamed, his expression one of unutterable joy, like that of a man rescued from death in the sea. "Are we glad you're here!"

Taken completely off balance by the impetuous welcome, he found himself forced to forget his intended severity and meet the natural friendliness of the pair with equal warmth.

"I'm glad to be here, finally," he said.

Remembering etiquette, Sidney Smith saluted formally. "I beg pardon, Lieutenant." He turned to the red-cheeked youngster who stood patiently waiting for recognition. "This is Midshipman Joseph Smith—no relation." The youth saluted smartly.

The Lieutenant responded to both salutes. "Now we can sit down and eat," he said quietly. "I'm hungry, and I'll take whatever you recommend. I judge you know the cooking here."

"Only too well," said Sidney Smith.

For an hour, while the trio ate lunch, the Lieutenant took bearings, listening to the two Smiths pour out the intimate details of their situation.

Sidney Smith had taken command of Lake Champlain in March of 1810, making his headquarters in Basin Harbor where, the year before, Lieutenant Melancthon Taylor of the Army had built two gunboats.

"Scows," Sidney Smith described them, "heavy, open, forty feet long."

"I saw them," the Lieutenant said. "Why are they on the beach?"

"Because they won't float," said Sidney Smith. Seeing the Lieutenant's angry frown, he hastened to explain. "They were badly constructed in the first place. In the second place, the shipyards around here make more money working on civilian craft; they refuse to repair them."

"You could make repairs with naval personnel."

"What naval personnel?" Sidney Smith asked bluntly. "The handful of incompetent hands we've received from New York or the farm boys we've managed to enlist here on the Lake? Mr. Macdonough, besides Midshipman Smith and myself we have exactly one man who's ever sailed on salt water—Master's Mate John Trumbull. Ask him to tell you some of our problems trying to keep the gunboats manned."

Midshipman Joseph Smith had bided his time, letting his superior officer sketch the broad outlines of the woeful situation. He spoke up now.

"We have no guns for the gunboats, sir," he said, and waited.

The pair's outpouring of frustrations had softened the Lieutenant to a point where he felt nothing could surprise him. But cannonless gunboats!

"The Quartermaster General requisitioned them away from us," said Sidney Smith. "Told us he needed them for defenses that General Bloomfield wanted thrown up at Chazy. Said they were Army equipment—and snatched 'em."

Incredible as the facts first sounded, they stood out clearly. The boats he had seen on the beach, the two officers at the table, a master's mate, and twenty-two so-called seamen (all of whom ate and slept wherever they could find board and lodging in the neighborhood, where they'd gone to lunch) constituted the United States Naval Command on Lake Champlain.

The Lieutenant looked gravely at his companions. He

voiced none of his turbulent feelings, no resentment at finding himself in such a situation, no criticism of the two officers. Undoubtedly they had tried hard, done their best with the limited means given them. They had shown their unhappiness over existing conditions, frankly admitted their inability to cope with Army idiosyncrasies, and in the enthusiasm of their welcome revealed their earnest wish to work with a man who would give them a reasonable opportunity to prove their capabilities. So be it!

Lieutenant Thomas Macdonough took over his command. "Let's look at the boats," he said.

PART TWO

THE SHIPS

The naval force on this lake consisted at this time of two gunboats and three sloops, the whole totally unprepared. Went to
Whitehall and commenced fitting out these vessels. All hands
(including myself, a midshipman, Joseph Smith, and a master's
mate named Trumbull) employed in this business. After all the
difficulties to be expected in such a part of the country where
nobody knew anything that was necessary to be done, I succeeded in getting these vessels in a poor kind of order. . . .

Autobiography

1

Lieutenant Thomas Macdonough's inspection quickly and clearly showed what he must do to make the boats at his disposal into a fighting fleet—everything from complete hull overhaul to refitting!

The gunboats—if you could dignify them with the name—needed retimbering from stem to stern. Three of the sloops —only a landlubber, and a blind one at that, could have let slick civilians con him into buying such hulks—the Army could keep. The other three would have to do—*Hunter,* 60 feet long; *Bull Dog,* 64 feet; *President,* 65 feet.

"What do you know about the yards at Whitehall?" he asked Sidney Smith. "Can we hire competent carpenters there?"

Sidney Smith shrugged. "Carpenters, yes—competent, no."

"Where can we find cannon?"

"Well, the Army's set up an arsenal at Whitehall. But I doubt if they'll—"

The Lieutenant cut in. "Here are your orders," he said. "You will have your men haul the galleys well up on the beach this afternoon to dry out for temporary caulking on Monday. Tomorrow—yes, I know it's Sunday—you'll have their sails and sweeps overhauled, ready for use Monday. Meanwhile, you'll get hold of Joseph Barron and tell him we'll need him Monday afternoon to pilot to Whitehall."

Speechless, Sidney Smith stared.

The Lieutenant turned to the midshipman. "Can you pilot me to Plattsburg?"

Joseph Smith nodded eagerly. "Yes, sir!"

The Lieutenant turned back to Sidney Smith. "I'll arrange with General Bloomfield to let General Dearborn know what armament we'll want delivered to us at Whitehall," he said, "and by tomorrow afternoon Midshipman Smith and I will return here to pitch in with the rest of you."

Recognizing action after so long a period of paralyzing frustration, Sidney Smith could not contain his delight. "Yes, sir, Commodore," he said, "we'll have the fleet ready for sea Monday evening!"

Completely disarmed again by this spontaneous outburst, the Lieutenant laughed loudly. What a fleet!

Sidney Smith quickly brought him back to the realities. "Do you think," Sidney Smith asked, "that General Dearborn will cooperate with us?"

"I don't know," he said slowly. "But that's Dearborn's problem. We can only try every resource, use all ingenuity, employ any conceivable means to prepare our"—he almost said fleet—"boats to defend the Lake."

At an appropriate hour Sunday morning, Lieutenant Macdonough and Midshipman Smith waited on General Bloomfield. The General greeted them heartily. But his farewell, following the Lieutenant's detailed listing of armament and other supplies to be furnished the vessels at Whitehall, lacked ardor.

"You're taking a lot on your own two shoulders, Mr. Macdonough. General Dearborn won't like it," he said. "He won't like it at all."

The Lieutenant shook Bloomfield's hand. "Neither will the British, I suspect."

Sailing back to Shelburne Bay, he went over his plans with Midshipman Smith. The flotilla would proceed up the Lake Monday night, the galleys under sail but rowed if necessary, to arrive in Whitehall sometime before evening on Tuesday.

Sidney Smith would command, in *President;* Joseph Smith would take charge of the gunboats.

The midshipman glowed at this first smell of action.

The Lieutenant liked his lone midshipman's earnest intelligence. "If the wind fails," he said, "just ask Lieutenant Smith to lend you men off the sloops to row. The sloops can always catch up if you get ahead." He added: "Meanwhile I'll ride to Whitehall and make arrangements with a couple of shipyards and the arsenal. If necessary, I'll go to Albany to see Dearborn." Unconsciously he rubbed his thighs. "In a carriage."

With Monday's preparations proceeding satisfactorily under Sidney Smith's supervision, the Lieutenant hoisted himself aboard the Burlington-Vergennes stage at Shelburne shortly after noon and eventually jounced into Whitehall and a Clinton House bed almost as sore as if he had ridden a horse.

Next morning he asked directions and walked to Moses Eggleston's shipyard.

In the early daylight, he found the village of Whitehall. Resembling a large lumberyard from the timber cut up and scattered everywhere, it lay snug in a wooded valley, beautiful with turning foliage.

On the brow of a hill to the west, a blockhouse built within the outlines of an old fort commanded the valley. Detachments of soldiers went about their chores in front of a good-sized barracks, and the Lieutenant idly tried to visualize the munitions stored behind the fort's stone walls. Out of the valley, Lake Champlain opened, the rising sun tinting its cold waters pink. A small river rushed into the Lake over a small cascade.

In the open shipyard where the fragrance of sawn timber sweetened the fresh early-morning air, the Lieutenant sought out the only building—serving as model loft and tool shed—located the master builder, introduced himself, and stated his errand.

Moses Eggleston listened impassively. A short, broad-shoul-dered man with a wrinkled face and a white frieze of hair showing beneath a peaked cap, he peered over steel-rimmed spectacles at the yard's activities while the Lieutenant talked. He mopped at his big hands with a dirty rag. Occasionally he spat the juice of a huge tobacco cud that stretched his cheek out like an infected molar. He made no comment.

The Lieutenant went on, almost casually, step by step enumerating the repairs and remodeling he wanted done. He had met dozens of Moses Egglestons in yards all over the Eastern coast and Europe; master builders, craftsmen of tre-mendous visual imagination, ingenuity, and skill, invariably artistic in temperament. Their way with wood, their affection for the work of their own hands, their pride in their ability to create ships from trees, gave them an amazing serenity and independence.

The Lieutenant finished with a question, directly to the point. "Can you do all this?"

Eggleston peered at him for several seconds through the glasses which had slipped down his nose so that he had to tilt his round head back in order to line up their lenses with the Lieutenant's face. He continued to mop his hands. He spat. Then he asked: "You say you're from the Navy?"

"I am."

Lowering his head, the builder looked over the top of his glasses at the men working in a nearby sawpit. "You say you're getting these vessels ready to fight the British?"

"That's right."

Turning back, Moses Eggleston tilted his head again, peered deliberately through the Lieutenant, and wiped his hands with the dirty rag to keep them busy while his mind ran over the possibilities. Finally: "You going to try to stop smuggling?"

The Lieutenant laughed. "That depends on whether I have time. Why?"

"Because I've turned out a lot of the boats on the Lake,"

the builder said quickly. "I'd kind of hate to see 'em shot up."
He spat once more, against a wood capstan.

"Well," he said, as the Lieutenant remained silent, waiting
him out, "I guess we can take the sloops, but only providin'
you accept full responsibility for results. We ain't built warships before."

The Lieutenant accepted the arrangement. "I'll be here all
the time," he said, "with a couple of good men. We'll show
you exactly what we want, where." He stopped, looked down
into quizzical Yankee eyes. "We'll expect you to show us the
how of doing it. Agreed?"

Moses Eggleston's round face glowed merrily. "Lieutenant," he said, "it's only because you're in the Navy that I'll
have any part of this job; sailors have got to stick together.
But I know you'll be bringing some soldiers in with the guns,
and that's all right, too. Exceptin', the minute one of those
pin-headed officers so much as opens his yap to tell me what
to do, out he goes—along with you and your boats. Agreed?"

They shook hands, and Moses Eggleston sent the Lieutenant to the Boardman shipyards with a message that paved the
way for retimbering the galleys.

Late that afternoon, blown by an erratic wind out of the
north, the Lake Champlain fleet sailed into Whitehall Harbor
in good order, to be pulled up on ways and cradled before
sundown.

In his bedroom at the Clinton House, the Lieutenant met
after supper with Sidney Smith, Joseph Smith, and Master's
Mate Trumbull to go over plans for the vessels.

"What kind of space did the Colonel find in the barracks
for your men, Trumbull?" he asked.

"Enough to swing their hammocks, sir. And the chow's
good."

The Lieutenant liked the laconic seaman, as spare in frame
as in conversation. Intense, with blue eyes that figuratively
clamped onto you when he talked, Trumbull took his job

seriously. In getting the galleys and sloops ready for White-hall, he'd shown ability as supervisor; the men worked will-ingly for him. A good hand.

"See that they continue to be taken care of," the Lieutenant said, spreading several large sheets of rough plans out on the bed. "Now, let's take a look at what's ahead of us. Speak up, everybody," he requested.

At the end of two hours they had preliminary procedures blocked out.

Trumbull and the men would work with the Boardman yard on the galleys, each of which would mount one long twelve-pounder. In the Eggleston yard, the three officers would work on the sloops—the Lieutenant on *President,* Sidney Smith on *Hunter,* and Joseph Smith (with the other two keeping an eye on him) on *Bull Dog.*

Being the largest and most recently built, *President* would mount eight guns, if possible. *Hunter* and *Bull Dog,* each with a quarterdeck that extended one-third forward and on which no guns could be mounted with safety, could accom-modate only six or seven guns at most.

"But that's all right if we can get a few eighteen-pounders," the Lieutenant said. "With those we can put the British gal-leys out of commission before they can come close enough to damage the sloops."

He answered their next, unvoiced question—Do we get the cannon we need?—by relating his afternoon's interview with Colonel Humphry, Commander of Whitehall's garrison.

"I showed him my orders to take command of the naval forces, I informed him I'd seen General Bloomfield, I told him how many guns and how much powder and ammunition the vessels would require, and I gave him instructions to start delivering them to us at the yards tomorrow."

Sidney Smith practically gasped. The master's mate nodded approvingly.

Joseph Smith, surprisingly, shook his head vehemently. His lips tight, he glowered. "It won't do, sir," he said, sounding exactly as General Bloomfield had sounded two days ago at Plattsburg. "General Dearborn won't like it. He won't like it at all!"

The Lieutenant laughed loudly at the boy's ability to interpose a sly, pertinent observation at the most appropriate time.

He agreed with the midshipman, but kept silent about his own misgivings. The seventy-eight miles from Whitehall's arsenal to Albany's Army headquarters would have to be a distance great enough to keep General Dearborn at arm's length, figuratively and literally. The Navy Secretary had given the Lieutenant authority to get from the Whitehall arsenal what he needed for the ships. Did his orders cover the method he'd used, however? Had his assured manner, had letting Colonel Humphry assume that General Bloomfield approved the Lieutenant's requisition, stretched the Secretary's instructions for the Lake's defense too far?

He refused to debate himself into the same hypnotized state of inaction in which he had found Sidney Smith as a result of serving two masters. The Lake could be properly defended only by ships and men who knew how to handle ships. His job was to obtain those vessels and the men to man them. Any obstacle to that clear-cut aim constituted aid to the enemy, whether the hindrance took the form of British cannon balls or American red tape.

"We'll all take off our coats tomorrow and go to work," he told the group. To the master's mate, he said, "Whenever we need your men to help place the gun carriages and guns aboard the sloops, we'll call on you. Meanwhile, keep them busy on the galleys. Do the best you can."

By the end of the week, with weather a mixture of warm and cold, dry and wet, the Lieutenant was forced to conclude that nobody in this part of the country knew anything about what needed doing to put a fleet on Lake Champlain. He did not disparage the ability of the Lake's builders and carpenters to fit out vessels for ordinary commercial use, but he found them ignorant of every detail pertaining to a ship-of-war. As he came to realize that their unfamiliarity with naval building in no way affected the skills in their hands, he spent more and more time going from sloop to sloop, from shipwright to shipwright, answering questions, explaining, showing. He found his attitude softening toward Bloomfield and Dearborn. As did these shipwrights, they undoubtedly found it hard to accustom themselves to Navy ways. They too probably needed patient educating. That he felt himself well able to provide. He could be patient; he believed he could teach.

Work progressed. With masts unstepped, the sixty-odd-foot-long, iron-keeled hulls whose beams averaged twenty feet and whose drafts ranged up to six and a half feet, proved strong enough for the duty expected of them. With proper shoring, their decks would support guns and carriages, staggered along the rails.

Beside each cradled hull, ready to hoist aboard, waited its armament. For *Hunter,* two long twelve-pounders and four six-pounders, with one long eighteen-pounder to go forward on a pivot. For *Bull Dog,* six long six-pounders, with a long eighteen on a pivot. *President* would carry six eighteen-pounders and two long twelves. Enough to stand off, batter, and sink any gunboat.

Sidney Smith and Joseph Smith had thrown themselves into the work with energy and, it seemed to the grateful Lieutenant, a solid knowledge of what needed doing. No problem fazed them. Their resourcefulness pleased him and excited the unspoken but obvious admiration of the local shipwrights they directed. In Moses Eggleston's yard, the United States Navy on Lake Champlain began to take visible, respectable shape. A feeling of achievement filled the men. They whistled, joked, and kept busy on the sloops from sunup to sundown.

2

Saturday night, as he went upstairs to his room after dinner with his officers, the Lieutenant heard his name called. From the landing he saw a soldier in the lobby holding out an envelope. Before he accepted and opened the letter, he knew what it presaged. His eyes took in the short note with a single glance.

"My compliments to General Dearborn," he said to the expectant messenger. "I'll wait on him within the hour."

The walk to Colonel Humphry's office, in the still-bright glow of the final quarter of a hunter's moon, gave him time to pull his thoughts together and get his emotions fully under control. Bloomfield and Sailly had dropped bits and pieces that gave him an inkling of the kind of man he might expect. Set up originally as a doctor in New Hampshire, a good soldier in the Revolution (a colonel at the end) with a strong constitution that pulled him through a killing fever while with Arnold in Canada, Secretary of War under Thomas Jefferson, intelligent, determined. "Don't underrate him," Sailly had cautioned. That he certainly would not do!

Ushered into Colonel Humphry's quarters near the barracks, the Lieutenant met Henry Dearborn, senior major general commanding the United States Army, operating out of Albany and Niagara since the start of the war. During the preliminaries and while General Dearborn closely scanned the Lieutenant's orders from Paul Hamilton, he took stock of what he saw.

Dearborn's hair was white, and he looked to be about sixty.

His rugged face and square jaw testified to the determination and integrity which Peter Sailly had pointed up. But, together with his big frame, heavy neck, and long, broad-based nose, they also testified to a strong element of unadulterated stubbornness. This man had accustomed himself to getting what he thought he wanted.

General Dearborn wasted no time. "It's late," he said abruptly to Colonel Humphry, "and I wish to start back to Albany at dawn. Will you arrange for my carriage and horses, please, while I discuss matters with Lieutenant Macdonough?"

Could you hear an emphasized overtone on the word Lieutenant, as if the General wanted to give it the lower rank it had in the Army?

"Tell me, Mr. Macdonough," General Dearborn said when Colonel Humphry had gone, "just what steps you're taking to prepare the fleet."

The Lieutenant made his recital short but sufficiently detailed to bring out all he felt the General could clearly comprehend. When he finished, he waited quietly.

General Dearborn found a paper, held it up. "These supplies have been delivered, I understand, without my approval."

The Lieutenant nodded. "As I pointed out to General Bloomfield when I requisitioned that armament, there would not be time to have the guns shipped from New York. General Bloomfield indicated a need on your part for naval support next month. He didn't give me the exact time and place. I plan to have the squadron ready wherever and whenever you require it."

The Lieutenant felt he sounded pompous. But a little self-importance would help, almost certainly, with Dearborn.

The General took off the gold-rimmed spectacles with which he had gone over the armament list. He put them down slowly on top of the papers on the desk, slowly got up, slowly went to a window, and looked out.

"I won't deny, Lieutenant," he said, "that you've got me over a barrel. I don't like it. I don't like it at all."

The Lieutenant's insides settled. Just as Bloomfield (and Joseph Smith) had said, "He won't like it." Now that the issue was joined, he had his thoughts collected, he felt calm, good.

"General Dearborn," he said, "I don't like it either."

General Dearborn turned. His rugged face held an expression of surprised curiosity. "You don't like what?"

"I don't like to have to scheme, use cunning, play tricks, in order to do for you what you and I both want—keep the British in Canada."

The General turned back to the window, looked up at the moon. "Keep your breeches buttoned, young man." He stood silently by the window for more than a minute. When at last he faced the Lieutenant, he appeared to have come to a decision. He said:

"According to what you told me, you've moved ahead fairly fast with those boats. I believe you know your business, Lieutenant. Can you be ready to sail with me to Canada by the middle of November?"

The Lieutenant's heart bounded. "I can have the fleet ready by the end of this month, provided—"

"Provided?"

"Provided you give me enough soldiers to man the galleys and to service the guns on the sloops. I'll try to enlist enough men off the Lake to sail the vessels."

General Dearborn sat down behind the broad desk again, and squeezed and rubbed the end of his broad nose several times. "Young man," he said very deliberately, "you confound me. You calmly walk into my district, give orders to my officers, and tell me what to do."

The Lieutenant smiled. "With all respect, General Dearborn," he said. "I came to the Lake filled with excitement, with high hopes of doing something important against the enemy. I found the naval situation fouled by lack of Army understanding of what to do on the water. I merely took charge, requested your officers to provide me with needed armament, and pointed out to you that, with your soldiers, we can make the armament effective."

"All right!" Dearborn said gruffly. "I'll see Bloomfield gives you the men. You have the boats moored off Plattsburg before the tenth of November." He looked sternly at the Lieutenant. "The boats will be under my command."

The Lieutenant shook his head.

"I'm sorry, General Dearborn. But I must retain command. Subject, of course, to the exigencies of your invasion plans."

Dearborn bridled.

"Do you mean to sit there and say you've got the nerve to try to take those boats out of my command? The War Department bought and paid for them!"

The Lieutenant could glimpse a thin edge of weakening. Too, he had warmed to the man and to the argument. "The War Department got stung, General. I can put only three into condition. The others you keep."

"Now you *are* telling me what I can do and what I can't do!"

The Lieutenant shook his head again. How stubborn did the General want to be?

"We've been all over this, General Dearborn. You've seen my authority for taking command of the fleet. I have the vessels in fair way to being useful to you. It's for you to decide whether to have them in action next month or wait until I can get naval supplies from New York, which may take until next spring. In either case, sir, I must assume responsibility for our vessels on the Lake."

Dearborn pinched his nose mechanically, his eyes going out toward the window and the waning moon. After a long silence, during which the Lieutenant could see signs of internal debate, the General stood up.

"Lieutenant Macdonough," he said sharply, "I will comply with my orders from the Secretary of War and yours from the

Secretary of the Navy—under protest. I will suggest an appeal to President Madison to retain but one commander on the Lake and to keep him under the War Department. I will comply, that is, so far as to turn *Hunter* and *Bull Dog* over to you. But *President* stays under my command, and I will not turn it over to the Navy until you and the whole fleet come under my sole command."

The Lieutenant stood up, his expression pleasant, he hoped, even friendly. No need to demand complete surrender. With this he could make do—with Dearborn's guns, munitions and soldiers.

"The vessels will meet you at Plattsburg," he said. "I hope you have a comfortable return to Albany, sir."

3

Lieutenant Macdonough reported progress the following week to Lucy Ann Shaler in Middletown, to Paul Hamilton in Washington, and to Captain Isaac Hull at the New York Navy Yard.

To Ann he wrote a description of the Lake, of the country surrounding it, of the colorful characters he'd encountered, of the kind of life they'd probably live together, and of his plans to have her with him very soon . . . in December, if all went well.

To Paul Hamilton he wrote a simple account of what he'd found on the Lake, what he'd done with the boats, and what support he foresaw for the Army's march into Canada. He made no mention of the difficulties he and his fellow officers had surmounted, nor did he touch on his meeting with Dearborn. By the time the Navy Secretary received the Lieutenant's factual statement about the Army's claim to command of the boats, the War Secretary would have had his ear—and the President's. And Paul Hamilton, he expected—well, at least he hoped—would stand fast.

To Hull he wrote a description of current supply problems. He had no expectation of getting either men or munitions from the New York base, but he felt it wise to set Captain Hull's mind on the needs of Lake Champlain as well as those of Lakes Ontario and Erie.

And on Monday, October 26th, via Colonel Humphry, the Lieutenant sent a message to General Dearborn at Albany that *President* sloop, eight guns, Captain Billings, had sailed from Whitehall that day to arrive Plattsburg Tuesday.

Bending over backwards to maintain the Army-Navy liaison agreed on with Dearborn, the Lieutenant had thrown all hands into getting *President* ready first. To Army Captain Billings, who unashamedly admitted to no previous knowledge of boats and, further, freely confessed to wanting no part of them, he assigned Joseph Barron.

"Deliver Captain Billings and *President* safely to General Bloomfield," he told the reluctant pilot, "and in good style. Make everybody at the Plattsburg garrison feel the Navy knows its way around the Lake."

"But, sir," protested Barron, "you put none but soldiers on her, except me and my mate."

The Lieutenant slapped him jovially on the back. "What more do you need, Joe?" he said.

On Friday he sent Dearborn a second message that *Hunter* sloop, seven guns, Lieutenant Smith, had sailed from Whitehall that day to arrive Plattsburg Saturday. To sail the sloop for Sidney Smith went *Hunter*'s former captain and two crew members, left on the beach when the Army bought *Hunter* from her private owners and now enlisted in the United States Navy.

The following Tuesday, exactly three weeks from the day the decrepit sloops and gunboats had gone on their cradles for overhaul, the Lieutenant sent a final message to General Dearborn, somewhat longer. It said that *Bull Dog* sloop, seven guns, Lieutenant Macdonough, and two galleys, one gun each, had sailed from Whitehall that day to arrive Plattsburg Wednesday, November 4th.

Thus the fleet assembled, ready for action.

Painted a conventional black, flying white canvas fresh out of Whitehall's sail lofts, the flotilla exercised daily on the Lake outside Plattsburg Bay. Under Midshipman Smith and the master's mate, the galleys rowed, sailed, and practiced with the twelve-pounders. Under the noting eyes of Lieutenants

Macdonough and Smith, the sloops, with men from General Bloomfield's artillery corps at the guns, handled as well as could be expected, and the Lieutenant took great satisfaction from Captain Billings' complete happiness in leaving nautical details in the hands of Joseph Barron.

The flotilla went three times to the line, north of Champlain, in part to scout the situation at the end of the Lake where it entered into the Sorel and Canada, in part to accustom British outposts to the fleet's appearance, so that there would be no special alarm when it led Dearborn's troops on their projected invasion.

The Lieutenant had maintained a strict silence regarding General Dearborn's plans, revealing the coming action to his officers only after agreeing with Generals Dearborn and Bloomfield on details of land-sea cooperation.

General Dearborn disclosed his objective to be Montreal. He pointed out that Captain John E. Wool on the western front had led a successful attack on Queenston Heights in Canada just four weeks earlier; proving that the British could be overcome. Captain Wool had withdrawn, however, because he had had no support from General Solomon Van Rensselaer and the New York Militia.

The Lieutenant kept discreetly out of discussions between the generals on deployment of troops. When, however, General Dearborn disclosed his intention of having the fleet cover the marching army, the Lieutenant agreed that this could be done as far as the line itself, the twenty-odd miles from Plattsburg to the border; but pointed out that before he could commit himself from there, in Canadian waters, he would have to know more about the conditions he would encounter.

General Dearborn called on Eleazer Williams. The Scout Chief had, himself, just returned from a clandestine visit to Montreal over the proposed line of march. The fleet would meet only the possible opposition of two gunboats. Lazare apparently had had time to assay his information this trip! When he saw them two days ago, the gunboats lay on the beach at Isle-aux-Noix being recommissioned.

The Lieutenant asked about conditions in the Sorel River —depth, speed of current. Williams had no accurate knowledge. The Lieutenant called in Joseph Barron. Barron described the river as easily navigable, though narrow, up to Isle-aux-Noix "if you have enough air to overcome a two-knot current on the way back," and beyond that to Chambly Falls not so good.

Final plans, the Lieutenant told his officers, called for starting to move supplies November 16th to Champlain and for the Army to jump off from there, with 5,000 troops, Friday, November 20th, for Montreal. The fleet would cover the troops as far north as the Lacolle River, where the Army would cross inland to its objective.

During the next four days, the Lieutenant learned the impossibility of hiding the movements of large numbers of soldiers. While his gunboats cruised day and night off Rouses Point to guard against a surprise foray by the enemy's galleys, the sloops escorted the Army's boats (the 150 bateaux he'd been told about) loaded with food, to Champlain, carried miscellaneous troops, ferried some munitions. His excitement mounted steadily.

He watched, pleased, the increasing agitation of the two Smiths (particularly that of the midshipman, who conned his galley like the captain of a frigate), of Trumbull, and of the seamen. The Navy stood ready, able and avid to fight.

On the morning of November 20th, under a dull, snow-clouded sky, the United States fleet on Lake Champlain weighed anchor and, led by flagship *Bull Dog*, Lieutenant Macdonough, tacked over the line into the Sorel River and Canada.

Four miles down, where the Lacolle River empties into the Sorel, the American advance troops ran into a contingent of

British soldiers. The warships joined the skirmish, firing from the Sorel. When the American troops, screened by the naval bombardment, abruptly withdrew, the fleet held its fire.

Impatient to see the troops on their way to Montreal, the Lieutenant sent Joseph Smith ashore with his galley to get in touch with General Dearborn.

An hour later the midshipman reported back. He saluted. "Sir," he said in a tone that warned the Lieutenant of the worst, "General Dearborn suggests the fleet drop back to Champlain." He waited.

"Why?" demanded the Lieutenant.

The eager, rosy look had left the midshipman's face. In its place the Lieutenant saw shock, shame, humiliation. Joseph Smith said: "Because the militia refuses to go any farther into Canada."

Two weeks later, early in December, with winter setting in, with ice forming on the Lake, with General Dearborn's recalcitrant troops back in their Plattsburg barracks, Lieutenant Macdonough took his disappointed officers and men and his poor, forlorn-looking squadron into winter quarters at Shelburne.

4

Lieutenant Thomas Macdonough married Lucy Ann Shaler on Saturday, December 12th, a clear, cold day in Middletown, Connecticut. The Navy Department's leave of absence had put him in Middletown the Wednesday before, via miscellaneous stages which, it seemed to the jolted Lieutenant, sought to break all previous records for speed over their rutted routes. He had found Ann waiting for him in front of the stage depot when the horses clomped to a much welcomed stop.[1] As he told her later, she hurled herself at him with the speed and impact of a Congreve rocket. She had only, she insisted, held out a maidenly hand in greeting.

Unlike most of the women he'd known, Ann seemed always to do, and say, what she felt. He'd never come on a woman so natural, so sound in every instinctive reaction to what her senses brought to her from the world of people and things. As a sixteen-year-old girl, she'd liked him immediately—and shown it. She seemed aware also that to him—a Navy officer of wide experience, a man of the world who had seen London, Gibraltar, Tripoli, Venice, and many other places—she was just a child. Like a friendly puppy, however, she didn't let it bother her. She just, he guessed, let him find out in nature's own good time that the reason he kept returning to Middletown on furloughs was to see her.

She had, for him, true beauty. Slender and graceful, she carried herself with gentle dignity. Her features and their total expression showed him a woman of quality, of character, a beautiful woman. Best of all he loved her buoyancy, her love of life. She seemed to demand nothing, gaily to make do with whatever came to hand, to enjoy whatever befell. For this quality alone he would have come to adore her. As he looked back now on his farm upbringing, his five sisters playing in the barnyard, on stream banks, in the underbrush of woods—smelly, muddy, scratched—had the same relish for all their adventures.

From the moment the Shaler front door flew open and the family greeted him, he saw very little of Ann. For the house, full even on that Wednesday before the arrival of Grandfather and Grandmother Denning from New York, practically bounded up, down, and sideways with activity.

His mother-in-law-to-be, as devoted to him as he to her, embraced him with affection. Taller than Ann, and slender, she overwhelmed most of the younger members of the family, who awesomely showed her great deference. But the Lieutenant turned her face up to his and kissed her on the lips.

The Shaler children—Amelia six, Louisa eight, Charlotte twelve, William (never Bill) thirteen, Augusta sixteen, Egbert (never Eggie) eighteen, Charles (never Charlie) twenty-three—surrounded their future brother-in-law. They plied him with questions that ranged from Amelia's simple "Why didn't you travel in your full-dress uniform?" to Charles's serious inquiries about the problems of transporting men and supplies to the Lake.

With sixty-six-year-old Nathaniel Shaler [2] there always had been and still was a certain constraint. The Lieutenant never had gotten close to his slight, violin-playing future father-in-law; during the hectic days before the wedding, he got no closer.

In William Denning, however, he found a kindred soul, a man who instinctively understood what the Lieutenant wanted to talk about, who needed no elaborate descriptive phrases to appreciate the depth of the Lieutenant's feelings—

particularly about the war. At seventy-two, the old gentleman had personality, great personality.

His thin rosy face, shaped almost like a triangle standing on its apex, topped a spare frame of average height. A mop of unruly white hair surmounted the face; bushy white eyebrows shaded blue eyes that seemed always to observe, never to rest in their ceaseless tour of inspection. He wore a white goatee.

His clothes, appropriately, showed his standing. They came from one of New York's best tailors, as everything he owned came from the best suppliers. His information, the Lieutenant knew, also stemmed from unimpeachable sources. He had known, respected, and been respected by Generals Washington and Lafayette when they visited back and forth at "Salisburgh," the Denning country estate a few miles from Army headquarters at Newburgh. He had frequently entertained General and Mrs. Washington and Alexander Hamilton and Mrs. Hamilton.

Because of his wide acquaintance and his prominence in public affairs, his role in the Revolution had been important, while out of the limelight. A member of "The Committee of Sixty," formed in 1774 "for the purpose of organizing and carrying on the War with England" and resolved "to stand or fall with the liberty of the Continent," he had gone to the Continental Congress in 1778. An original subscriber in 1792 to shares of the Tontine Coffee House, he still carried great weight in mercantile New York, and among public officers.

Friday morning before the wedding rehearsal, the old patriot and the young lieutenant went into the Shaler cellar, like conspirators, lighted there by a candle in a hurricane lamp. In a corner of the musty, crowded darkness stood two half-barrels—one open and a small board with a stone on it keeping the solid contents beneath a floating scum, the other sealed and addressed to "William Denning, Esq., 341 Broadway, New York City."

"These shad," said the Lieutenant, pointing to the closed

barrel, "go to you next week by sloop *Robert McCleave*. They'll get better with age. Those in the open barrel are three years old, and the family think they're tastier this year than last."

In the light of the single candle, the old man seated himself on the closed barrel. "How does it go on the Lake, son?" he asked abruptly.

The Lieutenant had great admiration for his bride's grandfather, and took great stock in his judgments of men and his observations on the public scene. He also trusted his loyalty and his discretion. He could confide in this fine old gentleman, and often had.

"For me, sir," he said, "things go as well as I suppose I can expect in a part of the country that knows very little about fighting ships. My problems can be licked with enough support from New York—enough men and materials."

"Are you getting them?"

"Not yet."

"Keep after the Navy Department for what's essential. You've heard, I suppose, that you're getting a new Secretary? A Philadelphia shipowner who refused the job two years ago."

"William Jones? You know him?"

"A good man. A very good man. I suggest you get some strong licks in right at the start."

"Thanks. I will." He said: "I understand there's a new Secretary of War coming up, too."

"General John Armstrong. I've met him once or twice only. He doesn't look as decrepit as those other museum pieces they're using for Army commanders."

The Lieutenant laughed at the old man's vehemence.

"I think the President's going to sign the bill increasing the Navy," William Denning went on. "It looks certain to go through next month. But that won't affect you, I imagine, except, perhaps, to make Navy agents a little more liberal." He paused. "What I really asked you before was what do you think of our strategy along the northern border?"

Visualizing the recent retreat from Lacolle, the Lieutenant countered: "Have we any?"

"In a way, yes. The Army's put the British on the defensive even though none of our attacks have been decisive. We've got upwards of 7,000 regulars with a reservoir of 400,000 militia available over the country. The British have only 5,000 trained troops, with about 8,000 Canadian regulars and militia, and maybe 4,000 Indians."

The Lieutenant nodded. "I've heard those figures, too," he said. "I know we've got seven and a half million population to Canada's half a million. I know that England's busy trying to cope with Napoleon, and needs her troops in Europe. I know all that. But I have a feeling, a very strong feeling, that unless the Army concentrates somewhere along the border, General Dearborn and the new Secretary of War will end us all up in a barrel—like those shad." He hesitated for several seconds.

"What's the matter, son?" William Denning asked.

The Lieutenant rubbed his chin. "Well, sir, I don't mean to sound psychic, but the longer I'm on the Lake the stronger I get a feeling that we'll have important action there. I can't exactly explain it."

"I can," said William Denning. "It's because there are several chances the British will try to come down your way from lower Canada to pay us a visit in New York. At present it looks as though they'll try to make us fight an offensive war on a wide front that's impassable in places—along the Great Lakes. I think they'll continue trying to get around our western flank. But, failing that, they're bound to try Lake Champlain and the Hudson."

The old man's eyes roved over the Lieutenant's face. "I think your feeling's soundly based. I think it's not a premonition so much as a genuine awareness that we're vulnerable along that route [3] and sooner or later we're going to have to defend it."

He stopped briefly, to pick up with increased seriousness.

"If this war goes on another couple of years, as it may in spite of the peace talk you hear along the seaboard, you'll see action, son. Take my word for it. If they fail to get around us in the West, the British'll sure as Moses try Champlain."

The old man got up off the barrel.

"Enough of this," he said, putting his arm around the Lieutenant's shoulders. "I suspect you've got plans for the day with Bill Van Dusen and Hank de Koven and some of your playboy friends. I just want you to know, though, how good I feel to have a man like you up there keeping an eye on things. The family has a mighty high regard for you. And thanks for the shad, son."

The old gentleman's affection and pride touched the Lieutenant deeply. It took the spoken confidence of just one man like this to shore up misgivings about your countrymen's love of their country, to minimize doubts of your colleagues' military ability, to dissipate worries about your own capacity to rise to circumstance. If this patriarch had such confidence in him, how could he doubt himself?

He almost failed, however, to rise to the occasion when Amelia, spokesman for the family, put a beautifully wrapped package in his hand after lunch and told him it was "something which is a little bit extra from all of us." Urged to open it at the table, he took the cover off a flat box to reveal blue bunting. A card lay on the folded bunting: "To Commodore Thomas Macdonough from all his in-laws with much pride and love." He unfolded a broad pennant.

He fought back tears. Until now he hadn't appreciated quite how close the years had brought him to this family. The Shalers had flooded his affections and filled the places of his mother and father—both dead before he reached his teens— and the nine brothers and sisters he had left to enter the Navy. He finally trusted himself to speak.

"I'm not a commodore, yet," he said, looking around the table at their faces, particularly the entranced, uplifted faces of the youngest girls—Amelia, Louisa, and Charlotte—"and you'd hardly call the vessels on Lake Champlain a fleet." He looked at William Denning for a second, letting his eyes come to rest on Ann. "But, God willing, we soon *will* have a fleet and then I'll fly this on my flagship—and think of every single one of you."

The wedding rehearsal went well Friday afternoon, with everyone properly anticipatory of Saturday's proceedings. But from that point on events left very little impression on the Lieutenant. At a table in a private room off the old Hotel Washington's taproom, he had greeted old friends boisterously at his bachelor dinner and the rum flip had proved good, he remembered later. He did not remember rendering poor old Dr. Graham's "The Night after Larry Was Born, the Boys They All Paid Him a Visit," nor betting with Bill Van Dusen that he could build better ships in Vermont with house carpenters than Bill could build in Middletown with ship's carpenters. He had Hank de Koven's assurances, however, that he'd acted sober as a judge.

"Not a single naval secret did you divulge. Not a single war plan did you reveal. Our country could be proud of you last night," his best man proudly reported next morning.

The wedding went off brilliantly.

For blocks, both sides of Main Street—and the church sheds —barely squeezed in the shining carriages that brought to Holy Trinity Church a major part of Middletown's elite . . . the Parsonses, the Sages, the Mortimers, the Watkinsons, Colonel Simeon North, the Nathan Starrs, the Allisons and the Childses (all four pairs), the Johnsons, the Talcotts . . . along with, as Hank pointed out at the reception, most of Tom's disreputable friends from the local shipyards. (Only twenty-eight years before, Main Street had harbored more livestock than carriages; the newly incorporated community's first adopted ordinance then restrained "swine and geese from going at large in the City.")

Inside the tall white church, the music selected by Nathaniel Shaler struck the wedding guests as eminently appropriate. And shafts of sunlight, piercing stained-glass windows over the marble altar, shed a glamorizing glow on the wedding party.

The Lieutenant waited at the altar in full dress, gold-lace-trimmed blue coat with gold epaulet on right shoulder, single-breasted white vest with three buttons on the pockets, white pantaloons, and low-cut black shoes with silver buckles. From his black belt hung his sword. In his left hand he held his gold-laced cocked hat.

"Five swooning women have been carried out already," Hank de Koven whispered into his ear. "I told you not to shine up your gear so bright."

The Lieutenant hardly heard. His eyes followed Ann down the aisle, on her father's arm, behind the attendants led by Amelia and Louisa. They were utterly self-conscious in soft green-and-pink dresses with their baskets of roses, and utterly captivating. Ann's dress of pure silk damask, hyacinth color, with fitted basque bodice (he read later in the *Middlesex Gazette*), gave her the appearance of a portrait. Its wide organdy overcollar, which had been re-embroidered by hand, was fastened low with Grandmother Denning's lovely hand-painted brooch. The elbow sleeves of the dress were finished in the same detail. The pointed toes of her satin slippers, with silver buckles, peeped out under her graceful floor-length skirt. Fashioned like a bonnet, her headdress revealed hair which had been curled and upswept for the occasion. She carried a dainty nosegay of sweetheart roses and lady's-breath.

The Lieutenant choked up. He wondered whether he could make the required responses, and found, when Ann stood by his side and he looked into her eyes while the bishop gave him her hand to hold for the ring, that nothing short of a miracle would make his voice come, normal, from his constricted throat. How could anyone be so lovely?

Holding the Lieutenant's chapeau bras under his arm,

Hank de Koven performed the needed miracle. Passing the ring to the bridegroom, he fumbled, lunged, groaned. And the tinkling of the small gold band—bouncing from marble step to marble step down the altar to the floor—echoed through the hushed church.

The best man recovered the ring with considerable skill, even grace, and the Lieutenant, slipping it firmly on Ann's slightly quaking finger, recovered his voice so that his promises to his bride came out strong and assuring. No one in the congregation could doubt the strength of this marriage!

5

In a chaise drawn by a black horse on loan from the Shalers, Lieutenant and Mrs. Macdonough took a full week to drive to Burlington, going where they wished, when they wished. They had no rigid schedule. When they chose to make a late morning start, they made it. When they found a pleasant inn for lunch and the wine was good, and it looked outside as though it might snow, and the landlord had a cozy room with brightly blazing fire, they stayed.

"The black horse," said Ann on an afternoon such as this, "must think he's on vacation."

"He can't be enjoying it," the Lieutenant said drowsily, "as much as I am."

On such another afternoon Ann took to reading a copy of the Burlington *Centinel* in which the Lieutenant had wrapped his good shoes to keep from soiling the clothes in his bag.

"You should have married me in Shelburne," she said. "I see the justices there always give back the dollar wedding fee to the bride."

He grunted, busy examining Bill Van Dusen's wedding present, a pistol. Bill had said: "It's something new, according to Colonel North. You can replace any of its parts with a similar part from any of the other twenty thousand cavalry pistols he's making for the government. A fellow named Whitney over in Hartford's doing the same thing." The pistol looked serviceable.

"The bride, in many cases, buys flax with the dollar," Ann

rambled on, "and spins and weaves it into linen for family use—with her own hands. I'm going to like this paper. Listen, Tom!"

She poked him.

"The Ebenezer Barstows have thirteen children," she read. "The Benjamin Suttons twenty-four. The John Hadleys have twenty-five!"

He laughed. "I keep telling you about Vermont winters."

"I'm also going to have books to read in Burlington," she parried. "Here's an announcement of the Burlington Library Society meeting at the courthouse." Then: "I like this, Tom! Under the heading of the paper, it says:

"If there be any among us who would wish to dissolve this Union, or to change the Republican form, let them stand undisturbed, as monuments of the safety with which error of opinion may be tolerated, when reason is left free to combat it.—Jefferson.

"I wish I could be so sure! You should hear some of the wild talk in Middletown about how wrong the Federal government is in fighting England."

The Lieutenant looked up from a long letter he had received from Ludlow Dashwood on the Portland station. "Do just what Jefferson suggests, Ann. Don't let it disturb you. Let 'em talk. This is a great country. Or will be once we start to pull together and get England off our backs."

The lazy honeymoon week brought the newlyweds very close in many small ways. To the Lieutenant, his wife proved amazingly easy to get on with, always eager to do whatever he suggested, always enjoying what they did.

"I never believed it could be so easy to live with anyone," he told her.

"You've only lived with men," she pointed out.

They stopped a night at Whitehall's Clinton House. In a tall-ceilinged "bridal suite" whose frescoed cupids capered on all four walls, the Lieutenant let the serious aspects of living start to seep back into his consciousness.

"We'll have to put up for a while at the tavern in Burlington where I've been staying," he told Ann. "I tried to find us lodgings, but I didn't have enough time, or luck. Most of the thousand good souls of Burlington, at least the ones I talked to, don't think much of military officers."

Ann took this quietly, seemingly unworried.

"When we get settled," he went on, "we can have your things meet my trunk and writing desk in New York, where Lud Dashwood's having them sent from Portland. The Navy will ship them for us, to Albany by boat and then overland to Burlington. Meanwhile, can you get along with that trunkful of gear you have in the shay?"

At this she bristled. "That gear," she told him with considerable heat, "comprises some lovely gowns for attending balls in, and some . . . some intimate finery on which my mother and I sewed our fingers to the bone so I'd be presentable to my bridegroom!"

Next morning the Lieutenant showed his bride the Whitehall barracks, and drove to Moses Eggleston's shipyard. The disheveled acres lay silent under several inches of snow, but he found the master carpenter in the model shed, peering through his steel-rimmed glasses at the half-model of a sloop and in the act of putting a fresh, huge handful of chewing tobacco into his mouth.

Moses Eggleston beamed at Ann over his spectacles, but kept the chew in his mouth and mumbled his greetings and congratulations. Yes, he told the Lieutenant after a five-minute recital of needs, he would keep an eye on any materials to be transshipped to Shelburne and, yes, he thought, with business on the Lake falling off as it had, that he could probably send him some shipwrights from time to time and also find him some Lake sailors who would sign on and help him work his ships.

As they concluded their affairs, shouts drew them to the shed door and outside. A short distance from the yard, on the ice of the Lake, a dozen men surrounded a large sleigh and two horses that had broken through the ice.

"They'll drown!" Ann turned her head away.

Moses Eggleston laughed. "Not at all, ma'am," he said. "Come along. You'll find this interesting." He ran to the shore with Ann and the Lieutenant, and out on the ice.

Where they had fallen through on their way from the opposite shore, the horses frantically struggled to free themselves from the frigid water and the entangling harness. Four of the men, wrapped in wool and fur to the ears and wearing big deerskin mittens, tried to shove long planks under the horses' bellies.

Moses Eggleston shouted to them. "That's no good. You better strangle 'em first."

Ann held the Lieutenant's gloved hand tight, but watched as Moses and a burly, redheaded man who appeared to be the sleigh's driver stood on planks close to the horses and proceeded, coldly and efficiently, to wind the reins and halters around the horses' necks and pull them tight. It took considerable doing, but the men had powerful arms and hands. After a few minutes, seemingly dead, the horses gave up their fruitless floundering and floated quietly.

"Get the planks under their forefeet now," Moses Eggleston told the men, and, hauling on the sleigh's tongue and the harness traces, they pulled the animals by main force onto the ice with the planks still beneath them to prevent their going down again. The light sleigh, which had not broken through, seemed undamaged.

"In ten or fifteen minutes the horses'll be right as rain again, ma'am," Moses Eggleston told Ann confidently. "This happens every other day when folks use the Lake for short cuts."

"Could we drive our shay on the Lake down to Burlington?" asked the Lieutenant.

Ann's pressure on his arm cut him off.

"Never mind," he finished. "We're not in that great a hurry."

Moses Eggleston nodded. "You'd need a pilot, Lieutenant, to steer you around the soft spots." He peered owlishly at Ann. "I'm sure your ma'am wouldn't want a third party to help finish her honeymoon." He peered at the Lieutenant. "You don't want one neither. I know I wouldn't."

On Saturday afternoon, December 19th, they arrived at Tousey's Tavern in Burlington. To woo the marriage gods, he not only carried Ann over the inn's threshold but up the stairs and over the tall bedroom's threshold as well.

"This," he said, kissing her chilled face where it stuck pertly through the fur of her cap, "is home."

She didn't even look at the room as she said, "I love it."

"I do, too," he said, quietly. "But tomorrow you'd better start looking for a place big enough to hold that trunk of yours and my writing desk when it comes. There's a war going on in these parts, and your husband has to fight a large part of it with pen and paper. I'll need a lot of elbow room."

6

Lieutenant Macdonough slipped quickly from his role of bridegroom back into his job as commander of the American fleet on Lake Champlain. As Ann told him, he became a different man at his work—so absorbed in what he had to do that she could only stand back out of his way, marvel at how concentratedly he applied himself to naval chores, and thank heaven for the small part of his attention and love she received on some few occasions.

It amazed him how she accepted their situation and never voiced or showed disappointment in his goings. Instead, she always gave him to know, when he came back to her, that with him came the joy that made her life full.

He first left her early Sunday morning when Sidney Smith, bearing wreaths of holly and a spring of mistletoe for the bride, arrived at the tavern in a two-horse sleigh to pick the Lieutenant up for an inspection trip to the boats in Shelburne Bay.

Lieutenant Smith brought his commanding officer up to date. "The boats look like snow mounds already, under their coverings," he reported. "The men have laid bets we won't get them back into the open Lake before May 15th."

The Lieutenant let a smile creep along his lips. "The Army thinks so, too, judging from the letters I found waiting for me. Incidentally," he said. "I paid a small fortune in postage last night to redeem our official mail from the Burlington postmaster."

"You think we can get out on the Lake earlier?"

The Lieutenant nodded. "I'm planning to take it over in April," he said. "Which means that between now and then we've got a lot to do, regardless of weather."

Before heading south for Shelburne, Sidney Smith drove down Pearl Street toward the Burlington shore front. At North Street, he pointed to the framework of a large building under construction.

"After you'd gone to Middletown," he said, "General Bloomfield asked if I could let him have some men to help put up that barracks. I thought it wiser to keep our men busy and comparatively warm working for the Army than try to keep them from getting drunk and disorderly sitting around in the cold for the Navy."

The Lieutenant scanned the enormous building, already roofed and with considerable siding in place. "If the men work as hard for us as they seem to have worked for General Bloomfield," he said, "we'll have a good flotilla come spring."

"They didn't do this alone," Sidney Smith confessed. "The General brought a big construction gang over from Plattsburg just before the Lake froze."

He drove to the foot of Pearl Street and pointed out where the Army planned to throw up embankments for protecting the village from attack by water. "The Army doesn't seem to have much confidence in our keeping the British off the Lake," he said.

"Don't let it bother you," said the Lieutenant. "It's standard practice for the Army to dig in, and Bloomfield's read the rule book from cover to cover." He looked quickly at his companion. "The Army didn't take back those guns we got from them at Whitehall!"

Sidney Smith laughed at the Lieutenant's obvious alarm. "No, sir," he said. "We still have them, right where we set them up to guard the boats before you left for your wedding."

As the sleigh covered the ground to Shelburne, the Lieutenant used Sidney Smith as a sounding board for his ideas on how best to make the fleet effective for the 1813 campaign.

"We'll have to make do with what we've got," he pointed out. "Commodore Chauncey's trying to sweep Lake Ontario clear for the Army's operations on that frontier, so all available men and supplies will go first to him. Lake Erie's second; I'm told the Navy's sending some of New York's best shipwrights there to build a fleet—Henry Eckford of Eckford & Beebe and Noah Brown of Adam & Noah Brown.[1] We'll have to take next best."

"You don't sound depressed at the prospect," said Sidney Smith.

"I'm not," he said. "With the grand strategy aiming to fight the British on the Ontario and Erie borders, we have time on our side here. We'll do all that's expected of us if we protect Lake Champlain while the Army sends every available soldier to the Ontario and Erie fronts."

"And after things get settled there?"

The Lieutenant's jaws automatically tensed. "That," he said, "is when New York and Boston better empty their yards of men and guns for us!"

The pair said nothing more for several minutes, while the horses guided themselves along the snow-packed road. Like himself, the Lieutenant felt sure, Sidney Smith heard the booming of cannon through battle smoke.

"My plans take advantage of what we have," he went on, "not what we wish we had nor what we'll keep hounding the Navy Department for—hoping to get eventually."

He paused again. Finally he said:

"Our problem revolves entirely around keeping the ascendancy on Champlain; and being able to support the smallest army that can adequately protect the towns on both sides of the Lake from predatory enemy raids.

"We kept the British off the Lake before we went into winter quarters. If then," he said, "we improve the fleet with whatever brains and brawn and materials we can muster before we go back, we should be able to cope with the enemy this year, too, even though they build more gunboats."

Sidney Smith looked skeptical. "We might conceivably put another gun on each of the two galleys," he said, "but there's nowhere on *Hunter* and *Bull Dog* to mount more."

"What about their quarterdecks?"

"The quarterdecks won't support that much weight."

"So we get rid of them," said the Lieutenant, "get down to solid decking that we can shore up to carry any weight we want."

A smile of admiration spread over Sidney Smith's boyish face. "Commodore," he said, "I wish I'd thought of that." After a moment: "One improvement I *can* think of, if it's all right with you and the Secretary."

"Yes?"

"Different names for *Hunter* and *Bull Dog*. Something like . . . well, anything but what the Army called 'em."

The Lieutenant laughed. He said: "Once we get those long quarterdecks off and four more guns on, those vessels will look so good they'll deserve new names. You pick them, Mr. Smith."

"Thank you. I certainly will."

When the sleigh reached the hauled-out boats, surrounded by their guns so placed as to command all possible avenues of attack by water and by land, a pair of bundled-up sailors, on watch over the dormant fleet, came out the door of a wood-and-tarpaper shack. Inside a small fire burned in a tin tub. The seamen saluted. Except for their salutes, however, they showed no signs of being in the Navy. They wore the heavy woolens of the French-Canadian woodsmen who, since the Revolution, had infiltrated the towns on both sides of the Lake, colorful clothes but not nautical.

The Lieutenant smiled inwardly at their incongruity. But he thanked his stars that he had even these men, and until he could provide them with basic Navy equipment he could only put up with whatever clothes they scraped together for themselves.

"Have all the men got everything they need to keep them comfortable?" he asked Sidney Smith, out of earshot range of the watch.

"Yes, sir," Sidney Smith said, "the Army's looking out very well for the men working on the Burlington barracks. And the ones posted here with the boats have good lodging with the townspeople—along with their regular issue of rum. They seem to regard that very highly."

"So would I, if I had to stand watch in this snow and ice!"

The Lieutenant retucked the heavy cloth robe firmly around his middle, and Sidney Smith made a sweeping circuit of the vessels which, with their masts out and covered with planks and tarpaulins, exposed very little of themselves under their snow blankets. The tarpaulin-covered guns on their wooden carriages stood completely free of snow, however, ready for instant use.

The Lieutenant gave Sidney Smith his full approval. "You've done a good job," he said, "you and the men. Thank you."

"Thank *you*, sir."

As the sleigh turned away from the sloops, Sidney Smith posed a question that brought a grin to his own face.

"What's the current situation with *President?*" he asked. "Is she going to be General Dearborn's or ours?"

Caught unawares, the Lieutenant looked nonplused for a moment. At length he let a frozen smile spread over his wind-whipped face, and said: "Since you bring it up, I've come to the conclusion that the outgoing Secretary of the Navy would dislike getting a final report that one of the ships included in the Champlain fleet belongs to a general quartered in Albany. So tonight, when I write Paul Hamilton to catch him up to date, I'll list *President* under Navy command. Do you approve?"

"I do indeed."

"Thank *you*."

After several restless seconds, Sidney Smith hesitantly said: "Do you think you can make it stick?"

The Lieutenant rolled back his head and roared. Then: "Figure it this way," he said. "We have the vessel in our possession. General Dearborn has a claim only and, by the time we put *President* into the water next spring, he'll probably be busy fighting the British on Lake Ontario. Meanwhile, when William Jones takes over as Navy Secretary from Paul Hamilton in a few weeks, he'll find my official report which includes *President* as part of our Champlain fleet. Can you see Dearborn come May, trying to straighten Jones and a new Secretary of War out on his side of it, by correspondence from Lake Ontario?"

Sidney Smith chuckled appreciatively.

"Commodore," he said, "it's a pleasure and a privilege to serve under a man with your genius for keeping the Army dragging behind like a cow's tail."

That evening, comfortable in a dressing gown of China silk and, to Ann, looking very handsome in the Brutus haircut she'd prevailed on him to get for their wedding, the Lieutenant wrote before the bedroom fireplace. To the outgoing Secretary of the Navy he detailed the state of the Lake Champlain flotilla, describing the three sloops and two gunboats with their armament. *President* led the list.

He outlined his plans for refitting the vessels, and reported his requests to Captain Samuel Evans, now in command of the New York Navy Yard, and John Bullus, Navy Agent in New York, for armament and men. The fleet was undermanned and poorly manned when it went into winter quarters, he concluded. To hold the ascendancy on the Lake during the coming year, the vessels needed officers and seamen capable of sailing them and working their guns.

He realized how greatly he understated the case. But he

deliberately sought—by not demanding at this time what Commodore Chauncey must desperately need on Ontario—to put himself on record as a knowledgeable, objective commander, able to improvise when necessary and unashamed to call for whatever help he needed to meet a situation.

7

On December 23rd, the Lieutenant waked to find a bottle of champagne and two glasses standing on the table beside his bed.

"Happy birthday, darling," said Ann. "How does it feel to be twenty-nine years old?"

Again, on Christmas morning, his bride produced a bottle of Grandfather Denning's wedding-reception champagne for breakfast in bed. And something of the Lieutenant's festive happiness reached every man in his command as he took Ann on a tour in a borrowed sleigh behind the black horse. The tour included the new Burlington barracks where she charmed Master's Mate Trumbull and his working detail and the Shelburne winter quarters where she captivated red-cheeked Midshipman Smith and his watchmen.

The day before New Year's the Lieutenant surprised her with: "We're leaving town this morning." He explained: "It's rough enough at any time for a man stuck up here in the wilds of Vermont without a family—more so when everybody else is celebrating. So I've arranged with Sidney Smith to see that our men have themselves a little New Year's Eve fun. What I don't know won't hurt me or them—I'm clearing out with you."

The Argalus Cobbs, rushing into their tavern yard when the Macdonough sleigh drew up, embraced both Ann and the Lieutenant as though they were family. A lovely large room

on the second floor awaited them, with blazing fire and a
pitcher of rum flip.

"Since you're a sailor's wife, ma'am," Argalus boomed
across the room from the door as he turned to leave after de-
positing their luggage, "we assumed you like rum, too."

When their host had gone, Ann remained so quiet that the
Lieutenant, opening a bag on the plaid-quilted bed, looked up
suddenly.

Ann smiled gravely at her husband.

"I'd like you to join me in a toast, Commodore," she said,
"to our son."

The Lieutenant folded her in his arms.

The tavern's old-timers, remembering the Lieutenant from
his previous visit, greeted him and Ann with almost as much
warmth as had the Cobbs themselves, and took them into
their upstairs inner circle for much loud conversation and
some passable singing. Downstairs the New Year's Eve noise
seemed even louder.

Through the din, the Lieutenant managed to get in a few
words with Lawyer Rich, who confirmed his earlier prediction
that the Vermont legislature would be forced to reverse itself
on its stand behind the Federal government. "The voters are
bitter," he said. "They'd throw the present rascals out today
if the next election wasn't until October. Meanwhile, they're
doing all the trading they can manage with Canada without
getting caught."

Ann looked quizzical. "Don't the laws mean anything to
Vermonters?"

"Ma'am," said Rich, "we're as honest as the day is long. It's
only after dark that folks forget the laws."

She laughed self-consciously with the lawyer and her husband. "It's all very confusing," she said. "I just read in the
Centinel about citizens having sent to the Army 'that which
money cannot buy,' as the piece put it ... onions, cheese,
fowls, and so on. And the receiving officer said: 'Here is

Patriotism (with a capital P) unfeigned and genuine.' I really don't understand."

The Lieutenant took his wife's slender hand. "You have to appreciate that Vermonters, like other people we know, are human."

From Argalus Cobb the Lieutenant learned that Jacob Dibble had left Waterbury for St. Albans. "To run contraband over the border," said Argalus. "Now the snow's on the ground, you can slip through the woods with little or no trouble."

"I'd put Peter Sailly onto Dibble," the Lieutenant told Ann, "only I want the scoundrel for myself."

"You always sound so admiring when you mention Peter Sailly; when will I meet him?" she asked.

"Soon—providing the sickness quiets down in Burlington and Plattsburg."

She looked at him closely. "Is that why you visit all your men every day? To see whether they've caught the fever?"

He nodded. Momentarily his mind ran over the names of the men he'd sent to hospital in Burlington. So far none had succumbed to what now had the name "spotted fever"—a pneumonia. But the Army had lost as many as twelve dead in a single day. One of their surgeons, Dr. James Mann, had vividly described its ravages—"inflammation of lungs, crammed with blood; heart reaches the point of being unable to move; the patient suffocates in a moment, dies without a groan." The doctor blamed "the drinking of ardent spirits" for much of its devastation. The Lieutenant smiled briefly; every man jack of the Navy personnel drank up his rum allowance every day!

At midnight, having greeted the New Year dancing to the scraping of a violin played midway on the stairs so that both bar and common room could share, the Lieutenant and Ann went to bed. Four hours later, he waked at the sound of a musket shot near the bedroom window. Instantly alert, he listened but heard nothing more—no smallest noise, no movement outside the inn. He tried to go back to sleep, but in fifteen minutes a second musket shot broke into his tentative slumbering; a pistol shot followed, and more musket fire.

In a few minutes, fifty or more noisy persons, chiefly children and young people, gathered under the bedroom windows, fired more pistol shots, and threw stones against the window glass.

Ann, finally aroused by the noise, opened one eye. "What do we do?" she asked, wryly. "Invite them up?"

A knock brought the answer. Argalus Cobb called through the door.

"It's in your honor, Captain," he said. "They're coming in to drink my liquor and wish you and your missus a good New Year."

The Lieutenant called back: "Please thank them for us, Argalus, and give them a few shillings for their kind wishes."

Argalus clopped downstairs in carpet slippers, his resonant voice continuing to pass through the bedroom door: "If only I can get them out before they get too drunk to stand up!"

The Lieutenant settled back to sleep. "I feel like a Roman emperor," he told Ann, "dispensing largesse to the people."

Next morning he learned that he and Ann had received no particular compliment, for Mercy Cobb explained that local custom took young folks, servants, and even Negroes from tavern to tavern—and to other houses—to wish a Good Year and ask for a drink from everyone.

Starting home soon after, he found last night's visitors on all sides, decidedly drunk but astonishingly able to walk, run, and slide on the icy streets without falling—without even making a false step.

"These Vermonters," observed Ann, "seem more than human."

8

Through President Daniel C. Sanders of the University of Vermont, Mrs. Thomas Macdonough located lodgings—the separate half of a huge white, wide-porched house near the University—and settled in with her trunks and the Lieutenant's writing desk, on which he worked long evenings after the day's chores in town.

Ann wrote her mother that she had joint use of a kitchen where artless Betsy Byrd—widow with twin daughters, Emily and Hester, aged sixteen—exchanged Vermont's outstanding cooking recipes for Connecticut's. She also wrote that she'd seen little of her neighbors, since her husband spent most of his time with the military.

From a small office in Pearl Street near the new barracks, the Lieutenant maintained liaison with the Army and kept his men busy doing needed chores (including raising a new carillon to the belfry of the Congregational Church) that sustained the seamen's morale and brought to the naval establishment the thanks and respect of Burlington's soldiers and civilians alike.

Mostly, he was involved in the bookkeeping details which Washington's Navy chiefs cherished and Ann found so hard to reconcile with a husband purportedly on active duty in a war area. He explained to her, in as much detail as he felt would convince, that he didn't spend his evenings with pen and paper because he liked to make ink by mixing ink powder in water. He showed her the Naval Regulations issued by command of the President of the United States of America.

"The first two duties of the commander of a squadron read: 1. Inform the Secretary of the Navy of all proceedings . . . 2. Correspond with all public offices."

Also, as he patiently pointed out, he had no purser; those duties devolved on him; he bought everything down to slops, of which he kept meticulous records. In addition, he had duties as captain of a ship. When he had partly detailed those —give constant attention and quicken dispatch of work, inventory stores, keep counter books, audit accounts of officers, keep a muster book—Ann took the well-thumbed 4 by 6½-inch pamphlet of regulations from him, investigated for herself, and found fifty-seven separate duties for a ship's commander.

"Since one of those regulations requires the captain to keep a journal of everything that happens," she told him, "perhaps you'll want to enter that Dr. Paton confirms my New Year's announcement. Our midshipman will report for active duty sometime in October."

Several other midshipmen already had arrived; one in particular. Early in February, while going over Sidney Smith's list of names and ratings of men available to help in refitting the boats, the Lieutenant had answered a firm knock on his office door and looked up to see a stiff salute framing a shining countenance.

"Midshipman Azariah Bellamy reporting, sir!"

The Lieutenant returned the salute, and for several seconds gazed silently at the boy. Aze looked taller, heavier, older in his uniform. For this dramatic moment, he'd put on his full-dress blue coat with six buttons, short lapels, and standing collar with a diamond of gold lace on each side.

When finally the Lieutenant felt he could trust his voice, he asked for news of Ludlow Dashwood and other officers at Portland.

"Mr. Dashwood said to tell you that Portland is as dull as ever since it lost your society," Aze relayed solemnly. "He says your friends anticipate a great deal from your next spring's movements. That's why I hurried here the minute I received my orders."

The Lieutenant smiled, gradually working his thoughts around to how best he could put Aze to work for the boy's own benefit and the Navy's.

"Oh, yes," Aze went on, "Mr. Dashwood would like you to write him about the shorthand, I think he said, that you've discovered."

The Lieutenant nodded. "That gives me an idea," he said. From a desk drawer he took his battered copy of Naval Regulations. "Read me what it says about the duties of a midshipman."

"Yes, sir." Aze held the book but did not open it. He stood stiffly at attention. "It says, sir, first, no regular duties; second, execute all orders; third, merit fostering care of officers; fourth, keep journals; fifth, study naval tactics—acquire a thorough and extensive knowledge of all duties to be performed on a ship of war. That's all, sir."

"You seem to have studied a little."

Aze beamed.

"Well, here's my idea," said the Lieutenant. "Suppose you work in this office for a while. I need a clerk. I'll show you that shorthand Mr. Dashwood mentions, and you can help keep my journal as well as your own. You'll pick up what you need to know as you go along."

"Thank you, sir." The boy seemed overwhelmed at this opportunity to watch the running of the fleet from such close quarters.

After a few minutes' further reflection, the Lieutenant asked, "How much will the Navy pay you for performing the duties you reeled off?"

"Nineteen dollars a month, sir," Aze said, "and one ration a day."

"Well," said the Lieutenant, "that puts you on the bottom of the list, all right, one step below a ship's carpenter who gets twenty dollars and two rations. Let's see what we can work out so you can get along on your pay."

"I can get along," Aze said hurriedly; "I can get along fine, sir, just fine." Nineteen dollars obviously loomed large to him as a country boy.

The Lieutenant kept his amusement to himself. He said: "I'm sure you can, Aze. But I'd like to have you live close by. Since you're going to work as my clerk, I may have to call on you at all hours."

Aze glowed. He'd never dreamed, apparently, that the Lieutenant would look out for him, need him, like this.

"Suppose," said the Lieutenant, "you get acquainted with Burlington right off by finding the Mills bookstore and getting two of the maps Mr. Mills advertised a couple of weeks ago in the paper. Here's the notice." The Lieutenant spread out the *Centinel:*

FOR SALE BY SAMUEL MILLS

Price: One dollar

A new and elegant map of Upper and Lower Canada and the United States

Contiguous, including every probable seat of war.

At this important crisis in the American history, the ability of such a work must be evident to every reflective mind. Public curiosity is at this time awake, and every class of citizens must be peculiarly interested in passing events. Who would not wish to trace the progress of the war, the path of conquest, and the loopholes of retreat? By paying Mr. Mills only one dollar for this map, the possessor can do it all, seated at ease by his peaceable fireside.

"Here's two dollars for Mr. Mills." The Lieutenant handed the money to Aze. "Ask him if he can provide charts for Lake Champlain. No, I'm just being facetious. There aren't any; we'll have to heave the lead." He smiled. "After you get the maps, pick up your gear wherever you left it, and find your way to Mrs. Boyd's—on the hill near the University. I'm sure she can spare a room for you in her part of the house." The Lieutenant added: "She has a couple of beautiful young daughters, but that, of course, won't interest you. You'll be too busy with your job."

"Yes, sir." Aze kept his face composed.

"Introduce yourself to Mrs. Macdonough," said the Lieutenant, "and give her one of the maps. Say you're my new clerk; she'll appreciate that." He clapped Aze on the shoulder. "Keep the other map for Navy use. Those are your orders, Midshipman Bellamy. Shove off."

Earlier in the month, too, word had come from Middletown that Ann's cousin Nathaniel Shaler had been lost at sea. "I hadn't seen much of him," she told her husband, "but I was very fond of him."

Also, Jacob Dibble, taken on his way to the enemy with a load of provisions, beat up an Army sergeant and a citizen who volunteered his services in the capture. Sergeant and citizen ended in the Burlington hospital, Dibble in jail with every likelihood of serving a short time for the beatings but, because of public temper, not for the attempted smuggling.

And, on February 10th, Ann had celebrated her twenty-third birthday. The event passed generally unnoted, except for a letter from home and, at supper, a carnelian seal with her initials—a very small token, wrote the Lieutenant on the accompanying card, of my love for my dear wife.

On a sunny and comparatively warm and windless Saturday, the Lieutenant and his bride sleighed the twenty-two miles across frozen Lake Champlain from Burlington to Plattsburg for dinner, overnight, and Sunday breakfast with the Peter Saillys. Midshipman Bellamy drove, and for lunch en route the trio ate fried chicken that had been kept moderately warm on a heated soapstone under their carriage robes.

The white-blanketed mountains of Vermont as they left

and the snow-covered shore of New York as they arrived glistened like a candle-lighted crystal chandelier.

Peter Sailly himself threw open his paneled front door at the Lieutenant's clop of the small brass knocker, embraced Ann with true Latin affection, and turned her over to an equally fond greeting from Mrs. Sailly. He directed a servant to relieve the midshipman of the horse and sleigh, and led the Lieutenant to a small library off the living room. For more than an hour he talked business.

The Lieutenant listened for much of the time because, as Collector of Customs, district of Champlain, Peter Sailly would have to rely on the Navy for considerable help in upholding the laws against smuggling.

"As you know from your own observation, Lieutenant," Peter Sailly pointed out, "my men have only a few boats to patrol about a mile of water at the border night and day. And I have only a handful of militia—not even uniformed—to keep watch at our customhouses at Rouses Point and, opposite in Vermont, Windmill Point. You may recall how the fishermen come out nights to spear salmon and sturgeon in the river— with pine knots flaming in an iron frame in the bows of their canoes and reflecting in the trees."

The Lieutenant laughed. "I remember thinking you'd have trouble telling legitimate fishermen from smugglers with contraband."

"You can help us there, by letting me call on you for a gunboat whenever my assistants need it."

"You'll know in advance?"

Peter Sailly laughed. "I wanted to impress you," he said. "Certainly I'll know. We have many sources of information to depend on. Men—and women with their children—constantly cross to Canada to visit relatives. Some Canadians come this way to live permanently; some desert from the British army. Then we have the Indians who move back and forth, like Lazare Williams' scouts. And smugglers; they peach on competitors. The point is, we get warning; and when they come by water we'll need gunboats. Especially when they're armed with cannon, like the big lumber rafts and privateers."

The Lieutenant almost leaped from his chair. "Privateers! Come now, Peter!"

"Yes, Lieutenant," said Sailly. "If you know whom to apply to, the government will give you a commission for privateering on Lake Champlain. Can you see, now, why I need your strong support?"

The Lieutenant's mind had raced far ahead. He brought his thoughts back to Peter Sailly's question, and gave his unqualified promise.

Glancing out the library window, his host said: "Here's General Bloomfield, with Colonel Clark, to talk about their problems. We'll have to finish working ours out when you bring your flotilla here in the spring . . . Commodore. I may call you that, yes?"

The Lieutenant showed his pleasure at this recognition from a colleague whose respect he valued, and said: "Not in public, please. Just to Mrs. Macdonough—Ann, if you and Mrs. Sailly will."

General Bloomfield sampled Peter Sailly's Madeira, found it excellent, and wasted no time relieving his mind of what filled it.

"Mostly," he said, "I'm getting my brigade in shape, on War Department instructions, to join Dearborn and move on York." [1]

This was indeed news; first intimation to reach the Lieutenant that the American Army planned an early attack on the capital of upper Canada. On Bloomfield's departure, Colonel Clark would command all troops left in Plattsburg, Burlington, Chazy, and Champlain.

"A handful only," said the Colonel. "I'll need your Navy for support, Mr. Macdonough." His voice boomed, louder even than Argalus Cobb's. Behind his cold gray eyes the Lieutenant thought he discerned competence.

"I can provide the vessels, Colonel," he responded in his

usual, friendly style. "I can't guarantee enough men to work them, though. You may have to help us with those."

"Don't count on it," snapped Colonel Clark, and his gaze rested chillingly on the Lieutenant's face.

"Colonel Clark," the Lieutenant said, "I count on only two things, sir, ever. Myself and the Almighty." He raised his glass.

Bloomfield broke the tension. "General Dearborn has suggested to General Armstrong," he said, "that Armstrong order New Hampshire troops to the Vermont side of the Lake. And, in a dispatch I received this morning, Dearborn further recommends protecting our Plattsburg magazines by moving them across to Burlington. Colonel Clark will arrange for their removal as soon as the Lake opens."

The meeting broke up on a note of optimistic expectancy for success of the forthcoming action along the northwestern frontier.

Before the group dispersed to their rooms to prepare for dinner, the Lieutenant addressed Colonel Clark. His casual tone glossed his feelings.

"I'll be sending you a memorandum, Colonel," he said, "from Joseph Barron, one of my volunteers who worked for you and Lieutenant Hatch as sailing master last summer. It's his bill for back pay. I'll endorse it."

Colonel Clark fumbled only momentarily. "Just send it along," he said. "Don't trouble to endorse it."

The Lieutenant's expression remained bland. "I don't mind the trouble, Colonel," he said. "And Barron's wife thinks the bill will look official and get prompt action with my signature on it." He bowed to the group. "You know how wives are!"

By February 22nd, the Lieutenant had completed preliminary preparations for the spring's naval activities.

As far back as December, he'd placed orders for 300 tons of cannon shot with the Monkton Iron Company at Vergennes, twenty-two miles south of Burlington. Following that, he'd visited the ironworks on Otter Creek, and met the managing agent, Colonel Benjamin Welles, an accomplished Boston gentleman with wide black mustaches, and they had inspected the coal barns and forges, and agreed that a major satisfaction in commanding a naval establishment so far from Washington lay in the ease with which you could pass on a contractor's production. No officious government inspector slowed things down searching out picayune flaws where none existed.

The Lieutenant had noted much more than the ironworks. The well-wooded, protected land along the river below the falls, seven miles back from the Lake, registered strongly. So had the Canadians in "French Village," some of them former Hudson's Bay Company voyageurs—droll, witty, original, and all fine woodsmen.

From John Bullus, the New York Navy agent, had come first concrete evidence that William Jones, confirmed by the Senate in January as Secretary of the Navy, realized the importance of Lake Champlain's Navy. Wrote Dr. Bullus under date of February 15th:

> I have been directed by the Secretary of the Navy to send to you Fifteen Ship Carpenters. I got Mr. Eckford to procure them, which he has done, all at the rate of One Dollar, seventy-five cents per day; and to be found Boarding and Lodging. The Ship Carpenters that were employed at Sackett's Harbor were boarded and lodged at from 18 to 24 shillings per Week. Eight Carpenters will leave here tomorrow and the other seven in the next Stage. I will thank you to have suitable accommodations provided for them. You will please advance to Mr. Lacy their Foreman, for the support of their Families to such as request it, Five or Six Dollars a Month, and take Mr. Lacy's receipt for the same.

To expedite launching of the refitted vessels as early in April as the Lake might open, the Lieutenant had erected at Shelburne Bay rough shacks in which carpenters and shipwrights could do many preliminary jobs before winter relinquished its grip on the snow-covered vessels.

And despite the obvious inefficiency of working around obstacles of climate and temperature, with only makeshift stoves in the shacks to ward off the worst of the cold, his Spartan plans had won enthusiastic support from more-than-willing officers and men.

9

With the arrival in Shelburne of the New York carpenters, time sped as inexorably as the muffled ticking of the big gold watch in the Lieutenant's vest pocket. Day by day his problems with the vessels mounted.

He had first concerned himself with finding room and board for the newcomers. This he had done in advance, sending Joseph Smith from house to house until the midshipman had adequately bedded the fifteen men down.

While they got themselves settled, he called their foreman to his office. To Doc (as fellow carpenters called him) Lacy, he carefully explained that he expected the foreman to maintain discipline even under existing primitive conditions of work and leisure, and put him on his own.

He then called Lieutenant Smith in, explained what he had done in regard to the civilians, and placed on Sidney Smith's shoulders the primary task of keeping the Navy personnel in line. As he made clear to both supervisors: they must see to it that every single man helped get the boats out on time.

Despite the rigors of their strange environment, the carpenters took hold with enthusiasm. Six days a week they started work on the vessels at dawn and finished at dusk. And they made visible progress as they cut and sawed and hammered to meet the Lieutenant's schedule.

Carronades, gun carriages, and ammunition from New York reached Whitehall in March, for forwarding to Shelburne by water as soon as the Lake opened. Since he intended, however, to have the fleet ready for action when the ice went out, the Lieutenant ordered Midshipmen Charles T. Platt and Walter N. Monteath to Whitehall to bring them immediately by land.

Neither young officer asked how this was to be accomplished. As Platt, dark-eyed and intense, told Monteath, stocky, ordinarily placid but now following himself around in circles: "The first thing for us to do is get to Whitehall."

Since Platt had joined the Navy from his home town of Plattsburg, Monteath trusted his companion's local knowledge to find Whitehall. Once there, he hoped, he would have calmed his nerves sufficiently to help Platt figure what to do about hauling the heavy guns and munitions back to Shelburne.

At home, the Lieutenant showed Ann a letter from Hull & Griswold, his shipping representatives in New York, and said: "We're getting around two thousand dollars from my quarter interest in *Jeannette Snow*." He continued to read. "Hull and Griswold say, rather despondently, that President Madison's resolved to carry on the war. I don't know how their minds work, if they think he can do anything but see the war through." He held the letter out to her.

She handed him the *Centinel* in return, saying: "Others besides New Yorkers wish the war would be called off. Read this proclamation."

He read it. It was signed by "his Excellency Jonas Galusha, Esquire, Governor, Captain General, and Commander-in-Chief in and over the State of Vermont."

> ... I have therefore thought fit, by and with the advice of the Council, to appoint, and I do appoint, WEDNESDAY, THE TWENTY-FIRST OF APRIL NEXT, to be observed as a day of PUBLIC FASTING, HUMILIATION AND PRAYER throughout the State. ...
>
> ... to beseech God ... to avert the horror of war, and restore peace, health and harmony to our State and Nation, and to the world of mankind!

The Lieutenant turned back to the official and personal correspondence that had piled up while he had been spending all his daylight hours at the ships and driving home after dark.

From the Lake Champlain Transportation Company's captain, John Winans, came word that General Bloomfield had put steamboat *Vermont* under charter to transport troops and supplies. (The Lieutenant visualized the time Colonel Clark would have for himself, speeding the Plattsburg magazines at four to six miles an hour to Burlington.)

From Eleazer Williams came reports that Lieutenant Oliver H. Perry had taken command of the fleet building on Lake Erie, under Commodore Chauncey . . . that General Dearborn had joined Chauncey for an all-out effort against upper Canada, supported by the Ontario and Erie fleets . . . that General Bloomfield had completed arrangements to leave Plattsburg for the northwestern border.

A letter from Ludlow Dashwood in Portland announced that James Lawrence in ship *Hornet* had sunk British brig *Peacock* in an action that lasted only fifteen minutes. The Lieutenant and Lawrence had served together in *Enterprise* with Decatur.

"The Navy's doing all right on the ocean," the Lieutenant said, getting up to give Ann several newspaper cuttings which Dashwood had enclosed in his letter, the first copied from *The Times* of London:

> The Public will learn with sentiments, which we shall not presume to anticipate, that a third British frigate has struck to an American. This is an occurrence that calls for serious reflection—this and the fact stated in our paper yesterday that Lloyd's List contains notices of upwards of five hundred British vessels captured, in seven months, by the Americans. Five hundred merchantmen and three Frigates!
>
> Can the statements be true, and can the English people bear them unmoved? Anyone who had predicted such a result of

an American war, this time last year, would have been treated
as a madman or a traitor. He would have been told, if his
opponents had condescended to argue with him, that long
'ere seven months had elapsed, the American flag would be
swept from the seas, the contemptible Navy of the United
States annihilated, and their maritime arsenals rendered a
heap of ruins!

Yet, down to this moment, not a single American frigate has
struck her flag. They insult and laugh at our want of enterprise and vigor. They leave their ports when they please, and
return to them when it suits their convenience; they traverse
the Atlantic; they beset the West Indies Islands; they advance to the very chops of the Channel; they parade along
the coasts of South America; nothing chases, nothing inter-
cepts, nothing engages them but to yield them triumph.

The second carried the *London Pilot* logotype:

We lament most deeply to have to state that another British
frigate, the *Java,* has been taken by the American frigate *Constitution* . . . the mourning of our hearts, which commenced
on the first capture of a British ship by an American, and has
been rendered deeper and more melancholy by every successive instance, and most deep by this last affecting event, can
never be laid aside, till the honor of the British flag shall be
redeemed, by establishing the same triumph and superiority
over the Americans, that we have ever heretofore had over all
the nations that traverse the seas.

The third clipping, from the *Baltimore Patriot,* quoted a
Jamaica paper received by a Baltimore gentleman:

Masters of vessels about to proceed to England with convoys
are informed that they may be supplied with a limited number of American seamen (prisoners of war) to assist in navigating their vessels *on the usual terms,* by applying to, GEORGE
MAUDE, agent.

"They're hiring our men out as slaves!" Ann cried.
"Like their Barbary allies," the Lieutenant said grimly.

"And they won't stop until we put the fear of God into them. They claim the high seas as a matter of *right!*"

At Shelburne the daily tasks got done, the daily problems solved. Because of the Lieutenant's thorough planning, time worked in his favor. The early start kept pressure off carpenters, shipwrights, sailmakers and gunners as they coped with cold, with trial-and-error methods of fitting and refitting, with the inanimate stubbornness of wood and metal against doing what frozen fingers directed.

With the help of Joseph Barron (eventually paid by Colonel Clark) and Moses Eggleston, he rounded up Abraham Walters to pilot for Sidney Smith on *Growler* and Samuel Graves to pilot for Sailing Master Jarvis Loomis, commanding *Eagle*.

Barron and Eggleston also prevailed on local sailors to enlist in the Navy so that he could put the sloops into the water with more assurance than the previous fall that they would be sailed adequately. Manning their guns was something else again; that required many more trained seamen. New York would have to send gunners or the Army would have to supply them from Burlington's artillery.

On April 25th—three weeks before anyone expected to see the sloops afloat—*Growler* (formerly *Hunter*), eleven guns, and *Eagle* (formerly *Bull Dog*), eleven guns, moored off Plattsburg. Carrying two additional eighteen-pounders and two more long twelves than in 1812, *President* entered the water a few days later with twelve guns.

And for the next two weeks, as the Lieutenant reported to the new Navy Secretary, William Jones, the flagship helped *Growler* and *Eagle* "in maintaining the peace of the Lake by keeping the Army from molestation by water and the navigation clear to our merchants."

10

When he managed a few hours at home, the Lieutenant could not hide his growing unhappiness from Ann.

"We look fine from shore," he said, "and we're strong enough to hold control of the Lake. But the flotilla's efficiency doesn't begin to approach its indicated strength in vessels and guns."

She attempted to relieve his depression by getting him to talk. "Translate that, please," she said, "into plain English!"

He gladly unburdened himself.

"In the first place," he said, "we had to do the best we could to improve old boats. We made ordinary repairs on the hulls so they're reasonably seaworthy, and we added twelve guns. That's all we could do. Even now, for what we have to work with, we lack much basic equipment. Mostly, we lack manpower; we've got neither enough good officers nor enough good men."

Ann probed. "You've always considered Sidney Smith a good man," she said, "and John Trumbull, and Joe Barron. And you've mentioned others like Freeborn, the master's mate, and Jarvis Loomis, and those young midshipmen—Platt and Monteath and Sawyer and Aze."

"Yes, dear," he said. "I remember what I've told you. When I say good men, I mean experienced men. Sidney Smith was only fifth lieutenant under Commodore Barron on *Chesapeake* in 1807 when *Leopard* fired those broadsides into her and she couldn't reply because her ammunition hadn't yet been put in place. He certainly hasn't had much chance since, stuck up here on a lake with a couple of decrepit gunboats, to learn how to fight a ship of war. I can only guess at what he'll do under fire. The midshipmen, God knows, show eagerness and they've proved intelligent enough. But all they know about handling the guns, or the sloops, comes from what they've picked up from the mates and the manuals they manage to get their hands on. I haven't enough warrant officers either. We need at least a hundred and seventy-five men to keep us functioning afloat and ashore—from bosuns to cooks. Thank heaven a couple of Doc Lacy's carpenters signed on with us."

"I think you're plain tired from doing too many kinds of jobs, Lieutenant Macdonough."

"Don't mind my grousing," he said. "As Joe Barron always says in the middle of a job, I guess we can make it if nothing's split more than it's cracked." He laughed, relieved to find that talking over his problems had cut them down to a size which he felt once more capable of handling.

He laughed a second time, and said: "You should have seen Colonel Clark last week when he had to ask our help to ferry stores from Plattsburg to Burlington. Seems the steamboat broke down again. A part came loose, and they can't move the boat until they fetch a new part from New York City. Clark sent a messenger after it on the fastest horse in the cavalry stables."

The splits and cracks began to show toward the middle of May. On board *President*, Joe Barron keeled over with "the fever." Put ashore at Burlington on the fifteenth, he left the vessel without pilot or sailing master, both of which duties he himself had filled.

On May 19th, the Lieutenant met in Plattsburg with Eleazer Williams, Colonel Clark, and Colonel Denny McCobb whose regiment of Maine and New Hampshire volunteers had moved into Burlington to occupy the Vermont and New York shores when General Bloomfield's brigade moved out.

The Lieutenant called the meeting—a council of war, Eleazer Williams termed it—to get a general understanding of the conditions the Army and Navy would face during the summer, and to make the Navy's function so clear that Colonel Clark and whoever came to Plattsburg as his superior would know at all times what to expect.

The group took their places around a huge mahogany table in a private room of the United States Hotel which the Lieutenant frequently used for official business that needed the loosening effects of good wine and good tobacco. He began: "The British are building gunboats at Isle-aux-Noix; they'll have four probably. But our sloops can—"

"—maintain the ascendancy of the Lake beyond question," said Williams.

"We must expect, however, that the enemy will stage raids and menace commercial shipping."

Colonel Clark took the clay stem of a churchwarden from between his teeth long enough to ask, "If the Navy has more strength than the enemy, why should you expect him to harass us?"

The Lieutenant explained the impracticability of blockading the Lake where it dropped into Canada: "The British can always slip out under cover of darkness or fog, row their galleys to Champlain and Chazy, and get safely back."

Plattsburg, Port Kent, Essex, Burlington, Shelburne, seemed out of raiding range, however. "Which," said the Lieutenant, "relieves you and Colonel McCobb of concern for the magazines at Burlington and whatever stores you've left in Plattsburg."

Colonel McCobb confirmed this. He was a quiet, capable-looking man, middle-aged, with reddish hair and mustache slightly touched with gray. He reported having sent Captain Hall, with the companies of Captains Snell, Bryant and Bodwell, to Swanton, nine miles north of St. Albans, on May 3rd. He expected no action on the Vermont side of the Lake.

"On the New York side, Captain Oliver Herrick's company will continue in Champlain," he finished. "But so far, our only enemy has been sickness."

Eleazer Williams took the floor. "You may see the enemy in the not-too-distant future, Colonel McCobb," he said. "General Armstrong, back in April, broached the idea to General Dearborn of attacking Montreal via Champlain. I talked with Dearborn at Sackett's Harbor two weeks ago. He's too busy planning his campaign against York to put his mind on Montreal now. But—" He paused for emphasis, and the Lieutenant's eyes went to those small, feminine hands that seemed so out of keeping with the man's work. Williams went on: "—but by autumn, troops may be available."

While the group considered this, Williams went off on another tack. He said: "Now that the British have put Sir James Lucas Yeo in command of their ships on all our Lakes, the Navy may find itself getting busy, too."

Colonel McCobb waved a deprecatory hand. "Don't try to frighten us with a bogeyman, Mr. Williams," he said. "You know that Yeo never showed up after challenging Captain Porter in frigate *Essex*.[1] And Mr. Macdonough and I read the newspapers. They say that if Captain Yeo doesn't arrive on the Lakes soon he may preserve his credit—because there won't be any British vessels left for him to command!"

Williams' hazel eyes darkened, as though he resented the New Englander's light treatment of his information. He said: "The Canadians rate Captain Yeo highly. The word for him, they say, is crafty. Don't underestimate him, Colonel McCobb."

The scout turned to the Lieutenant. "My men report that, besides building gunboats on Isle-aux-Noix, the British are preparing to fortify the island."

The Lieutenant nodded casually. "Other sources confirm that, Lazare," he said. "I would imagine the enemy has a long-range plan in the making. Please watch developments and keep me informed."

Obviously surprised at the Lieutenant's having his own spies over the border, the scout could not conceal his chagrin at the cursory reception given his intelligence.

The Lieutenant summed up. "As things stand today," he said, "the enemy, with his gunboats, can only appear in predatory excursions at the most favorable time for him. We can repel or defeat him. When the occasion warrants, we will seek him out on fair terms."

The following Sunday he related many of the meeting's details to Ann, putting emphasis on Eleazer Williams' reaction to competition.

"You should have told him that you have others working for you," she said. "How can you expect him to—" She stopped short. "Don't you tell me *everything?*"

He put his arm gently around her. "You wouldn't want that," he said. "It would spoil the surprises."

She nodded agreement. "Speaking of surprises, I went to the hospital to see Joe Barron again. Until today most of the staff didn't think he'd recover. He couldn't raise his head without help."

"What's the surprise?"

"Joe's suddenly got religion," she said. "He told me he's been reflecting seriously on his past conduct and feels self-convicted—his exact words—of many errors. He wishes he could recall his misspent time. Not that he trembles, mind you, for fear of finding a more unhappy place than this world but he's sensible—his word, too—that he might have been of more service to his fellow creatures. He also dreads to leave his little family to shift for themselves in this world of depravity—that's what he called it." Ann paused. "He's such a dear! He expressed a curiosity to stay a little longer to see the fate of our country."

The Lieutenant's eyes softened. "I have a feeling we'll satisfy his curiosity."

Ann went off on a fresh tangent, pointing to a *Centinel* advertisement:

> Ten dollars reward for John Fisk, an enlisted soldier from the barracks at Burlington, offered by Richard Bean, Lieutenant, 11th Regiment, U.S. Infantry.

"What does it mean?"

"It means a soldier ran off. The Army wants him back."

"What will they do to him?"

"That depends."

"What would you do if a seaman ran away?"

"That depends," he repeated, "on circumstances."

She gazed at him for several seconds. Then: "Well, that's a secret I'm happy to have you keep from me."

On Wednesday, May 26th, Joseph Barron's substitute pilot ran *President* on a rock off Plattsburg. The pilot later proved that no one else on the Lake knew about the rock either. The sloop struck, crunched, and slid off, her bottom opened. Only by sailing her hard onto the nearest shore did the Lieutenant keep from losing his flagship in deep water.

11

Wasting no time on recriminations, Lieutenant Macdonough immediately set about hauling the staved-in sloop out of the water. This required the aid of the two gunboats which, because of manpower shortage, had not yet been launched. To ferry them from Shelburne he sent Midshipmen Smith and Sawyer and most of *President*'s hands on board *Eagle*, Sailing Master Loomis.

Midshipman Bellamy went along to deliver two hastily written messages. The first gave Colonel Clark a quick summary of the situation, with an estimate of a week's time needed to refloat the flagship. The second notified Ann that the Lieutenant would stay with *President*, and not to worry.

Growler guarded the careened sloop while the Lieutenant planned with Sidney Smith, Master's Mate Trumbull, and the carpenters how most expeditiously to get her back into commission.

The gunboats arrived at Plattsburg from Shelburne the following evening, herded by *Eagle* and chased by a Champlain squall. At the bay's entrance a gust of the Lake's impetuous wind threw Midshipman Sawyer's galley on beam ends, and in the dark it took *Eagle* several hours to rescue the crew from the ice-cold water and to maneuver the overturned gunboat to shore beside *President*.

Midshipman Smith brought the other galley in smartly, and Aze reported having dispatched the messages according to instructions.

Friday at dawn, work parties started lightening the disabled sloop, putting guns, gear, provisions—everything that could be taken out of her—on board the galleys for stowing on shore. By dusk the vessel, still on her side like a wounded whale, lay ready for hauling out on Saturday according to the Lieutenant's plan.

Because no trees or other purchase stood close enough to the water's edge, seamen next morning buried a dead-man of crossed logs in a deeply dug pit on the beach and to it anchored a great triple block. From this block they passed and repassed a heavy line through a second block secured to the bitts on *President*'s forward deck. Other seamen laid a track of stone-weighted tree trunks from beach to boat and placed logs under her keel for rollers.

Beside canted *President*, *Growler* made her main halyard fast high up on the sloop's mast and hauled the flagship erect. The galleys came alongside and lashed themselves to the sloop to keep her straight. The men on shore then walked their line along the beach—and *President* cumbersomely rode up on the track and out of the water.

Crawling out of the bay with water spouting from her hold, the flagship looked like a half-drowned dog shaking himself. Tedious, slow, the job progressed by inches. Every few feet, the gunboats unlashed and took a fresh grip. When finally *President* stood cradled on dry beach, the Lieutenant's inspection showed that the water inside the sloop had wreaked havoc; cleaning would take all available hands.

Carpenters, after examining the crushed bottom planks, began their repairs.

In the midst of the Lieutenant's herculean labors came a dispatch on Wednesday morning, June 2nd, from Captain Herrick at Champlain. Herrick laconically reported the enemy's gunboats coming up to the line, and over, continuing to annoy. Could the Navy stop this?

The Lieutenant had met Herrick half a dozen times, a pleasant, easy-going Yankee given to understatement. If he found the British practice annoying, it must have assumed proportions requiring strong counteraction.

Summoning Sidney Smith, Jarvis Loomis, and their officers, the Lieutenant went with Midshipman Bellamy, acting as clerk, to *Eagle*. Here he instructed *Growler* and *Eagle* commanders to proceed to the lines "for the purpose of preventing the enemy's gunboats from harassing American craft at the end of the Lake."

Knowing that his fellow officers, like himself, had felt tension mounting with the mishaps to the flotilla, he made a special effort to ease their nervous excitement on going to the border without him—particularly since they had practically no gunners, armorers, or gunsmiths to work the guns and small arms.

To Sidney Smith, senior in command, he said: "You shouldn't have any trouble; they'll probably run as soon as they see you." He added: "In the event they don't run, send ashore to Captain Herrick for volunteers to help out on the guns."

Lieutenant Smith nodded silently. But his eyes shone, and their light gave the Lieutenant sudden qualms. For a man hitherto so far from the fighting, this first draft of battle command might prove very heady.

The Lieutenant spoke slowly. "My instructions are explicit," he said incisively. "Confine the British to their own waters. Under no circumstances will you let the enemy lead you into a snare. Stay on your guard on the American side of the line."

From Plattsburg he watched *Growler* lead *Eagle* out of the bay, long narrow coach whip streaming from each masthead and triangular blue pennant on *Growler* signaling Sidney Smith as senior officer.

"I wish I could have gone with them," said Aze Bellamy. "I expect they'll see action, sure enough."

The Lieutenant's expression remained grave. He thought:

"I don't feel right about those vessels"; and immediately scolded himself with, "You act like a mother hen."

Next morning at 6:30, while *President*'s crew reversed the process of the week before and let the repaired sloop slide back into the water, a cannon shot boomed distantly, followed by a broadside. The seamen stiffened like field dogs pointing, faces turned toward the north, ears strained for further sounds.

In the office he used in one of General Bloomfield's almost deserted buildings near the shore, the Lieutenant heard the distant cannonading against the light breeze blowing down the Lake. Feeling suddenly hot, he scribbled a quick note, gave the message to Aze, and hustled him to the door.

"Get up to the stables," he said, "and use this order for the fastest horse they have to get you to Champlain. Find out what's going on, and report to me immediately. If I know you, Aze, you'll make it to Champlain and back in four hours."

The cold quiet of the Lieutenant's voice told Aze how high his commanding officer's emotions blazed. Saluting sharply, he turned and raced toward the stables.

To ease his tension, the Lieutenant had himself rowed across the bay, where he kept busy supervising the restowing of *President*'s gear and the remounting of her twelve guns. From time to time, as the booming in the north went on with only momentary lulls, the men looked toward him. Despite his best efforts he could not entirely conceal a growing apprehension.

He should not, he told himself again and again, have sent the impetuous, high-strung Sidney Smith to the lines. . . . He should have waited until *President* had completed her repairs and led the fleet himself. . . . He should have waited!

He tried to convince himself that the vessels could come to no harm. They had the fire power to repel more gunboats than the four the enemy was known to have. They had pilots who knew the Lake. Sailing Master Loomis had big-ship experience. But . . . but when he'd massed all the positives, he still could not down the feeling that Sidney Smith had run himself into trouble.

At 11:30 the gunfire ended, and an ominous silence dropped over the shimmering Lake. To wait for Aze, the Lieutenant went back to his office where he tried to eat lunch. But though his stomach felt empty and his mouth dry, he had no appetite for either food or drink.

At 2:30 he began to pace, inside the office at first, then in the bright early-June sun outside where the shoreline's many-shaded green trees matched the glistening water on the quiet bay. But he saw neither trees nor water.

At 3:30 his impatience pulled him up short. Taking himself in hand, he worked at bringing his emotions under control. He slowed his pacing to a walk, loosened his taut fingers, shook his arms and legs until they felt limp.

When at 5:30 Aze arrived, the Lieutenant looked up casually from behind his desk, as though the midshipman's coming had no great import, and leaned back in his chair.

Aze looked beaten. His clothes torn, his face scratched, hatless, he saluted.

"I made notes, sir," he said, "in shorthand with a patented pencil. Do you want to hear them, sir?" His voice shook.

The Lieutenant's heart sank. "Sit down, Aze," he said, "and start at the beginning."

"Yes, sir." The boy sat stiffly beside the desk, and read:

"Last night, at eight P.M., *Growler* and *Eagle* moored off Champlain, one mile from the lines. Lieutenant Smith's guard boat brought information that the enemy was bearing up the Lake to attack. He gave orders to beat to quarters and clear the ships for action."

Aze looked up. The Lieutenant's expression told him nothing. He went on:

"At one A.M. Captain Herrick went aboard *Growler* with thirty-three of the Maine and New Hampshire militia, and

Lieutenant Washington Dennison went aboard *Eagle* with twenty. The sloops then stood on and off, apparently deeming it unsafe to lie at anchor because the land shaded the water within fifty yards of the vessels so the enemy could have come in that distance of them before being discovered."

The Lieutenant nodded. Sidney Smith had used good judgment.

Aze continued from his notes: "At five A.M. this morning, the guard boat having brought information that the enemy had gone down the Lake, the vessels followed. The British galleys, with about sixty men each, defied them, but retreated toward the river. At six A.M. the sloops came about, one mile below Hospital Island—"

The Lieutenant leaped from his chair. "They came about where?"

Aze said: "Six miles over the line and two and three-quarter miles from Isle-aux-Noix."

The Lieutenant sat down slowly. He could visualize the trap (exactly what he'd warned against) into which Sidney Smith had led the two ships. The channel, Joe Barron had told him, spanned about fifty yards at the point where it passed Bloody Island and Ash Island. The current there ran two to three knots—down the river, into Canada.

Aze went on: "The shores were lined with British troops—artillery, infantry, militia. Small batteries were hove up. The enemy did everything to make the trap complete." He paused, and gulped. "At this point three galleys turned and gave chase. And at six-thirty our sloops started firing, broadsides on wing tacks.

"At seven A.M. a gunboat shot went through *Eagle*'s larboard quarter and wounded Pilot Graves severely. No one on the sloop had ever been on this part of the Lake before, so *Eagle* was forced to follow the motions of *Growler* as much as possible.

"At nine A.M. all *Eagle*'s guns but one were disabled owing to the breeching parting and the ring bolts breaking. Sailing

Master Loomis had them repaired and commenced action again with a hot fire against the gunboats and the shore."

Aze looked up, saw the Lieutenant's tight expression, and went on evenly, his voice holding steady with a note of pride, as though he spoke in defense of the American fleet.

"At eleven A.M.," he read, "*Eagle* had everything prepared to board the enemy when she received a twenty-four-pound shot in her larboard quarter between wind and water, which went through and knocked three planks off the starboard side under water, and she sank to the bottom, and the enemy took possession of her."

Fumbling with his crumpled notes, Aze finished: "*Growler* kept up a hot fire until eleven fifteen when, her gaff being shot away she became unmanageable, and her ammunition being expended she was"—his voice quavered again—"obliged to surrender to the enemy."

After a few moments, he said in an apparent effort to explain Sidney Smith's chasing the enemy down the Sorel: "The soldiers left at Champlain told me that Colonel Clark planned to withdraw Captain Herrick's company to Burlington today. That would have left our sloops open to successful attack by enemy gunboats and their twenty-four-pounders, being poorly manned as we were."

When he finally could trust his voice, the Lieutenant very quietly said: "That's a good report, son. Who gave you the particulars?"

Aze told him: "A sergeant from the Eleventh Regiment who volunteered on *Eagle* and escaped in the confusion after Mr. Loomis ran her to shore. She heeled over with her hull full of water, and he surrendered." He added: "Some of it I saw for myself."

His voice took on a compelling excitement. "The cannon balls would strike the water halfway between boats, sir," he said, "and skip along before they sank. One struck half a cable's length from *Growler* and bounded through the air directly over her. There must have been three or four hundred British on both sides of the river, and they kept up a constant musket fire. Only one of our men was killed, sir, but I counted thirty British dead on one unprotected spot along the shore."

The Lieutenant's blue eyes searched Aze's face. "How did you get to Ash Island and back, Aze?"

The boy returned the scrutiny with an expression half-hopeful of praise, half-fearful of censure. "I stole—I mean requisitioned—a canoe," he said. "I hid it some distance up-river, sir, and crawled to where I could watch the action. On the way out I met the sergeant in a clearing near Rouses Point where I found the canoe originally."

"You could have got yourself captured, or shot."

"Yes, sir," said Aze. "But at the time I couldn't figure a faster way to get the details accurately and bring them back to you, sir."

Lieutenant Macdonough turned slowly away. He had the details all right—the British had captured two of his three ships! [1]

PART THREE

THE MAN

On our side, as I had directions at all hazards to maintain our
ascendancy, we were not idle.

Autobiography

1

The disastrous loss of *Growler* and *Eagle,* reported to the Secretary of the Navy with Lieutenant Macdonough's recommendations for regaining control of the Lake at once, extracted from the Navy Office in Washington prompt and vigorous orders to the New York and Boston yards for men, carronades, and munitions; together with a succession of competent officers who brought with them to Lake Champlain a deep appreciation of the urgent need for their skills and experience.

William Jones wrote to the Lieutenant:

> You are to understand that upon no account are you to suffer the enemy to gain the ascendancy on Lake Champlain and as you have now unlimited authority to procure the necessary resources for that purpose, I rely on your efficient and prudent use of the authority vested in you.

In the same communication announcing the appointment of General Wade Hampton to the military command of the Lake Champlain district and urging hearty cooperation, the Navy Secretary very emphatically declared:

> You are to observe that the naval command is exclusively vested in you, for which you are held responsible.

For the first time since Aze rode in from the border, the Lieutenant smiled. His report of last winter on *President* had got results; and joint regulations of the War and Navy Departments, which immediately followed the Secretary's instructions, stated:

139

> No officer of the Army of the United States shall, on any pre-
> tence, command any of the ships, or vessels, of the United
> States ...

Very consoling too, in this period of defeat, the Secretary
ordered a purser to the station to relieve him of an ever-chaf-
ing portion of the back-breaking detail he carried.

The Lieutenant moved fast. With Peter Sailly's technical
help, he seized two good-sized sloops, recently launched at
Essex, as their captains appeared at the customhouse in
Plattsburg to register them. He also requisitioned two small,
slow sloops to serve as armed tenders in liaison with the Army.

He then set carpenters, rushed from New York, to work on
fitting out the four vessels in Burlington and constructing
four new gunboats, with the help of Army mechanics and
laborers.

Meanwhile, he kept his ear to the north. From Isle-aux-
Noix, via Eleazer Williams and Lake seamen, he gathered reports on *Growler* and *Eagle,* the latter raised and both being
worked on at the Isle.

"They've been renamed," Williams reported. "They're
now *Broke* and *Shannon* after—"

"—after Captain Philip Bowes Vere Broke," the Lieutenant
cut in, "of British frigate *Shannon* which captured American
frigate *Chesapeake,* Captain James Lawrence, a couple of
weeks ago." He noted, with some surprise, the degree of his
irritability.

Meanwhile, Ann prepared to go home to have her baby.
She insisted, however, on staying in Burlington through July
5th, after calling her husband's attention to a notice in the
Centinel:

> NOTICE—approaching anniversary of American Independence
> will be celebrated by the Republicans of Chittenden County,
> at Burlington, on Monday, the 5th of July next ... at Eli
> Barnard's tavern ... procession forms at 11 A.M. .... oration
> ... exercises ... dinner.

Most ardently to be desired that friends of our country should punctually attend . . . any Republican friends residing without this county heartily solicited to come . . . Such of the American federalists as should wish to join in our celebration will be cordially received and the hand of fellowship extended to them.

> C. P. Van Ness
> Ebenezer Brown
> Henry Lowry
> Nathaniel Allen
> Committee of Arrangement

The Lieutenant always cherished the celebration because of his wife's presence. The day came off sunny and hot. Between fifteen hundred and two thousand citizens assembled on the commons, with a lavish spicing of Army and Navy.

The Lieutenant presented his newly arrived officers to her. "Lieutenant Robert Henley . . . Bob and I served together under Commodore Truxton in *Constellation.*" And he brought to her General Wade Hampton whom the Secretary of the Navy had heralded as a man of talent and energy.

Nearing sixty, still black-haired, well-groomed, with cockade in his hat, the General looked harshly effective, his turned-down mouth adding to the aggressive thrust of his sharp chin. He made a rousing speech, which Ann applauded.

"But I loved it most," she told the Lieutenant at the end of the day, "when they introduced you as *Commodore* Macdonough and the crowd cheered you so hard."

In the succeeding weeks, as he wrote Ann in Middletown: Joe Barron rejoined *President* . . . work on the sloops pushed ahead . . . Lazare Williams reported the enemy lacking seamen at Isle-aux-Noix to man the captured vessels . . . General Hampton wrangled with the citizens of Champlain, having withdrawn Colonel Davis from the garrison there in order to concentrate all troops in Burlington . . . only a handful of men remained at Plattsburg under a lieutenant . . .

Later:

Burlington overrun with troops, mostly recruits learning discipline . . . Joseph Smith appointed lieutenant, William Caton promoted to surgeon, Robert Henley advanced to master commandant . . . Lieutenant Macdonough, too, advanced to master commandant.

Toward the end of July he told her that all his men felt great pressure to get the new flotilla into the water . . . only *President* guarded the Lake . . . he needed several weeks more . . .

But the enemy did not give the needed time. On Wednesday, July 29th, Eleazer Williams arrived with the alarm. At Isle-aux-Noix had arrived from Quebec Captain Thomas Everard of English sloop *Wasp* with officers and sailors to man newly named *Broke* and *Shannon* and three gunboats. Forty British bateaux prepared to transport 1,000 men under command of Lieutenant Colonel John Murray.

The Lieutenant, meeting with General Hampton, flatly stated: "The enemy can scour the Lake. Our sloops have no masts in, but some of their guns can be used. With your shore battery, my men can help you defend Burlington."

General Hampton made an effort to hide his displeasure, and said: "With *President* and your gunboats, Commodore, couldn't we keep the enemy from entering the Lake?"

"We could not!" The Lieutenant kept his voice quiet but his tone firm. "We would, undoubtedly, lose *President* in an action at this time. By keeping her safe until we float the new sloops and galleys, we'll have the strength we need to control the Lake."

The corners of Hampton's mouth drooped. "Then," he said, "we'll have to stand by while the enemy raids Champlain and Plattsburg."

The Lieutenant nodded gravely. "That's right," he said. "We'll have to take a licking."

The British landed at Plattsburg July 31st, destroyed the

hospital, arsenal, armory, blockhouse, and military canton-ment, burned two of Peter Sailly's public storehouses and stripped his home, along with others rich and poor, robbed the Masonic Hall of records and jewels, and forced towns-people to provide horses and carts to carry off the invasion plunder.

On the morning of Wednesday, August 2nd, former *Growler* and *Eagle*, flying British colors under Captain Daniel Pring, appeared off Burlington with one gunboat. About noon, having failed to lure the Americans out into the broad Lake where the British galleys lay behind the islands, the British sloops and gunboat came within one and a half miles of the city and opened fire. The shore battery—and *President*, anchored under the battery—returned the fire, and the enemy withdrew to the southward after twenty minutes.

As the *Montreal Herald* earlier had editorialized:

> The *Growler* and *Eagle*, both repaired and fitted, will annoy the Americans on Lake Champlain and will teach them in future the danger of insulting our sacred borders.
> Those federal and democratic bloody packhounds may al-ways rest assured of meeting a suitable reception, until they yield to our mercy. . . .

Besides looting the Lake towns, the invaders took or de-stroyed eight or nine small vessels.

Forced to stand back from the taunts of the enemy, the Lieutenant, his officers, and his men bore the indignity as best they could. The Lieutenant had one consolation as he prepared to resume command of the Lake: the consensus of Burlington's men of judgment held him responsible for their present safety.

The British raid roused Washington. To the Champlain station William Jones ordered Lieutenant Stephen Cassin who had been in the Mediterranean with Decatur, Lieuten-ant George Pearce, Lieutenant John Stansbury, and Acting Lieutenant Charles A. Budd. Purser George Beale arrived.

From New York also came a draft of fifty seamen. And on August 20th the fleet stood ready for service—when a hundred more men could be found.

At that point—culmination of weeks of sweating labor, of galling inability to sweep the enemy off the Lake, of continuous improvising in order to make do with woeful lacks— the looked-for letter came from Mrs. Shaler in Middletown with news that Ann's baby had arrived—a boy. The Lieutenant's hand shook as he laid the letter down on his desk in *President*'s cabin.

Two days later Lucretia Ann Shaler's brief follow-up news reached the Lieutenant as he prepared to go ashore for a meeting with General Hampton. Midshipman Bellamy, handing him the letter from Middletown, discreetly retired. The Lieutenant opened the letter quickly. His eyes caught the first words. He sat down slowly at the desk.

Their son had died.

2

General Wade Hampton had requested a private conference
with Commodore Macdonough in the General's quarters,
where the Commodore found Hampton looking grimmer
than usual, his chin jutting out sharper and the corners of his
mouth turning down farther. He seemed to have himself
under control by the barest margin. He waved his visitor to a
chair and sat down behind his work table, then waited in
silence until his orderly closed the office door on the way out.

He turned sharply.

"I want you to know, Commodore," he opened abruptly,
his eyes dark with rage, "that I asked the War Department to
accept my resignation from the service."

Tearing his thoughts from Ann and the baby, the Commodore asked quietly, "General Wilkinson?"

"Exactly! I'm told to serve under him!" Hampton slapped
the table. "Wilkinson!" The hatred in his voice as he spat out
the name shocked the Commodore. "I know how he operates
—assumes authority he doesn't possess, intrigues, connives,
cheats, steals. I can't begin to express my loathing for him as
a man and my contempt for him as a soldier!"

The Commodore made no comment. He had read newspaper accounts of General James Wilkinson's maneuverings
as governor of the Louisiana Territory, with resulting court-
martial findings that included references to irregularities in
his accounts while clothier general of the Revolutionary
Army. The court's "not guilty" verdict President Madison
had approved "with regret."

145

Hampton's dark face glowed red as he went on:

"General Armstrong gave me to believe last June that I had a separate command here. Now he's replaced Dearborn with Wilkinson in the ninth district and tells me to take my orders from *him!*"

With General Armstrong's earlier formation of an Army in Vermont under Hampton, the War Department had appeared to give to the Champlain area the importance it warranted as a key invasion path to or from Canada. Now, evidently, the Army intended to make the old mistake all over again, and relegate Champlain to secondary status.

"Has the War Department accepted your resignation?"

"No!" Hampton looked toward the window. "Armstrong asks me to stay on until after his campaign against Montreal via Kingston *and* via Champlain."

The Commodore waited. On June 6th, before Hampton arrived, the Burlington barracks had rung with eighteen rounds from Colonel Clark's artillery at news of victory at Sackett's Harbor and the destruction of Fort George. The Army seemed on the move in the northeast.

"With Armstrong transferring the War Department to Sackett's Harbor, so he can be with Wilkinson in planning the Montreal campaign, I can't do anything else but go along with the Secretary's wishes." Hampton seemed to have lost much of his venom, as if accepting the inevitable now that he'd voiced his anger and put the case on a basis of personal service to the War Department head. "How about naval support? When will you have the fleet ready?"

The Commodore replied deliberately. "Putting the flotilla on the Lake depends now on just one factor—seamen. New York tells me the men I need are on the way. As soon as they arrive, we'll sail. That, I hope, should be within the week."

Hampton smiled, almost genially. "Good! That's fine! I'll let General Armstrong know I can have my troops ready to march on Montreal this month." He got up to say good-by.

"Incidentally," he asked, "what have you named your new vessels?"

"The tenders keep their old names—*Frances* and *Wasp*. We named the two big sloops *Preble* and *Montgomery*."

Hampton tugged an ear, obviously casting over the probable sources of the names. "Preble, yes; a sailor, one of the Navy's commodores. But what Montgomery?"

"Richard Montgomery—an Irishman, like me."

"But he was a soldier!"

"A good Revolutionary one," said the Commodore. "He captured the forts north of here, at Chambly and St. Johns, en route to taking Montreal."

Hampton still smiled. "I hope that augurs well for me. And I'm glad to learn"—his smile expanded—"that you naval fellows know a little American history." He shook the Commodore's hand. "I'm sure my command will appreciate your fleet's courtesy in naming the *Montgomery*."

Early on September 6th, *President*, flying the Commodore's broad pennant, led *Preble, Montgomery, Frances, Wasp,* and two gunboats, finally manned the previous day by a draft of two hundred men with a few officers from New York, out of Burlington Bay into the broad Lake.

Heading north for Gravelly Point, below Plattsburg, where the enemy's two sloops and three gunboats purportedly lay, the American fleet carried forty guns, from nine-pounders to eighteen-pound Columbiads. The Commodore found the British boats, finally, anchored near the line.

As he bore down, they up-anchored, crossed over the line, and stood down the river.

From Plattsburg that night, he reported on their flight to Secretary of the Navy William Jones:

> ... thus, if not acknowledging our ascendancy on the Lake, evincing an unwillingness to determine it.

Next day he consulted in Burlington with General Hampton, again at Hampton's request. To this meeting he took the commanders of all his vessels. In their quiet undress blues, the naval officers found themselves overshadowed by General Hampton's colorful staff in the blues, yellows, and reds of their services. But the naval officers maintained a quiet self-possession. The Commodore had consulted daily with them, had kept them abreast of developments. They knew their own strengths and weaknesses, and they presented a united front.

General Hampton greeted them effervescently, like a man possessing good news, and motioned them to places at a huge round conference table. To his left sat Eleazer Williams.

The General rose. "Gentlemen," he began, and stopped to clear his throat. "Gentlemen, I have the pleasure of announcing that we have orders from the War Department to march on Montreal from Plattsburg September 20th. We will proceed directly against Isle-aux-Noix." He waited for the impact of the news to register, letting his gaze fall on the attentive faces of his officers.

The Commodore smiled inwardly at the General's histrionics. Having anticipated Hampton's public staging of what should have been a private meeting for the announcement, the Commodore had prepared his men to take it in stride. He nevertheless deeply resented Hampton's discourtesy.

Having limelighted the naval contingent, the General proceeded swiftly to put them on a spot. He said:

"Having finally achieved their desired strength, our naval forces now can throw their full power against the British flotilla. We plan, therefore, to make a joint descent by water on Isle-aux-Noix." Like an actor waiting for applause, the General looked around the table for approval.

From Eleazer Williams and others, the Commodore knew that General Armstrong's instructions to Wade Hampton included an alternate plan for a land attack on Isle-aux-Noix. But the Secretary of War had set his heart on the attack by water, as the Commodore also knew, and Hampton had taken this opportunity to work off some of his own and the War Secretary's chagrin at staying on the defensive during the months of the fleet's rebuilding.

Their impatience to use him for their immediate ends he could understand, even forgive. But he could not overlook Hampton's cavalier manner of making public the news of the proposed attack. Nor could he permit the Army's impatience to jeopardize the bigger job—defending the Lake against invasion.

He rose slowly, bowing to the Army chiefs and glimpsing Colonel Clark's frozen face from the corner of his eye.

"General," he opened, allowing a smile to touch his lips in order to take the harshness off his words, "the Secretary of the Navy has assigned me the task, first, of keeping the enemy within his own waters; and, after that—but only after that—of cooperating with the Army insofar as practicable."

The effect on the group reminded him of dousing water on frolicking dogs. Hampton's usual grim expression returned; frowns replaced the smiles on the Army officers' faces.

"Our naval force," he went on, "can keep the enemy's vessels north of the line. It can transport and convoy troops anywhere on the Lake south of the line. And we can continue to do this, by maintaining our present strength." He paused to give emphasis to his next words. "But we cannot permit our power to be placed in jeopardy at this time. We cannot risk loss of our superiority by the capture or destruction of even a part of our fleet."

He looked toward Eleazer Williams. Then:

"As Mr. Williams has reported to General Hampton," he went on deliberately, his eyes ranging icily over the circle of Army faces, "Isle-aux-Noix stands so strongly fortified that only a decidedly superior naval force could attack successfully. We have no such superior force. To take our present force into the narrow channel would be to face disaster!"

Again he let his glance circle the table. Williams, he saw, took pleasure at this vigorous, relentless dissection of Army thinking on naval problems. His own men's expressions remained impassive. The scowls on Army faces deepened. Hampton's tightly pressed lips, with their down-turning corners, made a grim, unapproving line.

Objectively, coldly, the Commodore went on. "We can, and will, put our resources entirely at the Army's disposal for any movement south of, and up to, the line. But, if the Navy is to maintain supremacy on this Lake," he concluded inexorably, "we cannot, in my opinion and that of my officers, embark with the Army on a joint descent on Isle-aux-Noix."

He sat down and waited for Hampton, as Armstrong's surrogate, to express the War Secretary's pique at this outspoken, unyielding reaction to his favored proposal.

The Commodore felt himself caught up in this never-ending struggle with the Army, dealing again and again with willful, spoiled men unable to tie effect in with cause, incapable of anticipating the end results of present action but clamorous for action, burning for any immediate action whatever, regardless of future consequence.

Why had he been cast in the role of cautious mentor? Why did the onus of decisions made with the outward look of timidity fall on his head? Had this necessary prudence driven Sidney Smith to his disastrous action? No! Let the Army do what it would, for whatever reasons of favored tactics, pride, pique. He had no need to prove his aggressiveness or his courage; he had done that as a junior officer, among brave men. Now he had to prove his foresight (his hunches?) and his judgment! A much harder job, being a senior naval officer, than he'd ever dreamed!

On his feet, General Hampton grimly reflected in words the reaction he anticipated from the Secretary of War... "much to be regretted that our naval means on the Lake should have fallen so far short of their objective. To our operations an ascendancy in the narrow parts of the Lake is of infinite moment."

Caustic, barely short of insulting, Hampton at length edged

away from fiery disputation to frigid discussion of naval escort as far as the lines.

On Saturday, September 18th, four thousand infantry, cavalry and artillery (all but a squadron of horse and artillery of Hampton's entire Army, which had been transported back to Plattsburg) embarked in bateaux and moved north from Cumberland Head. Preceded by the light corps and flanked on the right by the Navy, they reached Chazy at midnight. After lying on their arms, they embarked soon after sunrise on the 19th for Champlain, and immediately marched to Odletown.

The Navy waited on the line.

Five days later, the Army returned.

Because of inability to obtain adequate water supplies, Hampton let it come to the Commodore, the General had abandoned the War Department's alternate plan of attacking the Isle-aux-Noix by land en route to Montreal.

Having hidden his elation at Hampton's ignominious retreat from Canada, the Commodore also contained his skepticism for Hampton's new plans. His resentment still burned hot over the General's castigation of the Navy for refusing to mount a joint land-and-water attack, and it gave him great satisfaction when word reached Plattsburg that Perry on September 10th had captured the entire British fleet on Lake Erie.

He had a laugh, too, when Peter Sailly wrote—urgently, irately, and quoting at length the Secretary of the Treasury on customs laws—about the strange actions of one John Banker, with a Commission for Privateering.[1]

"Maybe John Banker's serving the Navy as a spy," the Commodore amiably told the astonished Customs Collector.

The Navy continued to patrol Lake Champlain.

To cover plans for a fresh march on Montreal—this time starting inland via Chataugay, forty-four miles west of Plattsburg—General Hampton sent Colonel Clark with riflemen to Missisquoi Bay on the Vermont side of the Lake.

But the Commodore never learned how Colonel Clark made out at St. Armand against a small British force, because Benjamin Welles of the Monkton Iron Company sent the flagship word that officious Clark had seized Welles's bog-ore boat, *Maria,* off Hog Island as a smuggling vessel, thereby making it impossible for the company to fulfill its contract for the 300 tons of iron shot the Navy needed. Some of the Commodore's pent-up fury expended itself in taking *Maria* out of Clark's hands.

Then the Navy held Lake Champlain alone, as Hampton again headed for Canada. While the Commodore patrolled, a handbill from Montreal announced the surrender of General Henry Proctor's British army to General William H. Harrison on the River Thames in upper Canada. With Chief Tecumseh killed and the Indian Confederacy broken, the enemy no longer could outflank the northwestern army, firmly established on the southern shores of the Great Lakes and moving under Wilkinson toward Montreal whose capture now might mean the end of the war. Hampton had picked a good time to join Wilkinson!

But Hampton surprised the Commodore. Despite Wilkinson's orders to meet him at the St. Lawrence, the intransigent General abandoned the expedition. Deciding that he and Wilkinson had too few provisions between them for both armies, he turned back to Plattsburg and went into winter quarters.

The Army's invasion foundered, and Eleazer Williams reported the enemy rejoicing.

While the Navy cruised Champlain in the growing cold, the Commodore now felt absolutely certain that the British would mass their next attack on the Champlain-Hudson path to New York. What had transpired to date only led up to the main action. Now, he knew, would come the big drive.

As if to show him graphically how little the country appreciated the gravity of the threat from the north, Federalist Martin Chittenden, directly opposed to the war and to the national government, was chosen Governor of Vermont by the assembly as both Republicans and Federalists called each other tories and traitors and trading over the border with the enemy grew out of hand.

Until it became impossible for his sailors to handle the iced mooring hawsers, the Commodore kept the flotilla exercising. On December 3rd, he chased four enemy gunboats, evidently headed for Plattsburg and surprised to find the watchful American fleet still on the water, down the Sorel. And on Sunday, December 19th, he took his vessels into Otter Creek for winter quarters at the "Buttonwoods," three-quarters of a mile above Dead Creek at Vergennes.

Here he could find what he knew the Navy must have in the coming year—timber for ships, iron for cannon shot, protection from attack until the moment came to strike.

3

After thoroughly securing the fleet for the winter, Commodore Macdonough hurried to Middletown where, on January 17th, 1814, he slowly put his pen down on the mahogany work table in Ann's childhood bedroom. Aloud, he read over his letter to the Honorable Secretary of the United States Navy:

> "I have the honor to inform you that I shall return to Lake Champlain in the course of a few days, after a visit to my family of two weeks."

"You should make that 'a *wonderful* two weeks!' " said Ann.

> "Previous to my leaving that Lake, I made arrangements for timber, iron, etc., for building the gallies as you directed—"

"Instead of coming here for your birthday and Christmas."

> "—and have waited your orders to send for carpenters and commence building after the models you informed me would be sent. I think not much time should be lost in preparing our force to meet the enemy on the opening of the Lake, as we may look for vigilance and exertion on his part.
> The enclosed letter from a man I have employed to give me information on the enemy I submit to you. He is well acquainted in Canada, and with many from whom he can attain correct information." [1]

As he sealed the letter and addressed it, his heart filled with affection and tenderness that had grown every day during the seven months' separation from his wife. His mother-in-law had given him details of the doctor's efforts to keep his prematurely born son alive, and of Ann's grief over their loss. But she had recovered much of her vitality and zest. And the two weeks in Middletown had restored some of his own basic optimism.

After long months of frustration, of coping—for what seemed to him small results—with the vagaries of the natural elements on Lake Champlain and of the human element on each of the Lake's shores, he basked in the warm attention the Shalers lavished on him in their individual ways.

From Amelia and Louisa came insatiable requests for stories about the "foreign countries" he sailed to—Vermont, New York, Canada—and he'd entertained them for hours, especially with the tale of the bear that Aze shot with a musket at the edge of Vergennes the morning the Commodore left for Middletown.

Charlotte and William and Augusta, the in-betweens, had wanted, and got, vivid sketches of bearded sailors from *Philadelphia* and *Constitution,* of officers who'd joined him from *Constellation, Chesapeake, Wasp,* of the dozen boys—fourteen and fifteen years old—who worked the vessels as hard as any of the men. Aaron Fitzgerald, he'd told them, could ride down a backstay headforemost!

The three oldest, as well as Nathaniel and Lucretia Ann, had loved his descriptions of Seaman John Vance, grandson of a Narragansett tribe's chief, and of Peter Joe, West Indian gunner on *President,* whose wife, Phebe, had given him a son in November at Burlington. When Peter Joe had rejoined the ship after a night at home, some of the crew, joking, had asked what he'd named the boy.

The Commodore had overheard the answer in passing: "What you think? We name 'um Commodore Thomas Macdonough Peter Joe Phebe—in honor of *everybody!*"

On the eve of their return to Lake Champlain, the Commodore told Ann: "The best accommodation I've been able to locate for us is a big room in Painter's Tavern. That's the focal point for Vergennes society . . . stages all the big parties and balls. Tom Rich, the proprietor, was graduated from Dartmouth." He smiled as he added: "You and he can discuss English literature while I tend to the fleet."

Ann glared. "Thank you, Commodore Macdonough!"

As they rattled around in the several coaches that took them to Vermont over snow-covered roads, he briefed her on the town of Vergennes and the people she would meet.

With snow on the ground, he told her, Vergennes was a pretty town, without sidewalks. And while sleighing lasted lumbermen would bring in sawlogs to pile up everywhere for future use. Besides Painter's Tavern, Vergennes supported the American Hotel and Redington's Tavern, along with several general stores, printing shop, law office, hat shop, gunsmith, sheriff, constable, county court, post office, homes for about 1,000 population, two school districts, and a Congregational church—as well as iron mills and the boatyards.

"No brewery?" Ann tossed in lightly.

He laughed. "One. And between it and French Village, where the Canadian wood-choppers live with their families and heads get broken as quaintly as the English language, I'm going to have all I can do to keep discipline in the fleet."

Ethan Allen and the French Consul in New York had helped name the town in 1788 after Count de Vergennes, French minister for foreign affairs, in honor of French patriots in the Revolution. Most of the dwellings were log cabins then. Now daughters and wives of prospering merchants went to dances in calico instead of homespun and hand-woven linsey-woolsey.

"Who told you all this?" Ann interrupted.

"The postmaster, Joe Tomlinson, when I picked up letters from you and W. Jones, and Dave Edward, who's a representative in the state legislature."

"Are you sure it wasn't their wives?"

"You won't be jealous," he said, "after you meet the women

of Vergennes. They're too busy making homes to do much about appearances. The majority look very old for their age." He added: "I think you'll like the men, too."

At the age of fifteen, Samuel Strong, now mayor, had driven cattle in the Revolution for American soldiers at Crown Point after his father had been taken by Burgoyne's scouts. William White, one of Vergennes' leading merchants, had told how youthful Sam fell into the water below the falls on Otter Creek while loosening floodwood. Unable to swim, he'd kept his presence of mind—alternately sinking to the bottom and crawling toward shore and rising to the surface for air. A tall man now, spare, unassuming, and independent like most Vermont Yankees.

Many others had educated themselves and took a surprisingly broad outlook on life. When not busy selling property and serving as town alderman, Amos Barnum worked at improving local cattle and horses, introducing fine breeds of both. Captain Francis Bradbury had put the Monkton Iron Company together—ore lands, forges, steel foundry, slitting mill, nail-making shop—for a wealthy Boston group. He used to be a sea captain.

Beldon Seymour came from Newtown, Connecticut; made hats in the block between Elbow and Green streets; married an Abigail Beers. Abraham Dibble, assistant judge of Addison County Court, had a good sense of humor. The gunsmith, Benajah Webster, came from New Hampshire; had started as a blacksmith seven or eight years earlier.

Ed Sutton and Dan Harmon and his brothers had the brains, energy, and knowledge of human nature it took to make out as merchants and distillers in what had been a wilderness only twenty-five years before. Customers of Reuben Bush and William White expected them to stock dry goods, crockery, hardware, drugs, medicines, groceries, and liquors —especially all kinds of liquors. Instead of money, they had to take grain and produce for their merchandise, and then barter those. They had to extend long credits, and know when to collect without giving offense. No wonder, with that training, these men made such good public officials!

In spite of poking fun at him, Ann seemed to enjoy his rambling sketches of the Vergennes townspeople.

"You'll meet most of them very soon, I'm sure," he said.

He was right. Three party invitations greeted them on their arrival.

The first, for dinner aboard the flotilla, arrived by word of mouth from Lieutenant Henley, senior fleet officer during the Commodore's leave.

The second, awaiting them at the inn, requested the honor of their presence at a dance to be held the coming Saturday at Painter's Tavern to welcome the Officers of the Naval Fleet to Vergennes. As the Commodore pointed out, sponsors included most of the merchants with eligible daughters, and their wives.

The third invitation came from Mayor and Mrs. Strong, for a small dinner the next week.

4

After lunch the day of their dinner on board the flotilla, Commodore Macdonough drove his rented sleigh to Painter's Tavern and picked Ann up for a tour of Vergennes and the naval installation.

On this bright afternoon, white snow glistened whiter on the roadway and its background hills. Vermont's cold air nipped sharply at the Commodore's uncovered nose and cheeks, but bit less viciously than on the Lake in December, and Ann's fur-trimmed face and figure kindled in him a warmth he'd missed too long.

They drove south, the two horses trotting briskly, bells tinkling festively. They turned west past French Village's small houses with bright-colored doorways and second stories of yellows and light blues. Occasionally they glimpsed the men of the village far off the road in the fields on the edge of the woods, burning logs for charcoal in huge pits.

The Commodore pointed out the Monkton Iron Company's fifteen large barns for storing the charcoal, the forges, and the slitting mill which cut rolled iron into strips for the nail shop. And they watched the waters of Otter Creek tumble thirty-seven feet over the falls below the town and run through the flume by the side of the rocks on the river's west bank, carrying the water to machinery in the large yellow building below.

"That's where they're casting the three hundred tons of shot for us," he said.

Ann's interest lay in the fleet, not the factory. "I don't see the boats."

"You will," he said. "They're moored three miles from here, above where Dead Creek runs into Otter Creek."

Vergennes folk called the place the Buttonwoods because of the groves of plane trees whose round fruit hung down, brown and mossy in the fall, like Christmas-tree ornaments.

"Dead Creek and its contiguous swamps give us excellent protection from the south," the Commodore said. "The north has rugged terrain, and the river winds so much we can feel secure from surprise via the Lake."

For once Ann seemed truly surprised. "You mean the British would ever dream of attacking you?"

"They can't sail or row up the Lake because it's frozen over, but they could attack in several other ways," he said. "They could put runners on their gunboats and haul them here loaded with shot. They could bring troops and guns up the west shore, behind Plattsburg, or straight up the ice on sleds or sledges and try to destroy our vessels. Or they could come around Burlington, along the east shore and this road we're riding on—if they thought about it."

He pointed to the river bank, to a shallower backwater where the water had rippled over rocks to freeze in cascades of green-and-white ice that sparkled like diamonds in the sunshine. "I wonder," he mused, "how big the fish grow in this stream."

For half a mile he said nothing more. Then: "I spend most of my time anticipating," he said. "Anticipating what everyone else will do—what the enemy will do, what the Army will do, what my officers and men will do. In between, now and then, every once in a while it seems, I get a chance to figure what *I* should do."

The sound of the bells on the horses' bellybands fell to a gentle tinkle as the horses walked.

"My greatest concern at the moment," he said, "is to guard against incendiaries."

Ann showed surprise again, but did not interrupt.

"To destroy our vessels is, admittedly, the enemy's first and greatest aim on this frontier." Explaining to her, he felt exactly as he'd felt when he met with the commanders of the vessels following their mooring at the Buttonwoods and put the officers on their guard. "I don't doubt for a minute that the British will attempt to burn our boats, if not trying it themselves, paying some of our own people to do it."

Ann's fingers tightening on his arm showed how much the idea shocked her. "I can't believe Americans would do *that!*"

"Even citizens who supply the fleet or do work on the boats," he said, "can destroy us."

After a moment, he said: "You wonder what's on my mind? Well, possibilities of that sort. I have to have sentinels and a regular watch to guard against any articles being taken away. I also have to take care of the men, keeping the officers busy keeping the men busy keeping the vessels in order as to powder, sails, and so on, so they won't get on each other's nerves and come to blows below decks.

"We now have some two hundred and fifty officers and men. That alone brings plenty of headaches. Many of the men are rough and tough; all are lonely ... except for a few whose wives have joined them and a few who've married local women or are living with them. How can the single ones keep out of what our sedate citizens call trouble? How can I keep them from trying to find fun in town and resenting the pompous burghers who act as if all seamen are scum?"

Ann pressed his arm.

"It takes the personal vigilance of every officer," he said, "to keep the men regular in their habits, to prevent fatalities when they get drunk in this cold climate, and to see that they don't abuse or maltreat citizens in any way."

Ann appreciated that he took this part of his duties particularly seriously. "You have enough to do keeping order in the fleet. Can't you let the local authorities handle whatever happens in town?" she asked.

"What sort of commander would leave his men to the mercies of civilians?" His voice sounded gruff, even to his own ears. "The civil authorities don't understand our men. They'd be too harsh." He explained: "Our men know our rules, and we're strict with them. But we're not severe like the British navy, or the French, or the Russian. We handle discipline very simply."

The horses continued to amble. "Go ahead," Ann urged.

"Well, in general," he explained, "the commander of each vessel keeps his ship in order, through his lieutenants, masters-at-arms, and warrant officers. They're the—"

"I know, dear," she cut in. "Warrant officers are subordinate officers appointed, or warranted, by the President, including boatswain, gunner, sailmaker, carpenter—"

Paying no attention to her parody on an eager midshipman reciting memorized Navy regulations, he continued: "Each commander holds court, before the mast, whenever necessary. And so long as everything runs smoothly on each vessel, I keep hands off."

"What happens when the men go ashore?"

"I've made a deal with Mayor Strong and the sheriff," he said. "If the local constable or the sheriff finds our men at the scene of trouble, he turns them over to our naval shore patrol. If they're drunk and did no damage, we sober them up in the brig. They go before the mast next morning, and—"

"Yes?"

"Well," he said, "they're reprimanded and perhaps lose some pay or their next shore leave, depending. If they injure a citizen, they have to pay for repairs—to him or his property. If they steal, they pay back. And if we can't find the individual aggressor, all men in the fracas or the theft, or all men in the vessel involved, have to pay."

"And if you don't catch them, or can't find out the ship involved?"

"Then every man in the fleet pays." He patted her hand, still on his arm. "You'd be surprised how comparatively little serious trouble we run into, with the men, in effect, policing themselves."

After a few seconds he chuckled. "Probably the men who help most to keep things running smoothly are the cooks," he said. "We do what we can to get men who like to cook, give them the best supplies we can buy in the area, and let 'em have a comparatively free hand." He paused as if to pick his words. "With the vessels moored, we also look the other way if the cook's wife or lady friend comes aboard to make his job happier and easier." He laughed. "Too, rum and whisky rations make the men's food taste even better and their free time pass even pleasanter."

Ann added her laughter to his. "Life in the Navy sounds positively beautiful, Commodore," she said. "Why did you complain in your letters to me all last summer that you couldn't get enough men?"

He geed up the horses and flicked his black whip. "Because the New York Navy Yard didn't send them," he said. "The ones we got, we kept. At least we kept most."

"Deserters?"

"There're always some, everywhere."

"What do you do to them?"

He explained, above the tinkling of the bells: "We tell the local authorities. If they're caught nearby we put them in the brig. If they're caught far away they're turned over to the Federal authorities."

"Then you shoot them!"

He turned sharply. "Who told you that?"

"Why, Commodore, you're angry!"

He geed the horses again. After a long silence, he apologized. "I'm sorry, dear. I suppose I reacted so violently because I don't want to believe any man in this fleet would run out on us when we need him. But if he did, I don't think I'd feel sorry to have him swung from a yardarm. No, we don't hang or shoot deserters unless their desertion endangers other men or their ships, or the situation calls for a serious example to others. I haven't faced that here—yet."

Ann made her own apology. "I must seem very flip to you

at times, Tom," she said contritely. "About deserters, for example. I know you believe in good naval discipline, and I know you achieve it with a minimum of difficulty. I also know you must deal very fairly with your officers and your men, because of the way they respect and like you. I guess I wanted to find out whether you'd had to act really tough. I found out—you hadn't." She finished: "But you could."

Rounding a curve in the road, their sleigh approached a blockhouse. Built on a little rising ground, it stood two stories high, of hewn square timbers about twelve inches thick and bulletproof. The upper story jutted over the basement story by some three feet, with portholes through which to fire down on the enemy should he attempt to set fire to the blockhouse or blow it up. Portholes ran all around the building, in both upper and lower stories, so that the enemy could not surprise the garrison from any direction.

"These blockhouses also serve as barracks for the men not needed aboard the vessels," the Commodore explained. Saluting a bundled-up guard, he pulled the horses to a stop. "Would you like to see inside?"

The men in the building made much of Ann. Once at ease following the Commodore's appearance, which obviously they'd been expecting, they pointed out its salient details like excited, garrulous housewives showing a neighbor over a new parlor. Three rows of posts supported the roof-frame joists, on which lay a double layer of beams crossing each other in close contact. Wooden bunks, double-decked, filled the interior, all made up neatly, many with wooden, brass-bound lockers at their foot. Two iron stoves, burning wood, kept the blockhouse warm.

"Like to see how we made it bombproof?" asked a huge, barrel-shaped man whose red whiskers ran from one ear around his cheek and chin to the other cheek and ear, like a misplaced halo.

"This is John Roberts," the Commodore told Ann. "One of Moses Eggleston's best carpenters, before he joined us."

Without warning, the giant reached under Ann's arms and lifted her, like a doll, high above his head so she could see the layer of earth that had been laid on the roof beams to protect against bombs. Gently, he lowered her to her feet.

Almost breathless from the suddenness of her acrobatics, she declared: "You're so strong!"

The carpenter blushed, but obviously relished having taken the center of the stage so dramatically. "When you're on board of one of the ships some day, ma'am, watch me lift a barrel of brine-pork with my fingers takin' ahold on the top rim of the barrel only."

The Commodore confirmed the claim, and expressed the apparent wish of the men: "Mrs. Macdonough will visit us often, I hope."

Outside, he walked Ann toward a battery of three guns, so placed as to command three angles with Otter Creek at their back. He saluted the guards, commended them on the condition of the guns, and directed Ann along a cleared path to the river.

Otter Creek widened to about a hundred yards here at the Buttonwoods and, as far as Ann could see, the trees that had given the place its name ranged indefinitely. Ice edged the banks, but the current had kept the river open. At a landing stage waited a gig rowed by four sailors.

Saluting the Commodore and his lady, Aze Bellamy smiled wanly.

"Your bag's aboard, sir," he said. "And good afternoon, Mrs. Macdonough. We've looked forward to having you with us."

Ann gave him her hand. "Thank you very much, Aze," she replied affectionately, letting him assist her into the boat. She watched him closely, however, as the sailors rowed to *President*.

Dressing in the flagship's small, unpretentious cabin, the Commodore kept up a running commentary, very happy to show Ann, and to tell her about, everything he'd done since bringing the fleet into winter quarters.

"We have two more batteries, and a second blockhouse, on the east bank of the river facing north and east toward where the enemy's most likely to attack."

"Which I hope they won't do this evening," said Ann.

"We took all the guns off *Frances* and *Wasp* for the batteries. Those boats go back to their owners as soon as the Lake opens in the spring. Lord, what slow sailors they are!"

During a lull in his loquaciousness, she asked: "What's worrying Aze? He looked very solemn in the gig."

"As far as I know, nothing's bothering him."

"Then I'll just guess," she said cryptically.

En route to *Preble* in the gig, the Commodore pointed out how *President, Preble,* and *Montgomery* lay at their moorings so that their guns could be brought to bear on any point from which the enemy might possibly approach, up the river or over the land. Downriver a hundred yards, gunless *Frances* and *Wasp,* with shorelines fore and aft, angled opposite each other in midstream in a way to block any vessel that sought to come upstream from the mouth of the Otter.

Though sails had been stowed and the ship rode under bare poles, *Preble* looked busy and bright. But her inviting noise stilled abruptly on arrival of the gig. A boatswain's whistle shrilly piped the Commodore and his wife aboard and he answered what seemed to Ann to be fifty salutes of officers standing by for presentation.

In *Preble*'s candle- and lamplit wardroom, around its big mahogany table covered with a white linen tablecloth, festivities got under way pleasantly with Madeira and claret (shades of dinner with General Bloomfield!) from cut-glass decanters.

It immediately became apparent that the coming Saturday dance had aroused the younger personnel to a pitch of enthusiasm the Commodore had not before seen, and which he very much favored. Only then did he realize how many of his officers had joined the fleet since the previous July.

"You must have met some of the girls," he said, "the way you're looking forward to this affair."

"We have indeed, sir." Lieutenant John Stansbury's twenty-one-year-young face shone. "Caroline and Jane Sutton came with their mother and father to invite the fleet. Wouldn't you say they looked pretty good, Bob?"

Lieutenant Henley nodded gravely.

"You're from Maryland, aren't you, Stansbury?" asked the Commodore.

The youngster started. "Why, yes, sir."

"Well," said the Commodore, "Southerners like you and me must always remember that Yankees think anyone born outside New England is a babe in the woods. They probably sent the Sutton sisters because all other Vergennes girls would scare you men off in the daylight."

As far as he could, the Commodore remained in the background through the evening. Quietly enjoying the exuberance of the young officers, like any husband he basked in their appreciation of Ann's personality and charm. She looked radiant in a tan taffeta full-skirted dress whose fitted bodice left her shoulders almost bare. Over them she wore a jet-beaded cape; on her feet tiny black satin pointed-toe pumps. Of course her figure showed far more than staid Vergennes dames might consider proper, but far less than naval lieutenants (certainly those present) might relish. She had an air of quality.

First course, an exceptionally delicious soup, caused her to exclaim (as much, she told the Commodore later on the ride home, because of all the wine she'd had as because of the soup itself): "This is the most delicious calves' head consommé I've ever tasted!"

In the roar that filled *Preble's* wardroom, she nearly dropped her spoon. "What did I say?"

On her right, amiable Lieutenant Stephen Cassin explained. He was thirtyish, the son of Commodore John Cassin, and always courteous. He had assumed the evening's catering supervision and had specified calves' head soup, but Cookie had said, "They ain't no calf's heads I kin git, so I'll give you a small pig's head instid, and I'll bet you a dollar Mrs. Macdonough won't know no different." So that was what she had eaten, and everybody had wondered whether she would recognize it, and Cookie had won his dollar bet.

Amid much clapping and shouting, Lieutenant Henley ordered the steward to produce Cookie, who turned out, uncurled, to stand a very thin six-feet-four in the glow of the table's candles.

The Commodore whispered to Ann: "I'm not supposed to know he isn't married to the woman he's got in the galley helping him feed *Preble*'s crew so well."

Unself-consciously grinning to show two missing upper front teeth, with freshly shaven cheeks and eyes as brilliantly lighted as Ann's own, Cookie took the silver dollar from Lieutenant Cassin, made a quick gesture of salute to Ann with the coin in his long fingers, and fled—to his so-called wife, no doubt.

Ann had immediately liked almost everyone contributing to the evening's felicity. She already knew Robert Henley and Joseph Smith, now a lieutenant. Lieutenant Pearce, dark, with an air of experienced authority in spite of only twenty-one years; Lieutenant Budd (on *Chesapeake* when *Shannon* took her), stocky, confident; Acting Lieutenants William M. Robbins and Elie A. F. Vallette, both of whom had joined the Navy as sailing masters at the outbreak of the war; Lieutenant Stansbury, son of General Tobias Stansbury of Maryland, a gentle-looking, sensitive boy with a fine mouth; Purser George Beale, round and jovial like Santa Claus and stowing away quantities of Cookie's enormous roast of pork like Falstaff. Ann found them all to her liking.

"All but Lieutenant Henley," she told her husband later in

the sleigh as they drove home. "You'd better keep your guard up, Tom."

"Didn't he pay you enough compliments?"

"Too many. And in the next breath told me how *he'd* moored the fleet, how *he'd* placed the batteries, how *he'd* built the blockhouses."

The Commodore smiled at her vehemence. "He's right. He did do those."

"But *you* planned them!" she insisted. "He tried to take credit for being the brains as well as the brawn. Tom, I didn't like him the first time I met him at the Fourth of July celebration. Oh, I know he's an old, old buddy from the Mediterranean. But I feel he has a need to be top dog."

"Bob's a great man in a fight," the Commodore said. "I'd stake my life on him."

She shook her head solemnly. "Don't, Tom. He's out for glory. Take good care he doesn't get it at your expense."

"Otherwise?" he asked, after a pause.

"Otherwise," Ann responded heartily, "I think you can rely, sir, on the officers of the Lake Champlain fleet to give a good account of themselves—as I told them."

The tinkle of the horses' bells provided a musical flourish to the evening's end, paced by the soft clop-clop of their hoofs on the snow-covered road. Above, stars filled a clear, cold sky. The off-horse whinnied, once.

Ann's voice reached the Commodore through the scarf wound around his head and chin. "Thank you very much for such a revealing day," she said softly. "From now on I'll try not to bother you with my picayune troubles. And I hope I didn't disgrace you at dinner, before all your men."

His laugh echoed over the moonlighted fields. "Disgrace me! You raised me higher in their estimation than a Navy Office promotion to captain!"

5

On the second floor of a wood building opposite Painter's Tavern, Commodore Macdonough found office space. The lower floor, used by the Vergennes militia for a guardhouse, "gives the place a little atmosphere," Ann declared ironically while she helped get the Spartan headquarters ready for him. "These three tiny rooms of yours have less in them now that they're furnished than the cells downstairs!"

But for him and Aze, who continued to act as his clerk, and for Purser George Beale, the rooms provided ample space for the paperwork required to keep the immobile fleet's personnel housed and fed, to catch up on unanswered correspondence, and to plan tentatively for expanding the 1814 fleet.

With Aze, the Commodore laid out programs for putting the midshipmen to work at studies calculated to achieve the Navy Office's avowed aim of having them "acquire a thorough and extensive knowledge of all duties to be performed on a ship of war," and for the boys of the fleet to learn seamanship under the boatswains and gunnery under the gunners.

He called his commanders together on *President,* put the programs before them, and assigned Lieutenant Cassin to supervise "fleet education."

He pointed out: "We all know that when chaplains serve as schoolmasters, as the Navy Office suggests, not much of practical value gets learned . . . a little copying of the ship's log to improve handwriting, and that's about all. I propose these training programs as a means to keep our junior lieutenants and warrant officers profitably busy, to bring our midshipmen along fast in becoming useful officers, and to give the boys and any seamen that show a desire to go along a basic understanding of how to sail a ship sharply and fire its guns effectively.

"I expect Lieutenant Cassin to select men who enjoy teaching the things they know best. I don't care whether they use books or boat hooks or just sit on the rail and talk. I want to see all our men so well trained in their jobs and so well organized by April that it won't make any difference how many boats the British build—we'll know more about sailing and shooting."

Sensing the Commodore's unusual seriousness about this novel idea of taking theoretical education away from divinity students and putting it into the horny hands of practiced sailors, the officers of all grades responded wholeheartedly to Lieutenant Cassin's search for capable volunteer instructors.

"Even Cookie wants to take a class," Cassin reported after his preliminary survey had uncovered much likely professorial talent.

"We can always use good cooks," the Commodore agreed.

For the purser, he pulled bills and letters relating to fiscal foul-ups out of a seemingly bottomless pile of old correspondence.

"Aze and I had other things to concern ourselves with," he told George Beale. "We took care of the most pressing matters, and we've given you time to get accustomed to how we handle the Champlain fleet. Now," he laughed hugely as he handed a mountain of papers to the purser, "you can spend a day or two cleaning these up."

The purser frowned over the top letter: "Do you honestly mean you haven't cleared this one of September fifteenth from A. and N. Brown in New York—last spring's accounts of their carpenters?"

"Don't scold, George," said the Commodore guiltily. "The bills for the carpenters' expenses coming from New York, and

for boarding at Shelburne, and for allotments to their wives
became mighty complicated. And you know very well that
none of us line officers ever went to Harvard or King's College to study higher mathematics." He winked at Aze. "Be a
good fellow, George, and get me straightened out with the
Brown brothers before I go to New York to see if they'll come
up here and build us a ship."

Aze's eyes almost blew out of their sockets. "A ship, sir!
How many guns?"

The Commodore put a finger on his lips to signal caution,
and replied: "Only you and George and William Jones in
Washington know I've even thought of this. Not a word to
anyone until the Secretary says yes or no. Answering your
question, Aze, I think we should consider twenty guns or
more."

"That would make it as big as any of Lieutenant Perry's
ships on Lake Erie!" Aze's excitement contrasted sharply with
his recent unusual quiet.

"Perhaps, then," suggested the Commodore, "we should
build ours a little bigger, say twenty-five?"

Saturday night's dance for the fleet officers developed into
a naval ball. The local correspondent for the *Northern Sentinel* (changed from the *Centinel* during Ann's absence) reported that for numbers and respectability it had never been
surpassed in Vergennes.

Arriving from their upstairs rooms, Commodore and Mrs.
Macdonough found the hotel's large dancing hall decorated
with naval flags of all kinds. The American ensign hung over
the entrance door, also surmounted by an arch of evergreens
and laurel. Signal flags splashed a melange of colors on the
walls. Pennants and streamers of red bunting, and white and
blue, "tastefully arrayed, served as curtains. Wreaths and
crowns of laurel, etc., were handsomely disposed as ornaments
in different parts of the room."

Music came from Burlington in the brightly colored, brightly polished uniforms of a United States Army band.

"A purely voluntary appearance, sir," John Stansbury informed the Commodore, "suggested by our friends in Burlington."

"Colonel Clark, no doubt," said the Commodore with a straight face.

"And other friends of my father in Maryland," the young officer replied with utmost earnestness.

"You never know," the Commodore confided to Ann out of Stansbury's earshot, "when a general will come in handy!"

Ann sparkled. Once again, now before the women of Vergennes, her figure showed its best under the easy princess lines of a pussy-willow silk dress. Organdy ruffles trimmed the elbow-length sleeves. A cameo stick-pin caught her wide, bertha collar in place; small cameo earrings matched the pin. Gay and dainty silver buckles set off her dancing pumps. And her popularity with Vergennes' male civilians proved as great as her popularity with the Navy officers.

At supper, "prepared in a superior style suitable to the occasion and arranged in a manner calculated to gratify both the epicure and the admirer of elegant decorations," the Commodore had a few minutes to compare notes with her.

"I like your Sam Strong and Amos Barnum and Ed Sutton and Dan Harmon," she whispered. "I like their wives, too. Dowdy, but sweet."

As the Commodore watched, and talked to, and danced with the mothers of Vergennes, he found himself impressed with their basic soundness. Their outer shell of diffidence—a hard covering for mental insufficiency combined with ignorance of social graces—once penetrated, proved in most cases to cover a warm and friendly core. He felt especially touched by their frank admiration for Ann's comportment.

"Not only is she lovely to look at," Mrs. Sutton let him know with enchanting candor, "but she's delightful to talk to. You're a fortunate husband, Commodore Macdonough."

And he'd expected these women to throw up their hands in outraged horror at Ann's modish clothes, to raise insuperable defenses against liking her!

At every opportunity he took it upon himself to set the mothers' minds at ease on what he suspected they feared most —the way of a naval officer with a maid. He described what good homes and families the young men came from, how hard they worked in the fleet, how exuberant they naturally acted when free from their arduous duties. He used all his arts of persuasion to portray his staff as desirable guests-to-be in Vergennes homes.

"Don't overdo it, Commodore," Ann advised in one of the rare moments when she could tear herself away from the fathers. "Let these good people discover for themselves some of the minor virtues of your young paragons. Incidentally, where's Aze tonight?"

"He begged off to go to Burlington—on business, he said." The Commodore rubbed his chin reflectively. "I must ask him about it. You make me curious."

Ann changed the subject. "Has anyone offered to take us in yet?"

He shook his head. "Not a soul. We may have to stay at the Tavern."

She put her hand tenderly on his arm. "I'd like you to have more of a home than a tavern bedroom," she said.

6

When the Commodore tried during the following week to uncover the cause of Aze Bellamy's uncharacteristic dejection, he encountered resistance. And after Aze, unwilling to unburden himself, answered a few direct questions with a reluctant yes or no, the Commodore desisted and reported nothing to Ann about his fruitless effort. Other news absorbed his attention.

Word reached Vergennes of a fresh Army shake-up on the northern frontier. The Secretary of War had divided the border troops into two columns. One, under General Jacob Brown, went to Sackett's Harbor. The second column, in two parts, went to Lake Champlain: the first part to Plattsburg under General James Wilkinson; the second part to Burlington under newly made Brigadier General Alexander Macomb. A letter from the Secretary of the Navy confirmed the military reorganization.

"Now we'll have just twice as many problems as ever before," the Commodore ruefully declared to Lieutenants Henley and Cassin.

"That Wilkinson!" said Henley belligerently. "A hard old man to get along with sober—and drunk much of the time, they tell me."

Cassin shrugged. Over his rugged face spread an acquiescent smile. "Maybe being freshly married to a gal less than half his age will soften Wilkinson up," he said. "Let's hope he brings the bride with him."

Henley looked at the Commodore. A big man with strong hands, he carried himself with aggressive assurance. Now,

175

slumped in an office chair with his black-booted legs stretched out, his forehead creased under jet-black, shining hair, he looked like a man craving action. He asked: "Tom, what do you know about Macomb?"

Behind his plain desk, the Commodore leaned back, too, and said: "The information I have, mostly from Eleazer Williams, puts Macomb around our age, thirty-one, thirty-two; mixed American and French family, born in Detroit, brought up in New York, educated in New Jersey; and one of West Point's first graduates. As a captain of engineers, he superintended the erection of forts all along the frontiers. Served as aide-de-camp to Wilkinson before the war, and served with him again at Sackett's Harbor last year in artillery. Williams considers him a good soldier."

Cassin nodded. "He sounds all right. I'm glad he'll have the Burlington garrison. Maybe we can use him to keep old Wilkinson off our backs."

Like Henley, Cassin stretched at length in a chair beside the desk. But unlike Henley, he seemed relaxed. Gray eyes lighted his thin, unlined face, and he looked what the Commodore knew him to be, a capable, confident, self-contained officer. Pleasing and urbane on the dance floor with women, on a ship's deck he handled men with an easy temper and soft tongue that covered the hard iron of his authority.

The Commodore let the talk about generals trail off. He then released the news that had caused him to call in his senior lieutenants.

Holding up a Navy Office letter dated January 28th, without preamble he read:

"You are authorized and directed to build about fifteen gunboats, or a ship, or a ship and three or four gunboats, as you think best.

"The object is to leave no doubt of your commanding the Lake and the waters connected, and that in due time. You are therefore authorized to employ such means and workmen as shall render its accomplishment certain."

He looked up. "How do you like that?"

Henley's dark face glowed. "Great!" he declared. "Let's get started."

The Commodore glanced toward Cassin. "Steve?"

"I'm mulling over that part where the Secretary mentions the Lake and the waters connected," Cassin said in his deceptively soft voice. "General Armstrong must have made an issue of our not sailing down to Isle-aux-Noix with Hampton on his first try for Montreal."

The Commodore's jaw flexed. He said: "Now Wilkinson will probably ride us hard to get command of the Sorel, as Mr. Jones orders, in due time."

For weeks the Commodore had let ideas for a more effective fleet simmer on the back stove lids of his mind. Because he wanted time to work on his side, to help clarify his ideas so that he could call for their execution with full confidence in their soundness, he hadn't broached his thoughts to either of these men. Keeping his own counsel, he'd discarded ideas impracticable under conditions existing on the Lake and had come to the settled conclusion that first efforts should go into the building of a vessel big enough to overpower anything the British might conceivably assemble at Isle-aux-Noix. He hadn't exaggerated to Aze when he said they should consider a ship up to twenty-five guns.

When now he outlined his attempered ideas to the Lieutenants, they rose in their chairs, buoyed up as he had not seen them in months.

"The Secretary gives us a choice of one ship or many gunboats," he summed up. "But I recommend a ship, if only because a ship requires fewer men for many more guns. You know what a time we'll have again this year trying to get men."

Academically the trio discussed the pros and cons of ship versus galleys. But as the Commodore had confidently anticipated, the lure of a ship outstripped the attractions of prosaic gunboats. Both Henley and Cassin had worked under big sail and like every other naval officer of enterprise and ambition they considered command of galleys a practical demotion.

"I go along with you, Tom," said Henley. "I'm all for the ship."

Cassin nodded vigorously. "No question in my mind," he agreed. "A ship will boost our morale and impress the Army. And, as you say, it takes fewer men for more fire power." He looked closely at the Commodore and asked: "How do we keep this from the British?"

The Commodore ran a hand over his chin. "That's a problem," he conceded. "Once we start building, we can't hide it from our men or from the local people. The British will get word immediately. But I figure we can keep details secret until we get the ship in commission. After that..." He paused reflectively. Then: "I'll talk with Eleazer Williams; he's living nearby in Charlotte. He may have suggestions for throwing the enemy off by indirection."

Abruptly changing the subject, he went on: "Meanwhile I'm going to New York to talk with the Browns, who built Perry's fleet on Lake Erie and sent us those carpenters last year. Before I go, Bob, will you pull together figures on what officers and men we'll need not only for a ship but also for ten galleys? I'm going all out to get Mr. Jones's approval for not less than six.

"And will you, Steve, give me some idea of the lumber we'll need? You can start getting it brought in immediately so that carpenters can move the minute the Browns arrive."

Cassin nodded, and asked: "Where do you plan to do this building—Whitehall? Shelburne?"

The Commodore told him. "Right here on the Otter where we'll have all the protection we need," he said; "just below the falls and the iron works. There's plenty of flat land to work on, the lumber's handy, and so are the lumberjacks. Also, the New York shipwrights can find boarding places in town, saving us transportation problems."

Over Lieutenant Cassin's face spread an appreciative smile. "You never stop those think-gears of yours from going around inside that handsome head, do you, Tom?" he said. "I particularly admire the way you keep them from clanking out loud, so no one even knows they're grinding until they disgorge all the answers."

The Commodore laughed. "Don't feel bad, Steve. I had to keep you two in the dark until Mr. Jones gave me the go-ahead." He added, tongue in his cheek: "I couldn't have stood your disappointment if I'd raised your hopes and he'd knocked them down."

Cassin shook his head in mock sorrow. "If we believed that, Tom, we'd believe anything," he said and smiled warmly. "I don't mind your being so secretive just so long as you count on me in all your planning."

The Commodore got up and walked around the desk. He put one hand fondly on Cassin's shoulder and shook the Lieutenant's other hand. "That I do, Steve," he said. "I count on you heavily, old friend."

Turning to Henley, he gripped a shoulder as he had Cassin's, and held out his hand. "Bob," he said, "we've got hold of a big thing here on Champlain. I need all the help you can give me."

Henley's eyes shone at the prospect the Commodore opened. The deep furrows returned to his forehead. He gripped the proffered hand hard. "I'm with you every foot of the way, Tom," he said.

Later in the day, at the Buttonwoods, the Commodore briefed all fleet officers on the essentials of his building plans. They, too, had their sights lifted in anticipation.

"Now I understand," said Joseph Smith, "why you wanted us to train everybody so thoroughly in sailing and gunnery."

"Now you'll understand, too," the Commodore returned, "why I'm sending you to Boston next week to open a rendezvous." He watched the pleased expression race over the Lieutenant's rosy face. "I'll expect you to enlist nothing but superior sailors and gunners. Also, I want you to find me a good clerk. Midshipman Bellamy's too valuable on deck now to waste his time writing letters."

Walking with Ann through the lightly falling snow that evening to Mayor Strong's house across the river, the Commodore outlined for her the day's activities, assessing them again in his own mind as he ticked them off. They added up, he felt with a small glow of accomplishment, to the first forward steps in a campaign against the enemy that might make up for two years of discouragement and frustration.

He also put into words for Ann a thought he hadn't yet confided to his officers:

"Washington must suspect the war can be won or lost on this frontier. Why else would the Army set up separate commands on each side of the Lake?" he asked, not entirely rhetorically. "Why else would the Navy Office approve my suggestion for a ship? Mr. Jones has always backed me up, but now he puts a touch of real urgency into his letters."

Ann only asked, "How long do you plan to stay in New York?"

"Just long enough to start the shipwrights on their way up here and to push Dr. Bullus and his assistant Navy agents into procuring the ship's equipment and armament."

For several seconds Ann remained silent. Finally, in a small voice she said: "I suppose I must make up my mind to seeing very little of you from now on."

He brushed a snowflake off the top of her nose and bent to kiss it. "Don't sound so mournful," he said.

"Will you visit the family in Middletown?"

"Probably not," he said. "But I'd like to stay in New York with your grandfather, if he'd put me up."

"You know he and Grandmother Denning will love to have you!" she exclaimed. "I wish I could go with you."

He found it very hard to say no to Ann, and he tried to make his refusal gentle. "You'd take my mind off business," he said, promising, "I'll get through it quickly and hurry back."

Across the Strongs' dinner table she looked lovely as usual, and once again he took great pleasure in watching the admiring gazes she received from the men and the oblique scrutinies from the women. In a deep-red velvet basque-type dress, with jacket effect embroidered in black jet beads to form a border design around the high-standing neck and long tight sleeves, she looked slender and regal. She wore a mantle of black lace, and black lace mitts added a touch of formality to her patrician hands.

As he watched, he reminded himself that a ball or a dinner like this, or with the fleet, offered Ann's only excuse to get out of their hotel room. He must see that she got around more, not stay cooped up as last year in Burlington. Mud or no mud later, he'd have to see that she had frequent chances to dress up and show the clothes she and Lucretia Ann had assembled. When they found new quarters, he must insist on having dinner guests, much as he preferred spending his free time alone with her. He must consider her more. Compared to his, her days must hold much loneliness.

Before the half-dozen ladies left the damask-covered table to the gentlemen and their cigars, Mrs. Strong signaled her husband with small, round eyes. He nodded. Standing tall and spare, he raised his glass and looked around the table.

"I propose a toast," he said, "to our town's two newest residents—Commodore Thomas Macdonough, and his lady who has charmed us one and all."

The Mayor waited until glasses had been refilled. "Now I propose another toast—to Unity Waid, sister of Zebulon and Rebecca Waid, in whose home our distinguished guests will reside."

Ann's shriek of joy at this unexpected announcement brought a burst of laughter and, when she impulsively rushed around the table to kiss Rebecca Waid's thin cheek and then kissed Zebulon Waid's plump one for good measure, a burst of spontaneous applause.

7

To prepare for the Military Ball in honor of Generals Wilkinson and Macomb, Ann went to Burlington by Friday's stage and stayed overnight with Betsy Boyd. After a morning's work at the office Saturday, the Commodore sleighed the twenty-two miles from Vergennes, taking Aze Bellamy with him.

"Aze can drive us back," he told Ann when she greeted him in the rooms they had shared the winter before at Betsy's.

Ann led him mysteriously to a stiff Windsor chair. "Sit down, Commodore," she said, keeping her distance. "I have interesting news for you about Emily. She's a month pregnant, and Betsy's just found out."

"Aze?" he asked.

She nodded.

After a long silence he rubbed his chin, wondering where to break in on his milling thoughts. He decided to temporize. He asked: "What's Betsy said?"

Gravely, Ann digested for him her hours-long tête-à-tête with the distraught mother the previous night. Betsy had always felt Aze saw too much of Emily. She did not approve. They were too young. She had brought Emily up strictly. She had tried to make up for the child's lack of a father. She had failed. What was she to do?

"What *is* she to do?" Ann propounded.

He parried. "What would you do if you were she?"

Ann held her hands folded in her lap. "I'd report Aze to his commanding officer!"

His eyes clashed with hers. "Stop looking so outraged!" he exploded. "You know this doesn't mean the end of the world for Emily."

"It does for Betsy!" she said patiently. "Haven't you any idea how a mother feels about the way people in a town this size will talk about the girl?"

"Of course I understand," he assured her. "But why should Betsy give them a chance to gossip?"

Ann perked up, and he asked: "How does Emily feel about Aze? It always looked to me as though she thought he'd been sent from heaven just for her."

"Practically her own words!"

The Commodore rose from the chair. "Why don't we all talk this over right now?" he suggested reassuringly. "I wouldn't want you to have your evening spoiled."

He led Betsy, Emily, and Aze from the Boyds' cold and formal parlor into the brightly curtained living room where Ann stood in front of the fireplace. His arm around Betsy, red-eyed from too much crying, he talked as though the group merely awaited dinner, did not face a crisis in three lives. When he felt some of the tension had seeped away, he looked toward Aze and Emily.

The eighteen-year-old midshipman stood straight and very sober, but when he looked at Emily his face softened. Beside him, she stood self-possessed, even resolute.

"Aze," said the Commodore, "you know you're in trouble."

"I know, sir."

"Do you love Emily?"

The boy looked toward the girl again, nodding silently. He took her hand then and faced Betsy. "And she loves me," he said defiantly.

Betsy began to cry again. The Commodore withdrew his arm from her waist. His lips tightened.

"Aze," he said, "you should marry Emily."

The boy gazed at him, appealing, and cried: "That's what we've both wanted to do for months, sir!"

Ann's surprise at Aze's outburst told the Commodore that Betsy had omitted this facet of the situation from her story. Under his searching scrutiny, Betsy turned her face away and laid it on Ann's shoulder, sobbing.

He rubbed his chin thoughtfully for a long minute. "I suggest," he said finally, to the group in general, "that if Aze and Emily quietly eloped tonight, with help from us all, of course, they could spend a few days' honeymoon in W..terbury and work out with Mercy Cobb for Emily to have her baby there when it comes. That way, none of the good people of Burlington need ever know exactly when Aze and Emily were married or exactly when their baby arrived."

"How can they be married on such short notice?" Ann remonstrated. "They'll need to—"

The Commodore airily waved her objections away. To the midshipman he said: "Aze, you remember the Reverend Daniel Haskell, don't you?"

Aze beamed. "Yes, sir!" he said, and the Commodore felt good at seeing the boy's natural buoyancy back. "We put the big bell up in the Congregational Church for him."

"Well," said the Commodore, "I'm sure you can prevail on him to arrange a wedding—tonight."

Betsy Boyd's tears had dried. The Commodore turned to her and said: "You'll help Emily pack for her honeymoon, won't you?" Betsy's eyes answered as she took her daughter to her ample bosom.

Emily embraced her mother ardently for a second, then ran shining-faced toward her bedroom. Betsy hurried after.

In their own room, nibbling supper off a tray, the Commodore waited for Ann to confide first. She did.

"Of course Betsy led me to understand that Aze—"

"Yes, darling," he said in mock derision intended to exasperate her. "According to you gals, all men are beasts. And Aze is a man—all right, a boy," he hurried to amend. "But it just happens he's an unusually fine, upstanding boy. I knew he wouldn't have got Emily into the family way unless—" He stopped abruptly.

"Unless what?" she demanded.

He chuckled. "Unless he had to, to marry her."

"Oh, Tom!" She blushed, and tried to cover it with: "Do you really think they can make arrangements tonight?"

"I do indeed," he said. "Reverend Haskell feels indebted to the Navy. He'll be only too glad to stop work on tomorrow's sermon, get the proper papers for Aze, and perform the ceremony. But you? Do you mind leaving the ball long enough to be matron of honor?"

Burlington's Military Ball considerably surpassed Vergennes' Naval Ball in general grandeur. The Marsh Hotel's dance floor covered twice the space; its cut-glass chandeliers held dozens more candles; its supper table groaned under a huge roast turkey, aromatic ham and boiled tongue, breads, biscuits, custards, whips, floating islands, pies, and delicious pound, fruit, jelly, and sponge cakes. The liquor, wines and whisky flowed within decorous bounds, but not too far within.

The band, with three times as many instruments as at Vergennes, played three times as loudly for the contra dances and cotillons; in addition, it provided pirouettes and pigeonwings, the pudgy, tight-belted little bandmaster calling out the rollicking figures.

Commodore and Mrs. Macdonough arrived at a proper peak of the gaiety and with proper dignity went down the reception line, which included many old friends from both Burlington and Plattsburg, until they faced the guests of honor.

In the few seconds it took to perform the amenities, the Commodore saw men of two different stamps. Young General Alexander Macomb looked accessible, sociable; aging General James Wilkinson looked angry, and bitter.

"I had hoped to meet Mrs. Wilkinson," the Commodore said by way of polite small talk.

General Wilkinson growled. "You'll waste no time doing that," he said, "if you're like your own officers, Mr. Macdonough." He pointed to the center of the floor where a delicately formed woman of twenty-five or twenty-six, in a dress of dark red like the velvet gown Ann had worn to the Mayor's dinner, raptly danced an intricate figure with Bob Henley. "That's my wife."

Maintaining his interested, but not surprised, expression, the Commodore turned away from Wilkinson's rudeness to take Ann out on the floor. Already there, she gaily waved one hand; General Alexander Macomb attentively held the other. The Commodore and the General smilingly bowed together.

Watching the pair, the Commodore had to admit that handsome General Macomb, with his confident carriage—could he be Irish as well as French?—made a remarkably effective partner for Ann. His black curly hair and his blue, close-buttoned, single-breasted uniform coat, with ten gilt buttons whose gilt buttonholes ran upward like a herring-bone, complemented Ann's white silk perfectly.

Her strapless gown had a very full skirt caught up from time to time with soft blue velvet bows. At these points the Commodore could glimpse her elegant full-pleated petticoat. A matching blue velvet bow caught her piled-high hair, and she wore the same brooch she'd worn at her wedding; no other jewelry. Long white buttoned gloves concealed her arms to the elbows. She danced in white satin slippers.

"I wonder if I look as well with her on the floor as Macomb?" he asked himself.

When Ann at last came off the floor and graciously acknowledged General Macomb's thank you for the dance, the Commodore stood with an Army surgeon friend, Dr. William Henry Wilson, who'd sleighed over the Lake from Plattsburg with the Peter Saillys. "Bill Wilson's going to sail with me this spring," he said, "whenever he hasn't enough to do running the Plattsburg hospital."

Ann pulled him discreetly away. "Aze just came," she whispered. "I'll get my things and meet you at the door."

On the way to the church, crowded with the bridal pair and Betsy Boyd into the sleigh which Aze proudly announced he'd hired for the wedding trip, the Commodore felt Ann clinging closer to him than usual. He watched her brush a lone tear off her cheek.

"I know you like romance," he bantered when they got out and walked toward the rectory, "but I never thought you'd wallow in sentiment."

"Oh, hush!" she ordered. "They look so very young and happy, I'm sure I'll cry in another minute!"

The simple ceremony took only a brief time. The Reverend Haskell, still astounded at the speed with which he had organized the wedding under the eager spur of this Navy boy now holding the pretty girl's hand, solemnly completed the vows. And with good-bys quietly said, the newlyweds burned to start their journey.

The Commodore asked: "Think you can make Waterbury before too late?"

"Yes, sir!" said Aze.

"Think you can wake Argalus Cobb up?"

"Yes, sir!"

"All right, then, Aze. When he comes stumbling downstairs and bellows through the door with that foghorn voice of his, you just tell him to open up and give you and Emily the best room in the house. And when you leave to come home, tell him to charge everything to Mrs. Macdonough and me. It's our wedding gift to you and Emily, son."

8

Two widely separate building activities came to the Commodore's attention Monday, February 6th, in his Vergennes office. Steve Cassin brought news of the first, in the morning; Eleazer Williams delivered word of the second shortly after lunch when he arrived with a dark-skinned man who looked to the Commodore like a French-Canadian Indian, if such could exist.

Cassin had embarked on his project of getting timber laid down for the ship below the Otter Creek falls at the edge of town. He came to report progress; which he did. Then:

"You knew, of course," he said, watching his superior's expression closely, "that the Lake Champlain Steamboat Company uses land at that point on the river for a boatyard." His scrutiny evidently uncovered what he looked for. "So that's it! You figure to go after their workmen for our job, comes a pinch?"

"Why not?" said the Commodore. "Doc Lacy, their boat-builder, came up here with the New York carpenters last year to work for us, then switched over to the steamboat company."

"Have you any idea," asked Cassin, "what Lacy and his men started working on this morning?" For once, Lieutenant Cassin apparently believed, he could surprise the Commodore; he delayed presenting his information.

Leaning back at his desk, the Commodore gave the Lieutenant ample time to unburden himself. Then he asked: "You're not trying to tell me about the new steamboat, are you?"

Cassin's jaw dropped. "Why, yes," he said. "What do you know about that?"

The Commodore knew what the Vergennes business men associated with the company had revealed to him several months ago. That they planned a steamer to compete with *Vermont,* which the Army had used the past summer. That Captain Jahaziel Sherman would lay the keel and supervise the construction under Lacy. That her wooden hull would be driven by the newest steam engine available. That she would go into service in the spring. This he told Lieutenant Cassin.

"Well," said Cassin, "they've started to build her." Then: "Why don't you take her over?" he proposed out of a clear sky.

"A steamboat!" The problems of finding seamen willing to work on a mechanical ship, of making her engines perform, of keeping her repaired, all loomed before the Commodore like a mountain. He threw up his hands as if to keep it from falling on him, burying him beyond retrieve, and said: "I'd rather take my chances with galleys."

For almost an hour Cassin did his earnest best to make out a successful case for the steamboat. He got nowhere.

"All right, Tom," he finally conceded with good grace, "I can't argue any more. But I'm warning you," he said with a smile as he got up from his chair, "you haven't heard the last of me and the steamboat."

The second piece of news came when Eleazer Williams, having introduced the dark stranger as "a man I can trust," moved a chair to the edge of the office, sat back, and left the center of the stage to his companion. The French-Canadian Indian tossed his bombshell right into the Commodore's lap. "The British on Isle-aux-Noix," he announced in a sepulchral voice, "have started building a brig to carry twenty-four guns!"

No amount of probing cross-examination changed the man's story. He had seen the keel for the vessel, he had talked with men working on it, he had listened to local gossip about its design. "She will carry twenty-four guns," he repeated over and over, his voice changing only to become raspier.

Hugely enjoying the impression the news had made on the previously imperturbable Commodore, Eleazer Williams nodded sagely. "This brig may carry only eighteen guns," he said, "but eighteen, twenty, twenty-four—does it matter?"

Confirmation of Williams' information came shortly from Plattsburg, via Peter Sailly, in two successive letters rushed around the southern end of the Lake whose ice had shown signs of weakening in the February thaw. The first advised:

> All reports agree that a vessel to carry 20 or 24 Guns is building at Isle-aux-Noix. The information is contrary respecting row Gallies. Some persons say that two are building; others say no preparations are made to that effect. Intelligence, however, is expected tonight, the result of which will be given tomorrow.

The second letter reported:

> The account received last night is that no row gallies are building at Isle-aux-Noix, St. John's, or Chambly. But the large vessel to carry 24 heavy Guns is progressing at Isle-aux-Noix.
> The British know that they cannot conceal from us their exertions in Building Vessels in our vicinity. *They may build, however, Row Gallies at Sorel or even at a greater distance & bring them to St. John's in the Spring—there being but 12 miles land carriage & smooth road.*

The Commodore's problems mounted. The winter epidemic had necessitated his calling on Dr. Joseph Lovell of the Burlington Hospital to send Army medical aid. Despite this assistance, he lost many men to the same respiratory diseases that had decimated the Lake region the year before. His force was further weakened by desertions due to cold and loneliness, which he had not, and did not, tell Ann about.

To compensate for these losses, and to enlist seamen for the ship, he sent Lieutenant Joseph Smith to Boston, Lieutenant

Robbins to Salem and Marblehead, and Lieutenant Vallette to New York to open rendezvous. Complicating this, Robbins came down sick at Poultney, Vermont, and had to be sent for after young Stansbury went to Massachusetts in his place.

Since more men enlisted meant more officers needed, the Commodore also engaged in extensive correspondence aimed to convince the Secretary of the Navy that he should send officers immediately, and only commanding officers of experience. To make this point doubly impressive he gave Lieutenant Cassin leave to go home on a visit to his family, with instructions to drop in at the Navy Office and talk to the Secretary in person.

"But whatever you do," the Commodore cautioned, "don't let him send you to another station. I need you, Steve."

Cassin looked as relaxed as always. "I'll be back, Tom," he said, "with all the support you want from Mr. Jones."

Cassin's fixed grin bothered the Commodore, but not until Cassin left did it dawn on him that Steve might still have the steamboat on his mind. If the Secretary learned of that, he might want it in the fleet!

Ann had had their belongings moved into their new quarters in Unity Waid's not-too-large house where they quickly found themselves pushed almost past endurance to put up with the little widow's incessant jabbering about her own aches, the ills of all her relatives, and the particular pneumonia that had carried Phineas Waid off the year before, leaving her a widow.

Ann complained at the end of the first week. "This woman will drive me crazy, Tom," she said. "She follows me around like a hawk, pouncing on every stick of furniture I touch and don't put back in the exact same position—chairs, pillows, everything! I have to stay in my room to get any rest from her fluttering, and even there she comes in whenever she thinks I haven't refolded the towels neatly or replaced the soap proper side up on the washstand."

He cheered her temporarily with a birthday dinner on February 10th at the Tavern where Tom Rich, at the Commodore's instigation, had provided pig's head soup. But he found it practically impossible to drag his mind from fleet problems to console her as she wanted, and needed to be, on her domestic conflicts.

As they reluctantly headed back toward their rooms, he announced: "I've got to go to Albany next week about carpenters and guns and powder before riding on to New York as I planned earlier."

"Won't you change your mind—and take me with you?"

"I wish I could."

She shrugged philosophically. "And *I* wish this war would get over with so we can go to housekeeping in Middletown! I hate being so idle, Tom."

He started his New York trip further disturbed.

On the night before leaving, an excited courier routed him out of bed and drove him to the Buttonwoods where he found officers and men still searching the woods for two figures seen pouring oil over the hauled-out gunboats on the east bank of the river—in preparation for setting them afire.

No damage had been done, but the men fled successfully.

"From their descriptions," Aze Bellamy reported, "one of 'em could be our friend Jake Dibble."

"What brought *you* here?" the Commodore demanded.

Aze explained: "I get very tired, sir, of boardinghouse food and very lonely during the week, with Emily living in Burlington at her mother's. I came to eat on *President* with Charlie Platt."

Accepting that, the Commodore asked: "Why didn't the guards discover the arsonists before they could pour oil over the galleys?"

"I don't know, sir," said Aze.

The Commodore contained his anger until Bob Henley, checking on the sentries, reported that the marauders apparently had moved fast, taking advantage of a change in sentinels who'd lingered over the hot stove in their block-house.

When Henley completed his report, the Commodore snapped out his orders: "Have every man on both guard details, the master-at-arms included, before me in the morning. And muster the entire fleet complement at the same time— I'm going to throw the fear of God into these men!"

He finished the night aboard *President*.

Next morning he tried and sentenced the neglectful sentinels, and read the riot act to every officer and man on the station.

In private, he told Henley: "I hold you responsible, Lieutenant. Don't ever let such negligence occur again!"

Henley saluted sharply, his hand stiffly touching his furrowed forehead. "No, sir!" he said.

The Commodore returned to Vergennes in time to bid Ann a hasty good-by, pick up his bag, and catch the stage to Albany—still perturbed but feeling that officers and men at last fully appreciated the need for unfailing vigilance to keep Champlain's meager fleet secure.

PART FOUR

THE AXES

The keel of a ship was laid at Vergennes....

Autobiography

1

Delayed in Albany with details of reshipping supplies already brought up the Hudson by sloop, Commodore Macdonough reached New York late on Sunday, February 20th. William Denning welcomed him with the affection of a devoted relative and the esteem of a good friend. But until he had completed his business with Brown, Bullus, *et al.*, he wanted merely to talk family with Ann's grandfather and grandmother. This he did briefly to their great pleasure, and went early to bed.

New York had continued to expand, he found next morning when he walked out of the Dennings' beautiful brick Broadway mansion and took a roundabout route past the Bear Market in Washington Street; then past the Fly Market in Pearl Street to Lieutenant Vallette's rendezvous and the Browns' shipyard on the East River.

City Hall, finished in 1812, since he had last visited the metropolis, looked most imposing with its dome of copper supplied by Paul Revere and its graceful John Dixey statue of unblindfolded Justice balancing her scales.[1] Washington Hall impressed him also, because of the notification he had received in November of a meeting there of the United States Military Philosophical Society which had elected him a member, along with Masters Commandant Joseph Bainbridge, James Biddle, Johnson Blakely, and Lewis Warrington. Mayor DeWitt Clinton, Robert Fulton, and John Bullus had voted him into the Society. He hoped he could attend a meeting before too long.

In the otherwise unused Market Street store outside of which Elie Vallette's recruiting flag signaled the rendezvous for Lake Champlain, the Commodore listened to his Lieutenant's bare report.

"Enlistments," said laconic Vallette, "come in slow but satisfactory."

Very evidently this steady-going redheaded youth, whose shoulders looked even broader than those of the powerful John Roberts who could lift pork-brine barrels with his fingers, had New York's recruiting situation as well under control as could be expected. The Commodore expressed his approval of Vallette's efforts, and urged:

"Keep sending us the best men you can find."

The Commodore's call at the Adam and Noah Brown shipyard on the East River took even less time than the visit to the rendezvous. He found Adam Brown working side by side with his shipwrights on a nearly planked hull.

A retiring man of average height who seemed, like most other master carpenters, more concerned with the job in hand than with his appearance and the impression he made, Adam Brown rested a moment. Even more laconic than Elie Vallette, he greeted his visitor with: "We had your letters, Commodore."

"Good."

"You want a ship?"

"Yes, and some galleys. Can you build them for us?"

Adam Brown gave a bluff nod. "Noah took the stage north yesterday, with his carpenters," he said, and went on with his planking.

Business with Naval Agent John Bullus in his downtown office and with Captain Samuel Evans at the Navy Yard on Long Island took longer; because the Commodore had to reconcile differences of opinion between the pair as to what materials could go at once to the Lake and which guns, already promised to other ships, could find their way north with least outcry from outraged commanders.

But three days of arduous negotiating, bargaining, stipulating, cajoling and compromising (and appropriating, usurping, transferring, drawing off, and stripping what he needed), left the Commodore full of bounce and gave Dr. Bullus and Captain Evans renewed respect for the capabilities of the Navy's commanders on the Lakes.

"The sheet anchor, then, will go to you from Boston," John Bullus concluded on the third day, over lunch at Clark & Brown's. "That is," he said, "if Captain Bainbridge can figure how to send three thousand pounds of iron in one chunk over those muddy roads of yours!"

His last New York evening Commodore Macdonough spent in a huge and comfortable black-leather chair before a blazing fire in William Denning's high-ceilinged library. Here Grandmother Denning understandingly left him with Ann's grandfather and a huge silver urn of coffee.

After handing the Commodore a small cup and saucer of exquisite pattern, William Denning let his spare frame down into another large chair where his eyes could range over his guest from under his bushy white brows. He said, warmly: "You honor me, Tom, by staying with us, and particularly by giving your last evening to an old man instead of looking over the attractions of the young women at our music halls."

"I've wanted to do this, sir," said the Commodore, "for months."

He had indeed. In the midst of standing up against seemingly imbecilic Army decisions, of trying to stop smuggling by otherwise law-abiding citizens, of making plans for the Lake's future defense while coping with present death and desertion in the fleet, he often had wished he could sit down, as now. He badly needed the refreshment, the strength, he could draw from the knowing old patriot.

Though Grandfather Denning looked like a goateed, rosy-cheeked pixie under that mop of unruly white hair, this veteran compatriot of George Washington and Alexander

Hamilton and James Madison and James Monroe had, in the Commodore's opinion, an Olympian view of the nation's philosophical and political struggles. The old gentleman opened surprisingly: "I suppose you felt bad about the President's not mentioning Lake Champlain in his recent message to Congress?" [2]

"I did," the Commodore said frankly, "and I wrote Mr. Jones how uneasy I felt because the President might consider I hadn't done everything in my power to do."

"What did the Secretary say?"

"That the President 'entertains the highest confidence in your capacity, zeal, and patriotism, and is perfectly satisfied with your services,' and that he'd had no intention of slighting me by mentioning more important operations elsewhere."

William Denning nodded. "That sounds like Mr. Madison. You can believe that's how he feels, Tom."

"But has the Secretary given him any appreciation of what we're up against on Champlain; the severity of the climate, the distance from sources of supply, the difficulties of transporting stores and munitions and men, the impossibility of obtaining enough seamen, making do with soldiers in place of sailors when we can beg them from the Army?"

"I think he appreciates your problems, Tom. At least in a general way since, like you, he himself has problems that most people don't know exist. He's fundamentally a scholar and a writer, by nature opposed to force; but he's also a man of great ability, in my judgment. He entered the war reluctantly, partly because he had to cut away from his early political friends, the Federalists. You know, don't you, that he wrote twenty-nine of the eighty-five numbers of the *Federalist?* He's a patriot. His character cannot be reproached.

"I think, myself, Tom, he's got wrong men in some key places. I'd rather Monroe served as Secretary of War than as Secretary of State. We need someone in that job with Monroe's common sense and boldness."

"Amen to that!" said the Commodore fervently.

"By and large," the old gentleman continued, "I think Mr. Madison's doing very well reconciling the conflicting forces contributing today to our national character. There's much evil and much good come out of the war so far, in my estimation. We've lost many lives, the enemy has destroyed much individual property, and we face permanent taxes and the upkeep of a military establishment that sound thinkers consider inimical to national freedom and happiness."

He got out of his chair and crossed the room to the coffee urn. Refilling his cup, he seemed to marshal his thoughts.

"You must have seen even better than I, Tom," he went on after going back to his chair and looking up at his guest inquiringly, "how selfish people had become under our former way of living. We found ourselves so busy acquiring wealth that we confined our political activities to local and state interests; like ancient Rome, if I may dare compare a beginning nation with one that stood up for hundreds of years. We almost lost the biggest thing we won in the Revolution—our feeling of solidarity, of working together for a common purpose—our national character. I think this war will bring that back to us. I think I already see us acting more as a nation, feeling more that we're Americans, not just New Englanders or New Yorkers or Virginians. I hope, Tom, to see this war make us a permanent union!"

To the Commodore, William Denning's stern expression added force to the ideas which he voiced so eloquently and which the Commodore felt as deeply. The old man continued:

"Our fingers still clutch the freedom we won in the Revolution and which selfishly, and out of individual avarice and partisan greed, we let slip through our hands. By holding fast, son, we can regain our grip, even firmer, I trust."

He put down his cup.

"We've got a pretty good society, Tom. Social distinctions are marked, but no one pays servile respect to rank or wealth, as elsewhere. You can live in your own way, with becoming elegance and splendor or with equally becoming modesty and simplicity. Which makes for an agreeable community; except that to grow as a nation we need something to knit us all together, something bigger than the satisfying of our creature comforts, something to uplift the spirit. I think that that something is a union of states in which the individual can rely on everyone else's determination to maintain that union as the free and independent republic we set up with the Revolution. Right now, I see signs that our people have seen the issue and want to face and settle it now."

"But I've heard rumors of treating for peace."

William Denning nodded. "The British have agreed to talk," he said. "I expect we'll send commissioners over to Europe in a few months."

"That doesn't sound much like fighting for freedom. That's compromising, plain and simple," the Commodore declared. "We started out to keep the British from impressing our seamen and interfering with our vessels on the high seas. Unless we accomplish both, we can't claim to be a nation, or even a union worthy of the name."

"I know how you feel, son," the old gentleman said evenly, "but look at the practicalities of the situation. Right now, with no British troops on our soil, we can hold out firmly for what we want. And with commissioners of the quality of Albert Gallatin, who's had twelve years as Secretary of the Treasury and certainly should know his way around American and European diplomacy, I'm convinced we can win our points. If we don't act now, however, we may lose our golden chance."

The Commodore waited for the old gentleman's explanation of this conclusion.

William Denning put the finger tips of both hands together in front of his chin. "I predict the end of the line for Napoleon before too long," he said. "With him rubbed off the European scene, the British can turn the full blast of their military power on us. How would you like to face their naval veterans on Champlain?"

"They'd know they'd been in a fight," he replied, quickly.

"That I'm sure of, Tom," the old gentleman as quickly affirmed. "I only meant to get over that, as in every situation in life, the blacks and the whites merge in many places and we get grays . . . you call them compromises. We frequently can't avoid them; we must make the best choice of evils we can. At the moment, I think, the British have their bellies full with their war with us and their war with Napoleon. They'll make concessions that we can accept, now. But once Napoleon goes, they'll resort again to their same old bullying."

"I'm sure they will," the Commodore said softly. "That's why I think we shouldn't consider peace now or ever, until we make them respect and fear us so much as a nation and as a naval power that they won't *ever* try their bullying on us again!"

"Should we make them fear us, too, as a military power?" the old gentleman asked, quizzically.

"With the generals we've had leading our forces—" The Commodore saw the amusement in William Denning's laughing eyes and, of a sudden, grinned broadly. "All right, sir! You caught me out on that one."

William Denning offered more coffee and said: "I hope you don't mind my running on and on the way I do, Tom. It's so satisfying to have someone I can unburden myself to, especially," he smiled gently, "someone young enough to think my words hold pearls of wisdom."

The Commodore accepted the coffee. "I only know, sir," he said, "that when I watch what goes on in Vermont and get news about, and read about, what's happening in Washington and Philadelphia and New York, and Boston and Hartford, I feel bad. But when I talk to you about the men running the government and the Navy and about our people, I feel good."

William Denning showed his pleasure. He said: "Thank you very much, Tom. Thank you very much. You pay me a very great compliment." He put his finger tips together, with thumbs against his chin, again. "You wouldn't mind, then, letting me get one or two things more off my chest of a national and personal nature?"

"I'd like to hear anything you have to say."

"It's about Lake Champlain."

"All the more reason to listen."

The old gentleman sat quietly for a comparatively long time during which he gave the appearance of mulling over what he planned to say. When he spoke, however, his voice retained its easy, conversational tone, as though he revealed his thoughts in whatever order they chose to come out.

"However much it costs the country, in lives and money, to win this war," he began, "I agree with you that it will be worth the price only if we acquire a national character based on our determination to hold on to freedom. We must make England, the entire world, realize that our people stand together on national policy, no matter how bitterly we disagree over internal affairs. And I think, I feel, we'll have one, maybe more, dramatic opportunities to show that, when called on, we can, and will, fight and beat any bully—no matter how big —who puts us to the test."

He looked quickly at the Commodore, and hurried on: "What I'm getting around to, son, is simply this. That I don't honestly think we're going to have peace talks with England before war ends in Europe. That when Napoleon falls I do think the British will throw troops and frigates at us from north, south, and east. That they'll move first against New York from Montreal. And that, unless I miss my guess, you'll find yourself, with the troops on the Lake, staring right at what we've just discussed—the opportunity to show the British and the world that we're a united nation willing to fight together against any odds for our hard-won freedom, for every impressed sailor, and for every illegally taken merchant vessel."

Once more he paused. He took his hands down from in front of his face and looked squarely at the Commodore.

"Furthermore," he said, "I have a strong, let me call it an overpowering, inner feeling that if the British learn that fact once, thoroughly, we'll quickly have peace on the terms we've fought for since the beginning. In your hands, son, our whole national future may rest."

The Commodore had seen the way the old gentleman's thoughts moved, and had expected a strong statement. But not so strong as this! He felt overwhelmed.

"Why not?" William Denning asked, and answered: "Your fleet stands in the way of British invasion down the Hudson. If the enemy can destroy you and take control of Champlain, their veterans from the continent will swarm down on New York like lava down the sides of Mt. Vesuvius. But if you stop them on the water, they can't move on land. And the pride of the powers-that-be in London won't let them go on against determined, united opposition that they can't hope to beat down. They'll make whatever concessions will save face and call their forces home."

William Denning talked for an hour more. He talked about politicians in Washington. He talked of personalities in New York. He discussed the ways in which the British might attack through the Gulf of Mexico and along the Eastern seaboard. But nothing he said in that hour reached the Commodore's teeming consciousness through the ringing in his ears of those earlier words:

"In your hands, son, our whole national future may rest."

2

When Commodore Macdonough's stage dropped him off at Painter's Tavern on Tuesday, March 1st, Noah Brown and thirty shipwrights had reached Vergennes, found quarters, set up for business with mold loft, sawpit, and steambox, and sorted out the timber that Daniel Wright and one hundred and ten local lumberjacks had cut and laid down from upwards of two thousand trees.[1] In person, Noah Brown gave the Commodore details in the fleet office across from the Tavern.

Much more talkative than his brother Adam, Noah nevertheless had what appeared to be a family penchant for boiling reports down to a minimum of words. His description of the lumber situation at the Navy's boatyard on the Otter implied that before going on leave Lieutenant Cassin had done well in arranging for all the wood needed for a ship and the new galleys the Commodore had in mind.

"I'll build you six new gunboats right along with the ship," Noah told him. "With the four old galleys, which I also can rebuild as good as new, you'll have a fine round number—ten."

The Commodore found Noah Brown's incisiveness overpowering. Much like Moses Eggleston, the New York builder exuded the quiet confidence of the typical master carpenter, but in him this combined with a hearty, outgoing attitude that touched his statements and his movements with great personal charm.

Spare, like Adam, but shorter, with a strong, weatherbeaten face and big, powerful hands that continuously played with the thick, gold watch chain across his black vest, Noah seemed always on the verge of laughing. His dark eyes gleamed when he spoke, as though whatever he did, or had in mind, provided, or at any moment could be expected to provide, very pleasant fun. His voice had some of Argalus Cobb's resonance, though several tones higher. Altogether, Noah gave every sign of being a good man to work with. In no time, he showed his understanding of the Lake's problems.

"Commodore," he said, expansively, "I'll have a ship of twenty-six guns in the water for you in sixty days. Mind you, you won't get anything elaborate. I'll tell you now exactly what I told the men when we worked for Lieutenant Perry last year on Lake Erie. We want no extras; plain work is all we want. This ship and these gunboats are only required for one battle. If we win, that's all that will be wanted of them. If the enemy are victorious, the work is good enough to be captured."

The Commodore liked Noah Brown more with every word.

"Mr. Jones contracted with you for only twenty-four guns," he pointed out, with a smile.

"That's right. But your officers tell me the British brig will carry twenty-four."

"That's gossip. They probably won't go over twenty."

"But if they should go to twenty-four, with twenty-six guns you'll still have the advantage. Why skimp?"

The Commodore laughed.

"You never tried to pry two guns out of a Navy yard!" He went on, seriously. "Can you cut those sixty days to launching down to, say, thirty?" he pressed. "Every day will count for us once the ice goes out of the Lake, which I think may be early this year."

Noah Brown fingered his watch chain. "Can't promise you that, Commodore," he said, amiably, "but I'll ask my men to see how close to fifty they can come. Provided that is, you give us the help we need with mechanics and laborers."

"When can you start?"

"Tomorrow at sunup."

"In spite of the weather?"

"In spite of the weather."

The Commodore leafed a wall calendar and put a ring around April 21st. "That's the day we launch her, then, Noah," he said, decisively.

The shipbuilder looked at him with obviously heightened respect. "I can see," he said, "that from now on I'd better think twice before making rash promises."

The Commodore's expression remained bland as he threw out very casually that the Secretary of the Navy had sent none of the ship's plans and draughts he'd promised. To his surprise, Noah Brown revealed that he'd told the Secretary to forget them.

"They'd just get in my way," he said. "I told Mr. Jones that if he wanted my men's broadaxes to help you fellers fight this war he'd have to let us swing 'em after my own fashion, not his. So the Secretary ordered me to go ahead and build the ship I figure will best carry the guns you need to beat the British on this Lake. That's what I'm here to do, Mister Macdonough."

With the assurance of the competent artist, he started to figure on a piece of paper, and said: "You'll carry thirty-two-pounders, I expect."

"Plus some twenty-fours," said the Commodore, "and at least four forty-two-pound carronades, which Mr. Jones has just landed from *John Adams*."

As Noah Brown multiplied several digits and then added, he muttered to himself: "For the thirty-twos we can figure two feet eleven inches for each porthole and seven feet eight inches for each space between; then allowing two and a half of these spaces for the prow and the stern, and averaging for the forty-two-pounders and the twenty-fours...." His muttering trailed off. He finally looked up. "Well, Commodore," he said, "your ship will come out just about one hundred and thirty feet long."

Amused by the Commodore's startled exclamation, Noah Brown pointed out: "That makes her somewhat smaller than *Constitution,* but bigger than John Paul Jones's *Bonhomme Richard* and our present ocean-going *Wasp* and *Hornet.* You should be duly impressed."

"I am," said the Commodore. "Indeed I am."

The master carpenter put the scribbled-on paper in his pocket, and stood up. "Well, if I'm to earn my two dollars and a half a day from the Navy," he said, "I'd better get to whittling me a half-model so I can start the carpenters to work. Incidentally, have you got a name for her?"

The Commodore had spent much of his ride in the stage coach mulling over William Denning's graphic forecast. He told Noah: "If the Secretary will say no when I propose to call her *Jones,* I'd like to christen her *Saratoga.*" His jaw flexed. "That's where we forced Burgoyne to surrender the last time the British tried to invade us from Canada."

Noah Brown's eyes lighted in appreciation. "A fine name," he said. "That's what we'll call her."

The Commodore smiled at such optimism.

Lieutenants Henley and Cassin reported to him shortly after Noah Brown had left for the scene of his activities on the Otter; and the Commodore took the opportunity to impress on them the need for strict attention by all hands to the job of building the new boats and of manning them with men well-trained and well-drilled, in what now seemed like little or no time. Without quoting William Denning or directly stating his views on the situation, he managed to convey a strong sense of his own seriousness together with a sharp picture of the action indicated by reports on his desk that the enemy had started building galleys as well as a brig at Isle-aux-Noix.

"Since you'll command the ship, Bob," he said to Henley, "I'll relieve you of all duty other than supervision of her building. Join Noah Brown tomorrow at sunup and see that he gets everything he asks for." He concluded: "I have just one request. Impress on Noah that I'll sail in her, being our flagship, and will need a place to sleep. I wouldn't put it past him to build her without quarters, even a berth, for me. He's going to keep her very plain!"

After Henley left, he looked across his desk toward Lieutenant Cassin, unnaturally stiff in his chair.

"Mr. Jones writes that you dropped in on him," said the Commodore.

Cassin nodded. "We had a good talk."

"He says you told him the enemy's not building a brig but some large galleys."

Cassin shook his head. "With all due respect," he said, "the Secretary couldn't have listened too closely. I told him we understood the enemy were building a brig *and,* undoubtedly, some galleys."

The Commodore accepted that while Steve Cassin remained silent, frowning. Finally: "Did you tell him anything else?"

Cassin nodded. "I did."

"What?"

As if facing up to something very disagreeable, Cassin gulped. "Well, I told him about the steamboat," he admitted.

The Commodore rose slowly to his feet. Glaring down at the uncomfortable-looking man sitting so rigid in the chair, he said: "And you told him we could put heavy guns under deck"—he picked up the Secretary's letter from the desk— "between opposite posts—"

"That's *his* idea, not mine!"

The Commodore had worked himself up to a hot sizzle. He threw the letter down on the desk. He knew his face had reddened; he could feel it. He also knew he should hold his temper. This was too valuable an officer to alienate. But he couldn't stand for insubordination!

"I told you to say nothing about the steamboat. I gave you—"

"You know very well we need all the vessels we can get," Cassin put in, belligerent now. "I saw a chance to get us a big one."

"Well, you did!" snapped the Commodore. "I have instructions to buy her. And you're going to take command of her. You can wrestle with steam boilers and pistons and all the rest. You asked for it!"

Cassin scowled. "You're not serious, Tom!" he said. "You wouldn't do that to me. You know how tough it'll be to get men."

"It's your worry now." He turned away.

"Is that your last word?" he heard Cassin ask.

"That's my order!" he said. "We buy the steamboat on the Secretary's order, and you run her on mine!"

Cassin made no reply. After a long silence in which the Commodore found ample time to regret his outburst, he turned. Cassin had fallen back into the chair, stretched out completely relaxed, and let a beatific grin suffuse his face. When he saw the Commodore's amazed look, he let go a raucous laugh.

"Now I can go out and die for my country, for I have lived!" he declaimed. "I have hoisted Master Commandant Thomas Macdonough with his own petard. And it blew him to pieces in fine style."

Confounded, but relieved to realize that his anger had not lost him his old friend, he found himself first smiling, then laughing hugely, at Steve Cassin's private joke.

"I talked to Mr. Jones about the steamboat," the Lieutenant explained with enjoyment, "only after he brought it up as the result of a letter from some Congressman who'd heard about it. He agreed to having her made over for sail, with sixteen or seventeen guns."

Cassin stopped long enough to let his grin spread, and said: "Which fine vessel you just ordered me to command."

The Commodore sat down, but did not speak.

"I didn't go over your head, Tom," Cassin went on. "When Mr. Jones asked if I thought we should protect ourselves by buying the steamboat, could I say no to such generosity?" He smiled affably. "Of course I had to steer him to the idea of sail, and I'd dug details out of Doc Lacy and could give him an on-the-spot estimate of costs to convert her. So he said for us to go ahead, if you want. And I certainly hope you do want."

While the Commodore remained silent, weighing the problems of getting additional equipment and men against the value of sixteen more guns in a single vessel, Cassin put in a final serious word.

"I'll never surprise you again, Tom," he declared. "Your boiling point's too low for surprises you don't originate yourself."

"I guess I've lost my sense of humor," the Commodore said. "From dealing with too many generals."

Cassin smiled again. "At least you can still make decisions?"

Relaxed, the Commodore leaned back, amused. "That I can always do, and hope for the best," he bantered. "In this case, why don't you and I take Noah Brown over to talk with Doc Lacy as soon as Noah gets the ship well in hand? If the price is reasonable, Steve, I'll approve. Then you'll have your troubles, too. Agreed?"

Cassin beamed like Aze Bellamy, and in his excitement he looked almost as young. "Agreed!" he said. "I have her name already picked out, if you go along, Tom."

"What is it?" the Commodore cautiously asked.

"*Ticonderoga*—where Ethan Allen in the Revolution took the British fort just across the Lake," Cassin said gravely, "the way I'd like to take their fleet in this war."

The Commodore picked up his bag, put on his overcoat, and left the office with the Lieutenant. Downstairs he parted from Cassin and walked swiftly toward Unity Waid's house, to Ann.

3

Although Lieutenant Henley had the responsibility for the ship, Commodore Macdonough spent every minute he could find on the narrow flat of the Otter Creek waterside, where Noah Brown's men laid down her keel on March 2nd. He'd midwifed the birth of galleys at Middletown and doctored the merchant sloops into war vessels at Whitehall, but *Jones* provided his first experience with large-scale marine construction from original gleam through conception and parturition.

Noah Brown made the many stages seem simple. He'd fashioned a half-model, composed of layers of wood pinned together, which he could take apart. Off this model, shaped to his own visualization of the ship, he lifted dimensions and laid the offsets down full-size in the shack he had built for a mold loft. From these he made up templates or molds for shaping the timbers.

With the first rays of each day's rising sun, the freezing yard echoed to a chorus of saws, axes, adzes, sledge hammers, and blacksmith's anvil. Sawn and hewn timbers of oak, pine, cedar, elm, hackmatack, and locust gave the entire area a sweet fragrance.

Before the Commodore's eyes the ship took shape slowly, steadily, as inevitably as the opening of a flower's bud. He watched the bundled-up men lay heavy scarfed oak timbers lengthwise on keel blocks close to the river's edge and bolt the timbers together to form the ship's backbone. Hoisting the stem into place then with blocks and tackle anchored to a standing tree, Noah's men bolted it to the keel and fastened to it the apron and the stemson. They followed with the sternpost, heavy oak, rabbeted like the keel and stem to take the planking.

Meanwhile sawyers with long sweeps of two-man saws, one man on the staging above, the other in the sawpit below, shaped planks; and broadaxmen hewed out curved futtock timbers for the ship's frames, wielding their gleaming blades with utter recklessness and astounding accuracy.

For the framing, the men set up a large assembly stage on each side of the keel. Placing the futtock timbers in proper marked position, they alternately doubled and fastened the timbers with locust trunnels (treenails; pieces of wood with ends split to take small wedges) to form a complete frame, notched them to fit over the keel, and raised each frame into place with hand winches.

To give the vessel added strength, shipwrights laid the keelson's heavy timbers in the hold, drift-bolted to the frames and the keel. Sister keelsons on either side of the keelson further strengthened the ship's backbone.

Planking progressed rapidly. Adzed to perfect fit, and steamed for the extra bending at bow and stern, each strake showed the skillful, ingenious handiwork of Noah Brown's master carpenters... until the Commodore could see, and admire, the ship's graceful sheer.

Pleased with progress that went forward six days a week, he took time out to drive with Ann around the Lake to Plattsburg to attend a council of war called by General Wilkinson.

Among those present at the meeting he found, as usual, Eleazer Williams; and, for the first time, Alex Macomb. As at their introduction, he felt a warm glow at sight of the young General's friendly face and gracious greeting. After the meeting opened and Wilkinson disclosed what he had in mind, the Commodore found himself drawn even closer emotionally to Macomb.

The Commodore confided to Ann on the drive home that Wilkinson had reconnoitered Rouses Point and proposed to establish a heavy battery there in the belief that it would command the mouth of the Sorel and prevent the enemy coming out of the river into the Lake.

"Would it?" Ann asked.

"Well, it might help to deter," he admitted, "a little, perhaps."

Wilkinson's second project aimed at marching his troops through current snow and mud to attack the British on the other side of the line.

"As far as I could make out," the Commodore said to Ann, "he thinks the idea has merit solely because he has three to four thousand men against only fifteen hundred British plus whatever soldiers may join them from Isle-aux-Noix. The odds in his favor seem to intrigue him, though he has in mind no clear-cut objective that I can discern." He added: "I politely told him I could offer no help. Macomb, in effect, also told him he had nothing to gain at this time and much to lose in men and morale. Alex will have to go along, however, in reserve."

While the ship grew, the Commodore wrestled with the less dramatic but equally important business of getting her armament, supplies, and men to the Lake. Mostly, now, the difficulty lay in attracting men.

Lieutenant Vallette sent thirty from New York, hoped to send a good boatswain and a gunner soon, and looked forward to enlisting many crewmen from Captain John Rodgers' flagship *President,* hauled out at the Navy Yard for repairs. He denounced in no uncertain terms the competition of Lieutenant Stewart, recruiting for Lake Ontario with orders from Captain Chauncey to give $30 bounty and $15 per month to seamen, $12 to ordinary seamen, and $10 to landsmen, with bounty in proportion. Vallette wrote: "He will get all the men if I am not allowed to give the same."

Lieutenant Stansbury forwarded fourteen men from Marblehead and Salem.

From Boston, Joseph Smith sent twenty-seven, reported the same competition as in New York from the Lake Ontario service and, in addition, reported increasing difficulty getting the Navy agent, Amos Binney, to provide money with which to keep the Boston rendezvous open.

With his usual patience, the Commodore untangled the Boston situation, where Commodore Bainbridge declined to approve Joseph Smith's requisitions and thus tied Binney's hands. This he did by issuing orders, as Lieutenant Smith's commanding officer, directly to Binney. He also took the bull by the horns in the matter of competitive recruiting by instructing his officers at all rendezvous to give as high wages as for Lake Ontario while continuing the usual $20 bounty; then he asked the Secretary of the Navy for approval.

By the end of March he informed William Jones that he'd received seventy-one men, bringing the total of men on the Lake Champlain station to 329. He had written earlier:

I hold it correct to acquaint you that the men, with a few exceptions, sent to me last summer, are very inefficient, such as the command of this Lake, now of importance in our operations against Canada, should not be trusted to.

I speak of good men for the Ship; as for the men for the gallies, soldiers in my opinion, would answer in every respect as well as sailors, and probably better, with their small arms for close action. Can an arrangement be made for the Commanding General to supply me with men for the oars of the gallies (this is the case with the enemy's gallies) leaving the guns to be worked by sailors?

I much fear that when I get my vessels in other respects ready for service, there will be a great want of men. I perfectly well know that the enemy have good seamen and officers aboard their vessels.

He now wrote:

Marines will also be required for the Ship; of these men we have none on the station. I hope, sir, you will order some on

—and another surgeon's mate. It also will be necessary to have five or six lieutenants more.

I calculate to name the Ship we are building here the *Jones* provided you have no other name to be given.

One good man arrived, unexpectedly. Abraham Walters, pilot on captured *Growler,* escaped from Quebec, made his way to Vergennes, and asked to go again as pilot on one of the vessels. The Commodore immediately wrote to Washington to learn whether Walters could be subjected to any treatment other than that of a prisoner of war should he again fall into the enemy's hands.

And from Quebec Prison Jarvis Loomis, sailing master on ill-fated *Eagle,* wrote that he had read of his appointment to the rank of lieutenant and implied a hope for his exchange and further service on the Lake.

The Commodore sent requisitions for cannon, shot, and powder to John Bullus in New York; and to Amos Binney in Boston, where Commodore Bainbridge, apparently giving Joseph Smith a hard time, put the rendezvous Lieutenant to work employing men to prepare the needed thirty-two-pound shot. He made a deal with Army Quartermaster General Elisha Jenkins in Albany for a suit of sails. Through Purser George Beale, via the Navy agents, he ordered supplies: from pea jackets to glazed hats, from paint to sail canvas, from leather fire buckets to steel cutlasses, from medicines and hospital stores to cheese, horse-radish, rice and sugar, and from tea to whisky.

Materials for the ship, sloops, and galleys dribbled in from New York and Boston slop dealers, sailmakers, brass founders, coppersmiths, saddlers, shipsmiths, pump and block makers, plumbers and turners, tailors, victualers, hardware merchants, and stationers.

In the midst of the paper work, James Sloane arrived from a Boston bookshop, sandy-haired, gentle, imperturbable, to serve as clerk. "Bless Joseph Smith!" the Commodore greeted him. "It looks as though he's found me the good man I need."

By the time he got back to the noisy, aromatic attractions of the busy Navy boatyard, the Commodore found the ship's outside planking in place, together with the ceiling of the hold. Caulkers had payed all seams with oakum and hot pitch, and had salted the timbers to preserve them from rot. Sparmakers had moved along, too, in preparing the ship's three masts and a full quota of yards for each mast.

With Lieutenant Henley he examined the beams, posts, and heavy wooden knees supporting the gun deck, already full-laid, with men now working on hatchways, ladders, mast steps, chainwales, pumps, capstan, railings, hawser holes, and portholes for the guns.

When he complimented Noah Brown on the quality of his work, and its speed, Noah accepted the praise gracefully and pointed out that his men also had made good progress on the six seventy-five-foot galleys.

Though building moved fast and smoothly, the Commodore had little other cause to pat himself on the back.

On March 24th, Ann informed him that Unity Waid no longer chose to keep guests in her house and wanted the Macdonoughs to leave the following Tuesday, bag and baggage. "After I worked up that cap for her sister Rebecca, too!" said Ann.[1]

Ten days later, word reached Vergennes that General Wilkinson on March 30th had met Congreve rockets and disillusion at Lacolle Mill, five miles over the line, from which place the British threw him back to Chazy.

A week after that, word followed that the unfortunate foray into Canada had cost inept Wilkinson his command. Major General George Izard would relieve him; meanwhile the Plattsburg command fell to General Macomb.

"At last," said the Commodore, "a good man in the job."

4

More than by any other menace to his plans, Commodore Macdonough found himself disturbed over the danger from anomalous weather. An exceptional lack of snow had enabled Noah Brown's men to push ahead rapidly with their shipbuilding; but unseasonably mild temperatures also took the ice out of the lower end of the Lake up to Windmill Point.

On April 2nd, two British sloops and several gunboats left the Sorel to anchor off Rouses Point and, as the ice continued to go off the Lake, their threat to Chazy, Plattsburg, and Burlington, successively, gave the Commodore sleepless nights.

He wrote to Plattsburg, to Peter Sailly:

It will do no good to growl. But I may observe that we are going to be in desperate situation on the shore of this Lake as long as the British can navigate it, stop all communications, and plunder our shores.

Peter Sailly wrote, cheerfully:

Captain Thurber assures that there is no new British row Gallies afloat, and that two new ones only are building. Therefore the present force of the British is the Same as last fall, althou' it will be soon encreased by their Brig and afterward by their 2 Gallies.

Either way, with the brig or with last year's force, the enemy could strike crushingly weeks before anticipated!

When the Commodore pressed Noah Brown for more

speed, the accommodating builder responded with his customary goodwill. His men followed his lead, after a soft-voiced but very patriotic speech in which Noah made clear that he considered himself and them as much a part of the American fighting Navy as the Commodore. They finished construction of the ship as though their own skins and those of wives and children depended on its quick completion.

Painting went on apace, the usual black, with ornamental parts touched off with white. Under the stern cabin windows, Noah personally inscribed her name, *Saratoga.*

The Commodore remonstrated. "She's *Jones,* until the Secretary says otherwise."

"He will," Noah assured him.

So she was christened. With a bottle of champagne contributed by Mayor Strong for the citizenry of Vergennes, Ann solemnly sent *Saratoga* down the ways into the narrow Otter on April 11th. That night the Commodore wrote the Navy Office:

> I have the honor to inform you that the ship "Jones" [he put it in quotes] to carry 26 guns (20 32'-Carronades and 6 24'-Long Guns) was launched this day, being the thirty-fifth day after her keel was laid, and all her timber taken from the stump.

Thirty-five working days from tree to ship! (Noah had promised to build Champlain's fleet even faster than he and his brother had built Erie's.) Now to rig her, outfit her; to mount her guns, and to find her crew.

Into the race against time the Commodore threw every man who could help Noah Brown's shipwrights, for the most part now getting the clamps in the gunboats for the beams in the bottoms. Sailing masters, boatswains, sailmakers, carpenters, seamen, gunners, armorers, gunsmiths . . . officers . . . all who could lend a hand in any capacity fell to on spars, sails, rigging, tackles, anchors, cables, and ship's boats.

Using nature's derrick, a great elm tree, tall and axed clean of branches, Noah stepped and secured *Saratoga*'s pieced, pine foremast, mainmast, and mizzenmast. He then set up their tops, platforms around the upper part of each mast, and added their topmasts. Across the head of this prolongation of each mast went the crosstrees, a light, horizontal frame of timber, and finally, the topgallant mast—the third upright section of each skyscraping mast, bringing each to more than two hundred feet. Bowsprit, yards for the square sails on the three masts, boom and gaff for the mizzenmast's fore-and-aft sail (the spanker), and the flagstaff for the taffrail completed the ship's equipment of spars.

Rigging fell into place with remarkable adroitness—blocks, tackles, lines, each with its special function ... hundreds of single mortised blocks, iron-strapped twin blocks, threefold cat blocks, fourfold tackle blocks, hearts, bulls'-eyes, dead-eyes (more than a hundred of these alone); lifting tackles, quarter tackles, yardarm tackles; shrouds, jeers, lifts, braces, backstays, bowstays, running stays, bobstay, guys, and ratlines.

Sails made their appearance gradually: mainsails, topsails, topgallants, royals, spanker; with their tacks, sheets, bowlines, clewgarnets, buntlines, leechlines, between lines, reefpoints, and reef tackle.

Equipment went aboard. Anchors: heavy sheet anchor, for storms; emergency sheet anchor, bow anchor, stream anchor, kedges, grappling irons. And their cables: sheet and bower cables, in multiples of 120 feet (a cable's length). Boats: captain's gig, launches for carrying stores and passengers.

But not her guns, her officers, or her men. These *Saratoga* lacked.

Waiting, powerless as his ship herself, the Commodore needed all his stability and patience to cope with Wilkinson, apparently clutching his command until General Izard's arrival.

On the very day *Saratoga* slid down the ways, Wilkinson

sent frantic word that "the enemy's brig and other vessels are manned and equipped for service, and a large number of bateaux have been collected at St. John's and the Isle-aux-Noix." He warned that the enemy undoubtedly planned to seize all available shallops on the Lake, load them with stones, and sink them at the mouth of the Otter, to immobilize the American fleet.

Wilkinson already had requested Governor Chittenden to call out Vermont's militia to protect Burlington and Vergennes. And to Vergennes, on April 12th, from Addison, Chittenden, and Franklin counties, abutting the Lake, came a thousand soldiers.

Quartered in barns, schoolhouses, the now empty home of President Sanders of the University, and the guardhouse on the lower floor of the Commodore's office building, the militia found themselves with nothing to do.

In the guardhouse below the Commodore, one soldier kept himself temporarily occupied eating johnnycake and salt pork from his knapsack and washing the mixture down with dark and fragrant rum from his big canteen. The canteen finally exhausted, along with his ability to withstand ennui, he disgruntledly kicked his musket, which was standing against the wall, and a shot went through the ceiling.

It missed the Commodore. He was already angered by Wilkinson's blatant announcement that the enemy fleet stood poised to attack and by Wilkinson's equally offensive presumption in rushing the militia to Vergennes. When the musket shot pinged past, the Commodore, as the bored soldier below, had reached his limit. He called for a council of war with the General and the Governor.

Wilkinson came in his gig, across the Lake and up the Otter to the falls. He bustled into the Commodore's office, busy as a fool in a fit, the Commodore told Ann later, full of his own importance.

"I am equipping a battery of flying artillery to wait on

the enemy's vessels whenever the roads may permit," he proclaimed dramatically.

The Commodore ignored that news. Standing, he scowled down on his seated visitors. "If you will get your damned militia out of here," he fired bluntly at the General and the Governor, "I will take care of the fleet." Pointing to the bullet hole in the floor beside his desk, he said: "I'm in more danger from *your* men than I am from the enemy's."

His grim expression warned the General to tread lightly. Not that he had directly challenged Wilkinson's right to represent the Army; but he certainly would touch on Alex Macomb's status if he had to. He addressed Wilkinson:

"For your information, General," he said, "the enemy's brig has not yet taken the water."

He handed Wilkinson a dispatch dated April 18th from Macomb:

I have this moment received intelligence from Captain ——, who is employed to give information of the movements of the enemy. He has received information from an undoubted source that the new brig is not yet launched, that she is tarred and painted white; that the rigging is thrown over the caps; that she will not enter the water until the 24th of the month.

And that only two row gallies are building, and that their keels are laid and some ribs in, but not all planked.

That the sloop *Mars* mounts 6-pounders, and she is the only *addition* to the old establishment.

Taking back the dispatch, the Commodore said: "Your private sources have evidently misinformed you, General." He went on: "I have sent a very competent officer to Windmill Point to watch enemy movements. At the very first sign of action, he'll ride back to report." He meant Aze Bellamy, but felt it impolitic to name a mere midshipman. He added a clincher: "Country-bred, he rides very fast—almost as fast as rumors."

Sitting down behind his desk, he faced Wilkinson and Chittenden, and said: "Now let's talk practicalities based on facts."

Out of the meeting eventually came an agreement satisfactory all around. First, Governor Chittenden would, upon arrival of troops from Burlington, discharge the militia except for Captain William C. Munson's company of Panton; the discharged militia to hold themselves in readiness to turn out immediately on hearing an alarm signal of three heavy guns fired in rapid succession. Second, General Wilkinson and the Commodore would select a site for a defensive battery at the mouth of Otter Creek. Third, the General and the Governor would go home and leave the Commodore free to cope with pressing problems.

The Commodore named and officered Noah Brown's six magnificent new galleys, 75 feet long, 15 feet beam, to carry two guns each, and manned by forty men. One at a time over several days, each went into the water fittingly speeded with champagne by Ann, accompanied by the gunboat's new commander.

With full concurrence from Lieutenants Henley, Cassin, Pearce, and Budd, the Commodore had honored two contemporaries, former shipmates, killed in action during the war.

First into the water, Lieutenant William M. Robbins commanding, went *Allen*—named for William Henry Allen, fatally wounded commanding brig *Argus* when captured by British brig *Pelican*, 14 August 1813.

Second went *Burrows*, Sailing Master Samuel Keteltas commanding—named for William Burrows, commanding sloop-of-war *Enterprise* and killed by a musket ball capturing eighteen-gun brig *Boxer*, 5 September 1813.

Following, went the so-called DD's—"death-dealers"—*Borer*, Midshipman T. A. Conover; *Nettle*, Midshipman Samuel L. Breeze; *Viper*, Lieutenant Francis J. Mitchell; *Centipede*, Sailing Master D. V. Hazard.

With ship and galleys launched, the Commodore, Noah Brown, and Stephen Cassin descended on the Champlain Steamboat Company in the person of Doc Lacy. They found him in a rough ship house working with his carpenters on the steamboat's planking.

"What have you been doing all this time?" Noah Brown said facetiously when he saw how little advanced the boat was. "Waiting for the Navy to take over?"

"Mebbe," replied Lacy, a New Yorker speaking with true Vermont prudence.

Noah had looked the boat over earlier. He had estimated her present worth at $5,000, her hull as susceptible to conversion best into a schooner, and her capacity as twenty guns. He also promised (not rashly, Commodore!) to have her in the water by May 15th.

"All right, Steve," the Commodore told the expectant Lieutenant, "she's yours. Get to work on her while I negotiate with the owners. Doc Lacy thinks they'll go along with us. Hire him and his men to help you and Noah."

The Commodore gave Cassin a piercing glance and said: "Next time you make a deal with our Navy Secretary for me, make sure to put it in writing."

"What do you mean?" Cassin's surprised tone rang genuine.

"I mean that Mr. Jones insists he wants us to take over a *steam* boat."

"But he told me—"

Noah Brown intervened. "Stop worrying, Lieutenant! Mr. Jones'll come around to our way of thinking," Noah assured Cassin. "No false front about him, like refusing to have his name on the ship. Wide open for good ideas, like complimenting the Commodore on suggesting *Saratoga*."

The Champlain fleet now had, afloat and with the forthcoming schooner, more than enough tonnage to hold the Lake against enemy building, immediate or reasonably anticipated. But the vessels had only a few of their needed guns, only a few of their needed officers and crew. The flotilla could not enter the Lake in this condition.

As last year at Burlington, the Navy might have to stand back and watch while enemy vessels depredated the Lake towns, while anguished citizens begged for protection, while generals and politicians fecklessly scurried about screaming for action.

Too, with the opening of the Lake to navigation, Sir George Prevost, governor of lower Canada and commander in chief of the army, could use the British fleet to bring up a sufficient land force to destroy the ships at Vergennes and make it impossible for the Commodore even to appear on Lake Champlain.

He laid the facts before his top commanders. Had anyone, he asked, ideas for mitigating the situation, possibly for turning it to their advantage? When very little of constructive value came to light, he outlined his own strategy.

While awaiting Midshipman Bellamy's arrival with news of the enemy's approach, he proposed, every man on the station would work day and night—Sundays included—getting *Saratoga* and the galleys ready for action; he himself would sleep on the ship, in order to help in any emergency. They would hope for delay to the enemy's brig, every day of which delay would put them nearer to getting the schooner-to-be into the water, with the old galleys' guns mounted in her. Then they would take the Lake, with *Saratoga, Ticonderoga, President, Preble, Montgomery,* and the six new galleys.

And if the enemy came up the Lake too soon?

"That," said the Commodore, "will give us considerable cause for reflection."

To speed up arrival at Vergennes of armament and supplies shipped to Albany and Troy, he sent Sailing Master Keteltas to help the local agents. To speed up arrival of men enlisted in Boston, he sent Acting Sailing Master John Hazelton to help Lieutenant Smith. But for officers he had to depend on whatever speed Washington chose.

He had appointed Hazelton on the Lake Champlain station, his order reading: "You will accordingly assume the duties and uniform of a sailing master in the Navy, for which this will be your sufficient authority, and all officers junior to you in rank are required to obey your orders as sailing master." But, as he pointed out to his staff, "I can't create all the new officers we need. We have to depend on Mr. Jones to send them to us in his own good time."

Concrete results emerged from these activities.

Ferrying back and forth between Boston and Vergennes every seven days, Hazelton brought drafts of a dozen or so tolerably good seamen. . . .

In Albany Keteltas put ironwork for gun carriages, cannon locks, rammers, springers, muskets, and pistols onto Barent & John R. Bleecker's wagons and headed them toward Vergennes over muddy, almost impassable roads. Better still, he got twenty-eight cannons headed north. . . .

With Messrs. R. P. Hart & Co. in Troy, he rushed the loading of eighty horse and oxen teams, leaving three large cables to go.

On the last day of April, Commodore Macdonough wrote to the Secretary of the Navy at length. With his report he included a statement of his force, the number and grade of the officers, and the number of men. He attached, also, a statement of the enemy's vessels "from the best authority"—a combination of Alexander Macomb, Peter Sailly, Eleazer Williams, and John Banker.

Lest the numerical summary of the situation leave William Jones' imagination unfired, the Commodore painted the essentials in considerable detail, so that the Secretary could not fail to realize how largely Champlain's security hinged on expectations.

Saratoga he described as rigged, her sails made and ready to be bent, her below-decks ready to receive officers and men, her provisions stowed, and supplies of every kind aboard, with few exceptions. As to guns . . . "she has her gun carriages, and the ports ready for the guns, part of which have arrived, which we are mounting, the others expected daily. All the powder is expected here in two or three days."

The new galleys, he advised, "are also finished, and some of their guns have arrived, which we are also mounting; the other guns for these galleys are daily expected . . ."

Reporting on *Ticonderoga*, he indicated the impracticability of preparing her as a steamboat "in due time in the manner you have suggested" owing to "the machinery not being complete, and none of it here"; and of maintaining it, due to "the extreme liability of the machinery (composed of so many parts) getting out of order and no spare parts to replace . . ."

He nailed that down with: "I have scarcely known the steamboat, now running here, to pass through the Lake without something happening to her, and they have to send to Albany to replace what was damaged. The calculation by the carpenter was that the boat here would be propelled, at most, not more than five knots, whereas one of the enemy's galleys would move in a calm at the rate of six."

Assuring the Secretary of his prudence and attention to economy in the expenditures for the station, he revealed that for the benefit of the service he had made some decisions without orders. These decisions, he felt confident, the Secretary would approve when he understood the motives behind them. He included disarming of slow-sailing *Frances* and *Wasp* and putting their guns, and some spare guns, along with those of the four old galleys, aboard the schooner (nee steamboat) "which Mr. Brown engages to have done in two weeks from this day."

The Secretary could hardly fail to concur since, as the Commodore added, tongue in cheek, "the disarmed sloops will, with much advantage, be employed in the transport service, and in carrying provisions for the Army."

With most of his officers below lieutenants and with recruiting dull, he made very plain the imperative need for "three or four lieutenants to command such vessels as I have no commanders for . . ." and for 245 additional seamen to man all the vessels. Until more men arrive, he wrote, "I have not yet selected my crew for the ship."

Should he get these officers and men, should the guns arrive, and "should no unforeseen circumstances occur," the fleet could enter the Lake by the 15th or 20th of May.

Earlier in April he had earnestly requested these officers (including a surgeon's mate, "as the surgeon reports forty men on the day's sick list"), these men, and these guns. The Navy Office must see by now the need for speed. In case it did not, he goaded thus: "The enemy's largest vessel . . . is rigged . . . We are using every exertion to enter the Lake before him."

5

Though men and guns moved slowly to the fleet, events on the Lake moved fast.

Having helped the Commodore select a strategic battery site at the mouth of the Otter, General Wilkinson silently folded his tent. Major General George Izard arrived at Plattsburg May 1st and assumed command of the Army on the 4th; General Macomb returned to Burlington. And Commodore Macdonough burned midnight oil juggling, on paper, available guns and men to prepare for every eventuality from having to defend his vessels in the river to entering the Lake to fight.

Lieutenants Henley and Cassin rose to the occasion with the zest of veterans, smelling battle after long and galling hibernation. They agreed, however, that defense of the unequipped, unmanned fleet constituted the primary order of business; that keeping the Otter open so the vessels could enter the Lake once their guns and men came on board stood paramount.

"Which defense I think we can make like this," said the Commodore, laying before them a simply drawn sketch of Otter Creek's mouth, where the river had laid down a delta that jutted into a large bay to form two small bays, south and north.

A dotted half-circle from the far point of the south bay to the far point of the north bay, with the proposed battery as center, showed the range of the battery's guns—twelve-pounders, on ship's carriages. Four gunboats, the map revealed, could protect the south bay; moving out to a line east of the battery on approach of the enemy, they would enable the battery to concentrate its fire power over a smaller arc. Another gunboat, at the very mouth of the river, could protect the battery from the rear.

Upriver a hundred rods, two moored gunboats could completely command the north bay and its shoreline, their long twenty-four-pounder and their eighteen-pound Columbiad pointing north over a narrow strip of land overflowed by the creek.

"With that setup and a sailor and musket behind every tree," Cassin said expansively, "I'd say we can hold 'em off until doomsday."

"I'm glad you feel that way, Steve," said the Commodore, "because that's your assignment. To set up and command the fort..." He smiled. Why not? he asked himself... *"Fort Cassin*'s your assignment."

Lieutenant Henley pointed to the gunboats drawn in position on the map. "This plan designates seven galleys," he said. "We have only six in the water."

The Commodore acknowledged the discrepancy. Then: "I'm turning all building over to you to superintend, Bob, not just *Saratoga*," he said. "Since we'll need a seventh galley, put Noah Brown to work on refitting the two we built in Burlington. Steve can station the extra one wherever it will do most good."

Henley could see problems. "What do we use for guns?" he asked, practically.

The Commodore wasted no words. "Steve takes what he needs for the battery," he said, "and you and I juggle what's left for the gunboats, for the ship, and for the schooner."

Before the meeting broke up, Cassin put a long finger on the map's narrow strip of land between river and north bay, which two of the gunboats would defend. "How about digging a channel here?" he said. "Big enough for the galleys to go through to attack if necessary?"

"Go right ahead," the Commodore agreed. "If you have time, make it deep enough for the ship. We can take her out that way in the event the enemy blocks the mouth of the river."

Cassin looked at him quizzically. "I wonder if you really mean that?" he said.

"We want to cover every contingency, don't we?" replied the Commodore, and smiled equivocally.

While Lieutenant Cassin constructed the fort from native stone and logs, set up the guns, and prepared to defend Otter Creek, Lieutenant Henley, accompanied by the Commodore, took up the problem of the extra gunboat with Noah Brown.

On his stomach beside a square timber that he and two helpers sought to nudge into place, the master carpenter for the first time showed signs of strain. "Lieutenant," he said in agonized tones, "here I am as busy as a man on the town, try-ing to get your schooner in the water, and you ask me to fiddle with a galley!"

The Commodore waited for the explosion. Quick to take offense, Henley could wreck everything by saying the wrong words now. He had pulled himself up to his full height. His eyes flashed angrily. For a moment the Commodore debated whether to step in before the outraged Lieutenant could vent his feelings. Then he relaxed.

Lieutenant Henley's scowl dissipated. He looked down on Noah Brown with amusement. "Why, you old coot!" he said. "You don't know enough, as they say in these parts, to pound salt!"

Noah Brown turned over on his back and looked up. In his face the Commodore saw admiration for the human quality that made Bob Henley the idol of every crew that worked under him. "Did you say something, boy?" Noah asked, all tension gone from his voice.

"Not yet, Dad," chaffed Henley, "but here goes." Simply, earnestly, he outlined the problem.

The Commodore took great comfort from the way his Lieutenant enlisted Noah's sympathy, then concern, over the immediacy of the situation. Ann might have judged rightly that Bob wanted glory. But who didn't? Getting it, Bob would never let his ambition block the fleet's good.

"That's why we need a gunboat more right now than we need a schooner," Henley finished.

Noah Brown got up, brushed himself off. "I've been fixing all along to refit the two good galleys," he said quietly. "The old ones I'm getting rid of."

This was news to the Commodore!

Noah went on: "I'll build you two replacements, same size, along with the refitted boats," he said, "before I go back to New York. Brother Adam writes me we've got a lot of work waiting for me in the yard."

This too was news! "When do you leave?" asked the Commodore caustically. "If I may be so bold as to ask."

"Next week Friday, the thirteenth," said Noah blandly.

"What about this schooner?"

In his most fatherly fashion, Noah calmed the Commodore down. "She goes into the water Thursday, the twelfth," he said. "You'll be in good shape, Commodore. With Doc Lacy, you can rig and fit her in no time—faster even than with my men cluttering things up." He pushed the officers aside, his voice brusque, his eyes bright, a smile playing on his lips. "If you fellers want those galleys I promised, why don't you get out of a busy man's way? I expect a war to arrive here shortly."

Though Noah's speed with the schooner and the four gunboats might make it possible to take the Lake before the British could mass their vessels, in his heart the Commodore knew that the Navy Office's congenital dilatoriness in sending armament and men would inevitably work for the enemy. Aze Bellamy confirmed this.

Looking as beaten as the day he'd reported the loss of

Growler and *Eagle,* Aze rode 80 miles from the line and into Vergennes on the afternoon of Monday, May 9th. He reported:

"The enemy brig, a small sloop, and eight galleys came up from Isle-aux-Noix and joined two waiting sloops and five gunboats in the Lake early this morning."

The news hurt. The Commodore could not take *President, Preble,* and *Montgomery* against a brig, three sloops, and thirteen galleys. He could not take the ship, lacking guns and men. Nor could he take the six new galleys; they must stay to defend the vulnerable ship and the nearly completed schooner.

"We're over a barrel again," he apprised his staff. "We can't go into a one-sided or losing contest. We must conserve our full strength for later."

Lieutenant Cassin prepared the fort for bombardment.

Lieutenant Henley mounted *Saratoga's* guns as fast as the horse- and ox-drawn wagon caravan brought them from Albany and Troy and as fast as his gunners could hoist each of their several tons aboard. "We may get the ship ready to fight in time," Henley told the Commodore on Wednesday.

The Commodore shook his head. "Not a chance, Bob," he said. "Macomb sent an express this morning. The enemy stayed off Chazy Monday and Tuesday. They're now off Plattsburg. Macomb doesn't know for how long."

Henley clenched a big fist. "Let 'em dawdle long enough and we can get ready," he said.

"No use fooling ourselves, Bob," the Commodore counseled. "Izard told Macomb that from what his observers made out at Chazy the enemy may have twelve to fifteen hundred men." He looked at his Lieutenant resignedly, and added: "Izard hasn't yet sent me the two hundred and fifty soldiers we need to man the galleys."

Henley exploded. "Why can't the gold braid, Navy and Army both, give us what we need! How do they expect us to fight our ships without men?"

The Commodore nodded, and said: "That's what I asked Macomb when I sent to *him* for soldiers for the gunboats." As Henley still sputtered, the Commodore added: "I'm sure Macomb'll support us, and in time. He'll know the instant the fleet heads this way."

Waiting for the British attack, the Commodore solved the mystery of British "sloop *Mars,*" reported in Macomb's dispatch of April 18th.

Aze Bellamy described the vessel. "She's not a sloop, sir," he said. "She's a ketch, with a very tall mainmast stepped a little aft of midships, and a very short mizzen. And she hasn't got six-pounders; she's got a single mortar taking up most of her foredeck."

The Commodore showed his surprise. "She's a bomb, Aze," he said, "built to lob explosive shells onto shore positions. You'd better run down to the fort and let Lieutenant Cassin have details."

Aze took pride in being able to bring accurate, usable intelligence. "One other thing I noticed, sir," he said. "On her deck, fastened to her bulwarks, she had some tubes that seemed to be upwards of four inches in diameter. I couldn't figure them out."

The Commodore patted the midshipman's shoulder. "Firing tubes for Congreve rockets, no doubt," he said. "According to last summer's newspapers, the British had shipped a million rockets over here. But so far only Wilkinson's seen any. Tell Lieutenant Cassin about those, too. They'll make him all the more anxious to set up that furnace at the fort for heating his shot."

Ann had received unanimous sanction at the *Preble* dinner to sponsor all vessels launched in Otter Creek. When, in performance of her appointed duty, she came to the yard Thursday noon to christen *Ticonderoga* the Commodore did what he could to quiet her obvious apprehension.

"But the town's full of reports that the British will invade any minute," she said in a voice that failed to hide her suppressed agitation. "Some families have their valuables all packed. They're ready to run. Unity Waid's gone far inland already. I expect Colonel Fisher's womenfolk will have left by the time I get home."

"Please don't leave with them," he said, as the schooner hit the water and riggers and fitters swarmed aboard.

She smiled back at him.

Friday brought an express from General Macomb: The British flotilla, consisting of brig, three sloops, and thirteen galleys, Captain Daniel Pring, off Burlington the day before, had departed early Friday morning.

Macomb also informed the Commodore that he'd sent two hundred and fifty soldiers to row in the Navy's galleys.

He further advised that a detachment of fifty light artillerymen, under command of Captain Arthur W. Thornton, would leave immediately in wagons to man Fort Cassin and contiguous shoreline, to fight beside the Navy against any British effort to land troops and destroy the fleet.

With the enemy bearing down on Vergennes, the Commodore ordered Lieutenant Cassin at the fort and Lieutenant Henley on *Saratoga* to fire three warning guns, at intervals, to reassemble Vermont's militia.

6

Reports of the British advance sifted into Vergennes from points along the Lake front.

Soldiers of one enemy row-galley chased a rowboat (which escaped), landed, and plundered a farmhouse. Passing Charles McNeil's farm on Sloop Island, another gunboat fired a dozen times and shot the top off a poplar tree; its commander took a tongue-lashing from the irate owner before retiring, still drunk. Wilson Williams fired his musket at the entire fleet from Thompkins Point.

Steamboat *Vermont,* having earlier in the week eluded (through Duncan McGregor's timely warning) three gunboats lying in ambush under the shore of Providence Island opposite Cumberland Head, barely kept ahead of the oncoming flotilla. And when, on Friday, Captain Pring anchored his fleet off Split Rock for the night, Captain Winans prepared to blow up his steam vessel rather than have her fall into enemy hands.

Friday afternoon Commodore Macdonough took General Macomb on a final tour of inspection.

At the yard they found *Saratoga* with less than half her guns mounted, but with a hundred men aboard to handle those in case of emergency. Armed for action, the gunboats awaited the arrival of Macomb's soldiers to row them down the Otter into their assigned positions at the river's mouth.

237

Floating *Ticonderoga* hummed with riggers supervised, to the Commodore's complete surprise, by Noah Brown.

"I couldn't go home before I'd seen the war, could I?" said Noah.

At the Buttonwoods they looked over the sloops: *President,* Lieutenant Pearce; *Preble,* Lieutenant Budd; *Montgomery,* Sailing Master Joseph Middleton, all cleared for action and ready to slip their moorings on orders to attack, and dismantled *Frances* and *Wasp* blocking passage upstream.

At the river's mouth they went over Fort Cassin with its furnace for heating shot. With Captain Thornton's expected light artillerymen scheduled to arrive shortly after midnight, Lieutenant Cassin expressed himself as satisfied with the fort's ability to receive the British fleet.

With a touch of amusement, he added: "We even cut what the men call 'Macdonough's Dugway' through that overflowed strip upriver. We made it deep enough for the galleys to get through to the north bay if they have to," he said with a grin, "but not the ship."

"Just keep the river open, Steve," said the Commodore, "and Fort Cassin will go down in history, maybe. You with it! Good luck."

At the end of the inspection, Macomb expressed high praise. "Your foresight astounds me, Commodore," he said.

"Thank you, General," said the Commodore.

"And now," said Macomb, "what can I do for you?"

"First," said the Commodore promptly, "you can call me Tom," adding: "I've thought of you as Alex since the night you stole my wife at the Burlington Ball and left me to cope alone with Wilkinson."

Macomb laughed jovially. "That's easy, Tom," he said. "Now think up something hard." His fine face showed an easy assurance born of the same inner strength that the Commodore always found so comforting in the competent, creative master carpenters with whom good fortune had thrown him.

"The hardest job I know," said the Commodore, "is working with the militia. If you'll keep them in line for me, I'll see to the naval defenses."

When the Commodore and the General arrived at Theophilus Middlebrook's house in Vergennes after midnight, the militia officers and town officers, many doubling in brass, were still running bullets and preparing cartridges from the town's emergency deposits of lead and powder. Theophilus, agog with excitement, had brought the supplies from the town treasury. Young David Middlebrook, twelve, kept dashing out of the house and returning, wide-eyed, with late news and rumors that spurred the bullet makers.

While the General discussed deployment of militiamen with the officers, the Commodore momentarily relaxed. When Macomb's hand on his shoulder shook him, he came awake instantly and found he had slept for almost an hour. The militia officers had departed, to join their men on the Lake shore. And after Mistress Middlebrook's more than ample supper of cold ham, hot bread, and steaming coffee, the Commodore and the General also went out into the clear, still-cold May night to drive back to Fort Cassin.

At daylight they watched the British fleet move up from Split Rock toward the mouth of Otter Creek.

While Captain Pring in brig *Linnet,* sloops *Broke* and *Shannon,* and five galleys hovered out in the Lake two and a half miles off Fort Cassin, the British bomb and eight of the flotilla's galleys closed on the fort. When the attackers came within range, the Commodore took a ceremoniously proffered match from Lieutenant Cassin, touched it to a primed twelve-pounder, and let the roar of the blast serve as signal for the American galleys to open fire.

The British gunboats responded and, as an observer later wrote, "thundering cannon and rumbling echoes, bounding back and forth over the Lake and the shore, made a noise like twenty Fourth of Julys rolled into one."

Moving from post to post with Alex Macomb as the inde-
fatigable General checked the militia and his own men on
shore under Colonel Samuel B. Davis, the Commodore soon
realized that the American reception of the British visitors
came as a surprise to Captain Pring. *Linnet,* standing on and
off during the bombardment like a frustrated commander
pacing his quarterdeck, seemed to epitomize the attacker's
reaction to this unexpected resistance.

"I believe," said Macomb at the end of a half hour's spirited
defense of the point, "that Pring expected to sail right into the
river and shell your ships—or bottle them up."

The Commodore rubbed his chin reflectively with a thumb
callused from writing to Washington for guns and men. "His
sole objective may be to take a position at the creek's mouth
to keep me from entering the Lake—perhaps to fortify the
point. I don't believe it ever occurred to Prevost to send land
forces."

"I *hope* Prevost's that stupid," said Macomb. "Because
Pring's got more than enough sailors and marines out there
now to raise hob with us if he lands 'em!"

Inside the fort, Lieutenant Cassin and Captain Thornton
threw a continuous and heavy hail of hot metal at the bomb
and gunboats. Under Lieutenant Robbins, the gunboat division in the south bay wheeled out to take its planned line of
position west of the fort, all guns in action. And for an hour
the combined fire of American fort and gunboats kept the
attackers at bay while British cannon balls relentlessly
pounded the fort's parapet and the enemy bomb sought to lob
explosive shells into the fort. One ball dropped inside, dis-
mounting a gun and injuring two men.

At the end of the hour, General Macomb conceded that the
Commodore had accurately gauged the enemy's original
objective.

"I'm convinced he planned only on blocking the river.
Finding you so strongly fortified, he's upset—trying to figure
what to do next."

"Looks to me as if he'd fallen into the same pit I've struggled to get out of the past week," said the Commodore. "He doesn't dare risk loss of his brig and his sloops in an all-out attack, for fear of what I'll do to him later."

Of a sudden his eyes lighted. Hand on Macomb's arm, he called sharply for Aze Bellamy, flushed with the excitement of his baptism by gunfire, and instructed him to ride as fast as his horse could take him to the sloops and to the ship.

"Tell their commanders to bring the vessels downriver at once!" His sharp voice sent the startled midshipman racing on his way.

Turning to Macomb, whose questioning expression called for enlightenment, he explained: "If Pring should decide to take the risk and throw at us everything he has out there, he could overpower us, sink a few of his galleys in the river, and lock us up tight—as he originally planned. We'd have the devil of a time ever breaking loose."

Macomb nodded. "So?"

The Commodore let a smile crease his drawn, whiskered face. "I have a hunch," he said. "While Pring's trying to make up his mind about the risk, I'll give him a glimpse of our ship and sloops coming downriver as if to sail out and give him a beating. It may help him decide to forget whatever he originally came for!"

Macomb's broad grin registered complete approval.

Though none of the offshore fleet came into range, the heavy bombardment continued on both sides. And while the Commodore watched grimly, an enemy gunboat, hulled by a shot from the fort, frantically sought safety in the broad Lake. But with every passing minute his fear mounted that Pring would throw all his forces into the attack.

Firing continuously, the American gunboats continued to fight off the enemy's galleys. Unable to get close enough for its mortar to lob explosive shells effectively into the fort, the British bomb took to Congreve rockets which added a whining overtone to the heavy din of the "twenty Fourth of Julys."

As the minutes sped and the American ship and sloops failed to appear, the Commodore's anxiety greatened. And all the way from the south bay's southern tip to the north bay's northern tip, American seamen and militia and regulars hunkered behind trees, waiting to repel a landing.

Back of the fort, where he could see to the river's first bend, the Commodore paced in a vain effort to slow down the pounding of his heart while his eyes searched over the tops of the trees for a sign of the fleet. Macomb waited with him, silent.

And then, at the end of an hour and a half, the Commodore saw *Saratoga*'s tall masts descending the river; and the sloops appeared around the bend. His face lighted. To Macomb he said exultantly: "Pring can spot them even better from the Lake!"

But if Pring had seen the American boats, he paid them no attention. The British guns continued to boom, their shells continued to fall on the fort, their rockets continued to whish and bang over the American shore.

"What do you think, Alex?" said the Commodore. "Does Pring know the ship hasn't got enough guns to come out after him? Will he—"

Of a sudden the British guns quit. On signal from *Linnet*, the bomb and galleys turned and stood off to join the vessels that had stayed out in the broad Lake. Their attack repulsed, the entire enemy flotilla headed back for Canada.

The abrupt end to the attempted invasion left the Commodore physically and emotionally exhausted. And he knew that the long-awaited action on Lake Champlain had just begun.

7

In the next two weeks guns and officers arrived at Vergennes; and *Ticonderoga* joined the ship, the sloops, and the galleys at the Otter's mouth. On Thursday, May 26th, the American flotilla entered the Lake. And on Sunday, May 29th, Commodore Macdonough wrote William Jones from *Saratoga,* at Plattsburg:

> I have the honor to inform you that I arrived off here today, and having been informed that the enemy had retired to Isle-aux-Noix, the squadron was brought to anchor.
> There is now full communication between all parts of the Lake, and at present there are no doubts of the communication being interrupted by the enemy.
> I find the *Saratoga* a fine ship; she sails and works well; she is a ship between the *Pike* and *Madison,* on Lake Ontario. The Schooner is also a fine vessel, and bears her metal full as well as expected. The gallies are also remarkably fine vessels. I have not yet my complement of men, but as fast as they come in I shall relieve the soldiers, whom I have on board, by them.
> I have made it known to Maj. Gen. Izard that the squadron is ready for service.

The American fleet at last held the ascendancy on Lake Champlain.

Ann met the Commodore's gig at the wharf in Burlington, and threw herself into her husband's arms. As they walked up the hill from the bay toward Betsy Boyd's house, past his old office, the sun shone bright and warm. Mid-June heat had dried out spring's mud, and hard-packed sidewalks seemed almost in danger of crumbling into dust. In mid-term, Ann carried their second baby easily.

He felt as though he hadn't seen her for months. The fleet had left Vergennes three weeks ago, but the pressure generated in building the ship, the schooner, and the gunboats and in beating off the British attack had only begun to ease.

They tried to catch up in the peace and quiet of their rooms at Betsy's. Ann read him items she'd saved from the *Sentinel* . . . a recent notice signed by James Goodhue, Ensign, 11th Regiment, Infantry: "12 DOLLARS BOUNTY AND 160 ACRES OF LAND are now offered to every able-bodied man between 17 and 45 years of age, who will enlist into the service of the U. States for five years, or during the war". . . thanks from S. Buell of Burlington to his friends and neighbors "for their prompt and effective services in rescuing repeatedly his dwelling and property from destruction by fire, while he was absent". . .

But she obviously had no heart for her task. Finally, she pointed to an advertisement she'd circled with ink. "Could we sit for Mr. Lewis, Tom?"

MINIATURE AND PORTRAIT PAINTING

William Lewis respectfully informs the public that his residence is at the house of Deacon Jacob Williams, near the college, where he will attend to the above branches, in both of which he hopes to give general satisfaction.
Miniatures $10 . . . Portraits in oil colours from $15 to $20, and good likenesses warranted.

He nodded. A miniature of Ann on his desk aboard the ship might make the coming separation slightly easier to bear. To see her, smiling, whenever he glanced up from his writing chores, well, if an artist could make her look the way he always saw her in his mind's eye, well. . . .

"I'm glad you like the idea," she said. And now it seemed

easier to talk about her going to Middletown to have the baby. Lucretia Ann already had left the Shaler homestead for Vergennes, Ann informed him, in a carriage with two horses driven by Lewis, the Negro boy, via New York, where she planned to visit with Grandfather and Grandmother Denning for a few days. "But I told Mother I had no wish to return through New York this year," she said, "because it makes the trip too long."

Already he missed her.

The miniatures turned out beautiful. Framed in black and gold, Ann's good-by gift to the Commodore stood on his desk when she accompanied him to Vergennes for rigging changes on board *Saratoga*.

Sharing his quarterdeck cabin, she seemed to know when to sit quiet, knitting, while he went over supply accounts complicated by passage through the hands of many shippers and agents. Inspecting the ship with him, she appreciated the fine points of her design and construction. And waiting off Otter Creek while shipwrights came from the yard at the falls to modify the rigging, she faced the moment of departure almost with serenity.

The Commodore took her over *Saratoga* only once. But in that tour he showed her everything from guns and gun deck to powder magazines and shot lockers, from binnacle to pump well, from church (used for divine service, for armory, and for officers' messroom) to blacksmith's shop. He showed her the orlops (light decking) over the ballast, dividing the main hold into rooms for water casks, provisions, and carpenter's timber. He showed her the berths for the sailing master and the boatswain and his mates—space for the sailors' chests, during an engagement, on which to lay the wounded—the cockpit.

He showed her the galley, with Cookie, drafted from *Preble*, grinning toothlessly. He showed her the quarters where sailors and marines slung their hammocks at night, and told her that the Navy Office apparently had no intention of sending any marines to Champlain. He described the head, a projection with railings and lattice-work floor on the bow, where the men accommodated themselves and did the ship's washing and butchering.

Ann saw, as part of daily routine, how the men stowed their hammocks daytimes, and when preparing for battle, in a network of small cords fastened to the bulwark railings and covered them with tarpaulin. She watched the men exercise at the guns. And she observed Lieutenant Henley dealing out justice before the mast.

Completing her sponsoring chores, she christened the four galleys Noah Brown had finished as his last piece of business, only one of which saw action in the defense of Otter Creek. At Fort Cassin appropriately, she gave the fifty-foot, lugger-rigged gunboats, each with one long twelve-pounder, names which the Commodore and his officers had chosen to honor more shipmates.

Ludlow, Master's Mate John Freeborn (captured in *Eagle,* now exchanged)—named for Lieutenant Augustus C. Ludlow who died in the action which finally saw frigate *Chesapeake* strike to British frigate *Shannon,* 1 June 1813; *Wilmer,* Sailing Master Daniel S. Stellwagon—for Lieutenant James P. Wilmer, killed only last March 28th when British frigate *Phoebe* and corvette *Cherub* captured frigate *Essex,* Captain David Porter, off Valparaiso; *Alwyn,* Acting Sailing Master Bancroft—for Lieutenant John Cushing Alwyn, impressed into the British navy at fifteen, killed by a British musket-ball 29 December 1812, while helping Captain William Bainbridge in *Constitution* take *Java;* and *Ballard,* Master's Mate Stephen Holland—for Lieutenant Edward J. Ballard, killed with Ludlow in *Chesapeake.*

On Ann's last night aboard *Saratoga,* Lucretia Ann joined them for dinner with the ship's officers. Thanks to Cookie's special efforts with another pig's head soup, Bob Henley's excellent wine, and the youthful gusto of Lieutenant Joseph

Smith, happily back from his Boston recruiting ordeal and overflowing with ludicrous anecdotes of Back Bay behavior, the dinner proved a great success in spite of the Commodore's frequent abstraction.

He found it just as hard to talk next morning when he took Ann ashore and drove with her to Vergennes where her mother's carriage waited at the Fisher gate. Ann's baggage was already in place under Lewis' ministration. Good-bys took only a few minutes.

Before his mother-in-law stepped into the carriage, she put her face up for the Commodore's kiss. Reaching into her braided handbag, she brought out an envelope. "Grandfather Denning asked me to give you this."

He kissed Ann, and handed her into the carriage. "Take good care of yourself."

Motioning the solemn Negro boy to start the journey, he turned away to hide his utter wretchedness.

8

Back on the Plattsburg station, the Commodore threw himself into the business of keeping tabs on an enemy whose activities, as reported by a variety of spies, shifted radically each week; of cooperating with an Army whose ideas of working together with the Navy changed every day; and of running a flotilla whose myriad complexities multiplied every hour.

Early in June he had notified the Navy Office that "the turpitude of many of our citizens in this part of the country furnishes the enemy with every information he wants," while "it is very difficult for us to get correct intelligence ... until they have got in forwardness with what they may be building."

After he wrote, he played a hunch. Ashore, in the Plattsburg garrison office he had used the year before, he sent for Eleazer Williams, and requested Peter Sailly to join them. He laid his cards on the table.

"We've all gathered intelligence about British activities," he said. "Some of it we've obtained through sources we've openly admitted—"

"—and," Williams cut in, "some of it from sources we've kept secret from each other."

The Commodore laughed. "I freely confess having used citizens like John Banker with his privateer," he said, looking at Peter Sailly, "and—"

"—and some of your own seamen," Williams finished.

"I've also picked up information from deserters off British

vessels," the Commodore said, "but that's beside the point."

He expected Williams to break in again. But Lazare, he quickly realized, could not anticipate the thought coming up. He said:

"The point I want to make is this: I think we should pool our resources and let Lazare take full responsibility for authenticating what they uncover."

At this implied compliment to past services, the secret corps Chief clasped his delicate feminine hands on the round table in front of him and remained silent. His satisfaction with the proposal lighted his dark eyes and softened his heavy, coppery features.

As the Commodore had told himself on his first meeting with this intriguing character, Lazare wanted, needed, the confidence of others. Looking across the table to Peter Sailly, he said:

"I remember General Bloomfield saying that if Lazare ever misled him, he'd have his ears. Well, seeing as how we both spend too much time sorting out misinformation, why don't we turn the entire job of intelligence over to him on the same basis as Bloomfield?"

With a minimum of debate, the Commodore and the Customs Collector gave the Scout the names of their spies; and Williams, after making it clear that the Army that had first employed him held his first allegiance, passed his word also to provide intelligence for Lake Champlain's water operations on the most accurate observations.

He gave his hand to the Commodore, and said: "I'm happy to have the trust of a pious, God-fearing man like you, sir."

Nonplused, the Commodore blinked. For an instant his mind raced. He had heard that Williams had taught among the Indians for the Congregational Church, had leaned also to Episcopalianism, and had shown no aversion to Jesuits who approached him, but he'd had no suspicion that the scout Chief brought religion into his work for the secret corps.

"Thank you, Lazare," he said, to avoid committing himself.

Williams filled the gap. He said: "The Reverend Daniel Haskell never tires of singing your praises for helping his church raise their carillon. And I've been aboard your vessels, Commodore, on the Sabbath and seen you with the crew assembled for worship; the Reverend Daniel Sanders of the University tells me you frequently invite him to conduct these services."

Again the Commodore held his tongue. He had helped get that bell into the church belfry as an ordinary civic duty, and ship services on Sunday constituted part of standard naval procedure. Lazare seemed to have missed, he thought with some amusement, his greatest religious work—throwing the fear of God into his men, but for mundane not heavenly purposes.

He smiled at the Scout, recognizing that a reputation of the kind Lazare ascribed to him could do neither him nor the fleet any harm in the local community. "Thank you, Lazare," he repeated. "Thank you very much. I just try to do the best the good Lord lets me." Which was the simple truth of the matter.

Within the week, Williams came up with solid information from four deserting British sailors: the enemy had laid the keel for a thirty-two-gun frigate at Isle-aux-Noix!

Supported by other sources, the intelligence left no doubt of British intent to outbuild the Americans. And to the Navy Office the Commodore at once suggested three plans of action: The first was to fortify the narrow part of the Lake (à la Wilkinson!). The second, to post the flotilla at the line and help the battery keep the British from entering the Lake until the Army could send an expedition against Isle-aux-Noix. He urged the third alternative, however: to build a bigger United States fleet, started at once by Messrs. Adam and Noah Brown of New York, of schooners or brigs to carry eighteen-pounders.

He stated the situation to Mr. Jones clearly and succinctly:

I hoped for no more building and that the enemy would meet us with what force he had complete, which three years ago he would have considered equal to ours. But now, sir, I am sure he intends to risk nothing, but will endeavor to outbuild us.

During the weeks he waited for the Navy Office to make up its mind on a course of action, the Commodore several times read over his letter from William Denning. In it the old gentleman talked to the Commodore as in his New York library, through a firm handwriting that set his thoughts out on a heavy, cream-colored note paper.

He confirmed the news of Napoleon's April abdication, which left Britain free to send veteran sailors and troops to fight the United States. Inevitably, as he and the Commodore had discussed, the enemy would invade at Niagara, Champlain, New Orleans, and along the Eastern coast—simultaneously. Champlain, in his judgment, still loomed as the critical target. Breaking through there, the enemy could inexorably sweep over the country from all other attacking points.

The old patriot's final paragraph burned deeper into the Commodore's spirit with each rereading:

Only men who value freedom can win, hold, and enjoy Liberty, and I feel, my dear boy, that you make one of that worthy group. I believe that you and your fleet will be given the opportunity to repel the invaders who today seek to deprive us of the Liberty we so-dearly won from them yesterday. And I have every confidence that, by that meeting, you will evict them *forever* from our country.

God bless you, Son, and keep you for us all. [Signed] Your devoted Grandfather.

Beyond doubt the old gentleman knew what he talked about in visualizing the probable British strategy; the Commodore already could discern the outline of their intentions on Champlain—holding back from an immediate test of power, frantically building at Isle-aux-Noix. But could

Grandfather Denning see truly into the future? Might the Lake Champlain fleet indeed hold the final balance of military power in this war? Could fate have plans to put its finger on him, Commodore—no, Master Commandant only—Thomas Macdonough? After several seconds, he clenched his hands and quickly released them to dissipate the sudden tightness that gripped him. Lazare Williams, he told himself, would have thought he had been praying. Had he?

While he waited, figuratively squirming, for official approval to start another vessel, the Commodore took the fleet toward Isle-aux-Noix, intent on luring the enemy into action. But the British would have none of his artful snares; Eleazer Williams' scouts reported them busy on their frigate, apparently content to wait on her completion before meeting the American flotilla face to face.

On the very same day that General Winfield Scott at Chippewa turned back the British on the Niagara frontier, July 5th, the Navy Office authorized an eighteen-gun brig for Lake Champlain. But the Secretary's notification reached the Commodore after Adam Brown arrived on the Lake to start her construction!

Adam resembled his brother Noah in most of the respects that counted importantly in the work they did. He just talked less, the Commodore decided, sometimes in shorter sentences. In the Commodore's cabin on *Saratoga* near the lines, July 18th, Adam showed a half-model of the vessel he had in mind to build. It called for twenty guns.

"But Mr. Jones authorizes only eighteen guns," said the Commodore.

"You know you can use twenty," replied Adam. "Just as easy to construct, and you have enough timber at Vergennes. I saw it."

Adam had Noah's same sound sense of values!

Sending for Lieutenant Henley, the Commodore gave his senior officer just time enough to meet the New York shipbuilder and settle himself in a reasonably comfortable chair. Then: "Bob, I'm relieving you of the ship, to command our new brig," he said. As Henley's face lighted, he added: "I'll take over *Saratoga*. You proceed at once to Vergennes with Mr. Brown to start building."

Henley made no effort to hide his enthusiasm, though speechless.

"I'll visit you as often as I can get away from the squadron," the Commodore went on; "and you can have Joseph Smith for your first lieutenant, as soon as I can spare him. I know you and he get along well."

Before Henley and Adam Brown left for the boatyard on the Otter, the trio prepared an ident for the brig's stores, to go to Dr. Bullus; agreed that Adam would immediately send to the Navy Agent dimensions of her spars for the sailmaker; specified the guns and cables desired; and approved opening of new rendezvous in New York, Boston, and Newport, Rhode Island.

As the meeting broke up, the Commodore showed the others the letter authorizing construction of the brig, with the Secretary's lamentation that he could "see no end to this war of broadaxes."

The Commodore shook Henley's hand, and said: "I'll cheer him up, Bob, by assuring him that our squadron matches any vessels on the Atlantic. I'll tell him how healthy our crews have been lately. Then I'll suggest that, along with a couple of lieutenants, a sailing master or two, and a surgeon, he send a master commandant to command the brig."

As Henley's face registered consternation over this apparent contradiction, the Commodore slapped him on the back. "Don't worry!" said the Commodore. "When the Secretary regretfully informs me he can't spare another one, I'll notify him that I've assigned you." He glanced at the quizzical shipbuilder, absorbing the by-play. "I'm only taking a leaf out of the Brown brothers' book on how to finesse the Navy Office into providing me with an experienced captain, for the country's good!"

Adam's fatherly smile looked exactly like the competent Noah's when the pair left for Vergennes. And five days later Adam sent word that he had laid the brig's keel.

From General Izard arrived an express telling of General Jacob Brown's savage drawn battle with General Gordon Drummond at Lundy's Lane, near Niagara, July 25th. In the Commodore's mind the shape of William Denning's predictions came into bolder relief.

He found himself continuously annoyed by British forays aimed to blast shore installations and magazines with rockets, and vexed by Vermonters' determined efforts to destroy themselves and all other Americans with aid and succor to the enemy. With repeal in April of the 1813 Embargo, commercial restrictions had come to an end, and Vermont's shrewd merchants found it so difficult to distinguish between legal trade and treasonable giving of aid and succor to the enemy that, as he wrote Ann, they compromised and did both. Their large-scale cattle drives to Canada over open roads continued, he wrote the Secretary, only because of "a great indifference on the part of the Governor or some other authority of that state."

He guarded the Lake as best he could.

On June 29th, while patrolling the Vermont shore in gunboat *Burrows,* Lieutenant Elie Vallette (replaced in the New York rendezvous by Lieutenant Charles C. B. Thompson) had come on four citizens towing two spars, eighty feet and eighty-five feet long, obviously intended for mizzen and foremasts on the British frigate. One of the captured smugglers, recognized as a seaman named George Smithson who had deserted from the Buttonwoods garrison the same night Dibble attempted to fire the galleys, went to the brig for an indeterminate period.

"Before I pass final judgment on Smithson," the Commodore told Lieutenant Henley, "I want to find out what the Secretary chooses to do with the civilians. If he instructs me to press charges in the local courts, they'll get off scot free— like the good citizens we get word about every day ... driving fat cattle publicly to the enemy. We can only charge Smithson with simple desertion then. Otherwise, Bob, we can make an example of him for giving aid to the enemy."

On the night of July 7th, Midshipman Joel Abbot had landed a party four miles inside enemy country, chopped, set fire to, and otherwise made useless four more spars—mainmast and three topmasts.

And on July 22nd word came via Eleazer Williams' scouts that more "citizens of the United States" had a large raft of plank, timber and tar ready to run into Canada through a narrow and unfrequented passage.

The Commodore summoned Elie Vallette, lately assigned to *Saratoga,* and sent the broad-shouldered Lieutenant in the launch to capture the raft. "Take volunteers," said the Commodore.

Among the volunteers accompanying Vallette went Aze Bellamy. As Aze meticulously reported later to the Commodore, "we discovered the raft about a mile from the line. It looked a quarter of a mile long or longer, with wooden cabins on it, and three or four masts with square-sails that were blowing her toward Canada."

Aze's excitement seemed about to burst through his throat as he went on: "Lieutenant Vallette and I went aboard with twelve men, sir, over the after end," he said. "The men on the raft shot at us from the cabins after we'd silenced their two guns, but we took cover behind the tar barrels and piles of lumber and bombarded them with bullets. They finally came out of the cabins with their hands in the air."

The midshipman paused, to pull himself together. His voice sounded controlled now, by great effort. "That is, seven of them came out without muskets," he said, and added quickly: "After we had them tied up, another man rushed out of a cabin back of me, trying to jump off the raft. When I turned, he raised his musket and I shot him with my pistol. He fell off the raft and disappeared."

The Commodore wondered at the midshipman's effort to tell with experienced nonchalance of his first hand-to-hand encounter with death.

"It was Jake Dibble I killed, sir," said Aze.

The Commodore understood the youngster's suppressed intensity then and felt a great urge to give forth with something sententious about the renegade Dibble. Instead, he smiled and said: "The raft's worth upwards of six thousand dollars, Vallette tells me, Aze. Your share of the prize money should pay for Emily's baby." Unable to contain his emotion, he declared: "I never met a man I detested more thoroughly. Dibble was a disgrace to his country, and to the human race. Those with him are no better!"

"I don't feel very sorry either, sir, for what happened," said Aze.

Vexed by smuggling, the Commodore found himself harassed by payment demands for building and equipping the fleet. With George Beale and James Sloane, he tackled a seemingly insurmountable stack of bills.

When the purser properly questioned payment for provisions, stores, cables, cordage, ordnance, or small arms not checked in by the sailing masters, boatswains, and gunners, the Commodore wrestled with the suppliers; over a single cask of powder "burst in going from Troy in consequence of the hoops not being well-fastened." He prepared proofs of pilferage, with promises to prosecute for delays and losses.

The bookkeeping supervision seemed endless, the trail of one account crossing another like animal tracks in a forest. From Boston, as a minor example, Amos Binney informed him that a thousand thirty-two-pound round shot to complete the number quite properly ordered from there could be made up better at the Monkton Iron Works at six cents a pound;

"this price is enormous yet, considering the cost of transportation, it would be a saving to the Government rather than to send them from this place." Previously, from Charlestown, 67,000 pounds of other sizes had come by oxcart.

When the purser receipted a bill for the Commodore's approval and attached a sight draft on the appropriate Navy agent, the Commodore signed both bill and draft. For everything from spy glasses to hawsers, from powder to spirits, from battle lanterns to surgeons' supplies, the bills ranged from a few hundred dollars to many thousands. The figures loomed mountainous to the Commodore.

Getting the bills paid brought fresh problems. As when Mel D. Woolsey, a large and reliable contractor, got stuck for days in New York with a fleet draft for $10,000 which, despite prompt acceptance by John Bullus, the New York bankers refused to discount.

"This detention, this want of confidence in the Government, shows the necessity of fore-laying for every necessity," Woolsey wrote, as if the Commodore didn't already know. "The language here is plain, undisguised—they will not trust the Government, even those institutions which have hitherto given them every support," the contractor concluded, shocked.

The bills mounted staggeringly, their total—particularly in view of the banks' attitude—fabulous. The Commodore had spent $17,140 to build and equip *Saratoga;* her guns had cost $12,420. At this rate, he estimated, William Jones's battle of broadaxes on Lake Champlain would chop more than $200,-000 out of the Navy's treasury.

And the steamboat company, having given the Commodore and Noah Brown good reason to believe that $5,000 would buy *Ticonderoga's* hull, now brought forward an account of $22,000. This one he turned over to William Jones:

> This is so extraordinary a sum that I have considered it proper to refer them to you. This sum they make out by damages sustained and by anticipated profits in running the boat.

I only observe that there appears a great inconsistency in their wishing so anxiously to dispose of their vessel, to their own loss, as they seem to wish to make it appear.

Writing to Ann, he wondered whether he'd ever appreciate these Vermont Yankees fully!

PART FIVE

THE BATTLE

The issue of this battle is well known.

Autobiography

1

With warm weather, officers and men flowed into the station at a somewhat faster rate than earlier when the rigors of Vermont's winter so effectively had deterred enlistments; and had caused the Commodore to call a halt to shipment north of Negro seamen who fell victim, almost on arrival, to the Lake's endemic fevers.

For *Saratoga* he now had experienced Raymond H. I. Perry, who had asked his cousin Oliver to procure him a situation with the Champlain fleet, as first lieutenant; Joe Barron as pilot; Philip Brum, a veteran Lake sailor who had served on *Erie* and had come aboard the ship through Moses Eggleston and Joe Barron, as sailing master; young Peter Gamble, methodical and thorough in everything from eating and sleeping to training and disciplining his men, as a lieutenant; along with Midshipmen Bellamy, Monteath, Graham, Platt, and newcomers Montgomery, Williamson, Thwing, Baldwin, and Duncan. John Stansbury he had appointed executive officer.

To the brig, he tentatively assigned Lieutenant Loomis, back from Quebec Prison along with several dozen other exchanged *Eagle* and *Growler* prisoners whom the Navy Office had just cleared as "competent to serve against the enemy"; Sailing Master Daniel Record; Boatswain John Wilson; Master's Mate Francis Breeze; with Midshipmen Chamberlain, McChesney, and Tardy.

Sailing Master Joseph Lindsey and Midshipman Hiram Paulding, that bouncy fifteen-year-old whose father had captured Major André in the Revolution, went to *Ticonderoga*.

To Lieutenant Budd on *Preble* went Sailing Master Rogers

Carter and Boatswain Joseph Rose. Lieutenant Pearce on *President* got Sailing Master Trent, also back from Quebec Prison. Newcomers Drury and Ellery, lieutenant and midshipman, took over *Montgomery*.

Besides making his own sailing masters out of Lake skippers, the Commodore got warrants from Washington for carpenters and other juniors to augment his establishment. Occasionally he lost a prospective addition; leaving the New York rendezvous, Hendrick Johnson had died when Seaman William Connor threw him overboard into the North River.

Human nature assailed the Commodore from all sides.

From T. Charlton Henry in Middlebury came six Bibles, contributed by the Philadelphia Bible Society "for the benefit of your fleet. The little acquaintance which I have with you [a mention by Eleazer Williams, no doubt!] induces me to take this liberty." To his clerk, the Commodore dictated an equally formal note of thanks.

From Albany: Governor Daniel D. Thompkins wrote, as a family friend, for the release of young Joseph Nelson, a carpenter recently come to the Lake after enlisting in New York. The boy's story, told in the Commodore's cabin, brought prompt action.

Three years before, Nelson had left home to go to Ireland for some property left him by an uncle. On the voyage, the British had impressed, then imprisoned, him. He heard nothing from his family. Escaping, he reached New York after three years, penniless, friendless, and enlisted for Champlain so that he could get in touch with his family in Washington County en route to the Lake. He found his father had died, and his mother trying to support five of his younger brothers and sisters. He could set up a good stand in the town of Cambridge for his trade of cabinet maker. He would return the bounty.

The tall, haggard youth might just as well have stopped as soon as he mentioned impressment. For the Commodore, no more was needed.

"What do you want to do, son?"

"I want to stay with you, sir, and fight!" said the boy. "But I guess I'd better go home and help my mother."

The Commodore gave him his release and stage fare to Albany.

From Washington:

> You will convene a Court of Enquiry to investigate the cause of the loss, by capture, of the U. States' vessels, the *Eagle* and *Growler,* on Lake Champlain on the 3rd of June, 1813; and report the result of the enquiry to this Department, together with the opinion of the court on the conduct of the Commander, officers, and crews of said vessels, on that occasion.
>
> You will request the attendance of such officers, who were attached to them, as you may deem necessary.

Now, in the middle of everything else, the Navy Office wanted this! Well, it was all water . . . down the Sorel! He put the order under a pile of correspondence which, eventually, Jim Sloane would get around to.

More immediately, he wanted to clear up the Briggs-Caton feud. Dr. John P. Briggs, *Saratoga's* surgeon, had notified him officially that the ship's cockpit lacked flannel or linen bandages and had neither spirits nor vinegar. Should the squadron engage, he apprised the Commodore, the want of these articles would subject surgeons and wounded to "distressing inconveniences." Deftly, the good doctor made his point:

> As these articles are abundantly provided for the use of the fleet, I presume you will not think that Doct. Caton has use for the articles, at the hospital, which were furnished for the ship.
>
> In my present situation, I wish to be as useful as is in my power, should necessity require it; to that end I wish Doct. Caton to furnish the above-named articles, as he must have a greater quantity than is necessary for the use of the hospital; as these things, I am confident, you suppose I have in my possession.

Of course he supposed the cockpit held all the equipment needed for battle wounded! Had he not paid through the nose for surgical instruments and supplies? His note to Dr. William Caton, Junior, went straight to the point; less tactfully perhaps than at a time when no other problems burdened his shoulders and his mind. He called the Surgeon's attention to a lack of proper equipment in *Saratoga*'s cockpit.

Dr. Caton's immediate response floored him. After stating that, on receipt of the Commodore's letter, he had sent hospital stores, including mattresses, pillows and everything necessary for *Saratoga*'s present sick and future wounded, the shore surgeon waxed hysterical:

> As my conduct has been so improper, I must ask of you, sir, to have examined the medicine chest and locker.
> Conscious myself of not having erred, I solicit—not only solicit, but beg for—my arrest. What you think of the charges, I cannot say. In justification of my feelings and character, I ask of you, sir, my arrest.

The Commodore called for his executive officer, and brought Stansbury up to date.

"Before I make my mind up on this, Lieutenant," he said, "get me a few facts."

Late one night a week later, having left the ship and gone to Plattsburg to see what he could find, Stansbury reported back. His summary included the observation that hospital attendants at Plattsburg for some time had considered the doctor overworked, because of temperament, not necessity. He said: "I think Dr. Caton's excessively sensitive, sir."

The Commodore eyed Stansbury. "This is no place and no time for undue sensibility."

He called his clerk in and dictated a short note to Dr. Caton:

> Your letter requesting your arrest has been received. I do not consider the charge of inattention sufficient to deprive the squadron of your services.

But as all men should be of a disposition to be spoken to without running into extravagances without cause, you can at a more favorable time make it appear, if you so wish, to the Department that you were not inattentive or neglectful to your duty.

"I hope," he said to Stansbury, "that Dr. Briggs doesn't wake up some morning to find himself mysteriously dead at the hand of Dr. Caton."

Still short of men despite frequent drafts from New York and Boston, the Commodore continued vigorously to exercise seamen and gunners. The training program had produced seeable results on all vessels, and he complimented his officers, senior and junior, who had brought the fleet to a precision equaling any on the Atlantic. He had not exaggerated in the slightest to William Jones; come the need, his sailors could handle their ships smartly, his gunners shoot accurately.

But a certain amount of sickness still plagued the fleet, necessitating transfer of men from back-breaking galley berths to lighter work on the larger sailing vessels. And from everyone but the doctors he had hidden his own frequent attacks of ague and coughing. He had no time, he told himself, for pampering. A little wine, a little rum, a little whisky, must suffice to hold the attacks down.

Dr. Briggs and Dr. Wilson, who came aboard, as he'd promised, on every possible occasion, did their best to keep the Commodore's coughing to a minimum.

"If you'd get out of this climate for a few weeks, your cough might clear up," Dr. Wilson had insisted since January.

And since January the Commodore had retorted that he would take a change in scene the minute the enemy went back to England. "Bill," he said, "you're like every other physician. You prescribe expensive medicines for poor people who can't afford them or tell them to travel for their health. You just ain't practical."

The doctor had taken the chaffing easily. Now he gave in.

"All right, Tom," he said, "you've heard the last of my advice. I've got orders to move West. I leave tomorrow."

"No!" Taken aback by the unexpected news, the Commodore of a sudden realized how much he would miss this good companion. Walking slowly across the cabin to his friend, he tugged from his pocket the plain gold watch he had always worn. Detaching the watch and its gold chain-seal and key from his fob, he held it out and said: "Then I want something to remember you by, Bill ... you and your impractical advice! Take this in exchange for yours."

The doctor made the swap. "Tom," he said fondly, "I'll pass this on to my grandchildren as a cherished heirloom." [1]

With Dr. Wilson's unexpected and regretted departure, the Commodore plunged back into fleet detail, to face a decision he had held in abeyance for nearly a month. He sent for sixteen-year-old John Kortz, Jr.

In work trousers and striped cotton shirt, the boy stood at attention before the Commodore's desk, wiry body rigid and a frightened look in his almost cerulean eyes.

"Relax, boy. Stand at ease," said the Commodore, his voice exceedingly soft. "I just want to find out how you like your life on *Saratoga*." For several seconds the boy continued to stand stiffly, hands at his side, and the Commodore sought to loosen him with a friendly grin. "Too tough for you?"

"Oh, no, sir!" the boy almost shouted. "I think it's wonderful." His frightened expression vanished like blackboard chalk under a wet cloth. His eyes shone. He relaxed. "I'm a topman, sir," he said, pride literally exploding from the simple statement.

The Commodore picked up a lengthy letter, and observed how the boy almost cringed at sight of the handwriting. "John," he said, "this is the second letter I've had from your father. Listen to what he writes." The Commodore read aloud:

"It is now one month since my poor Son John Kortz Junior was in the City of New York inveigled by Charles C. B.

Thompson, a Navy officer, through the instrumentality of one Acker, who enlisted at the same time, to enlist. Acker is a very bad fellow & undoubtedly was paid by the recruiting officer to bring him in.

"Thompson confessed to me that Acker brought him there to Market Street, formerly George Street, the worst place in New York, where to the disgrace of America the officer has his flag up to kidnap unwary children & any whom he may entrap."

The Commodore looked up. The boy's frightened expression had come back. The Commodore asked: "Did Acker take you to the rendezvous by force?"

"No, sir!" the boy cried shrilly. "I met him in a restaurant and got talking with him. I told him I'd run away from home, up in Hudson, and wanted to get into the war. When I asked him if he knew whether the Navy would take me, he said we could find out around the corner. He became interested after Lieutenant Thompson told us we were bound to see action on Lake Champlain, and he joined up with me."

"Are you sure neither Acker nor Lieutenant Thompson enticed you in any way?"

"Yes, sir, I am," said the boy. "They couldn't have been in cahoots, either, sir. Why, Acker's my best friend in the fleet today!" His voice had lost its shrillness, his face its evidence of fright.

The Commodore read on:

"My son enlisted without my knowledge, I repeat, or consent. I have discovered that he was sorry for it before he came to Albany. But they had him fast, & he could not help himself. They undoubtedly made him intoxicated & got him to sign his name to the Role. The officer told me he had orders to enlist all the boys he could get & would do so, & sneered at me by way of contempt."

"Your father sounds like a violent man, son."

"Yes, sir. I left home to get away from him and his temper,

sir." The boy's manner clearly showed that his earlier fright stemmed from fear of having to go back.

The Commodore skimmed through the body of the letter, digesting it for the boy: "Your father's appealed to the Governor. Says Acker may persuade you to desert, whereupon you'll be hanged or shot, and I'll become your murderer. He says your mother's in tears, your morals will be corrupted, you'll die of distemper incident to fleas, or be killed in battle. And his heart will be broken. What do you say to all that?"

The boy's poise surprised the Commodore, though he had had his eye on young Kortz and seen him develop under the ship's training and routine. Agile as a monkey on the yards, the youngster seemed always to enjoy his chores.

"If you want the truth, sir," said the boy, "I'd almost rather be shot here and now than have you send me home." Of a sudden tears flooded his eyes. "My mother gave me money to go to New York, sir. She said she only wished she could run away, too."

While the boy surreptitiously swiped at his eyes, the Commodore glanced over the letter's last paragraph:

> ... I shall expose to the world the whole transaction ... call you to account in a Court of Justice ... get my son discharged by habeas corpus ... seek my rights. ...

The Commodore laid the letter on the desk and said: "John, do you think we should take on your father, the Governor of New York State, and the Supreme Court—along with the British?"

The boy's eyes lighted. "I will, if you will, sir!" he declared.

The Commodore's guffaw brought his clerk's balding head into the cabin. He waved to Sloane and said: "Come in, Jim, and take a letter to John Kortz, Sr. Tell him his son's too busy learning to be a midshipman to come home just now."

The Commodore sent the boy back to his watch, bouncing all the way.

2

At Major General George Izard's invitation, Commodore Macdonough met with Izard and Alex Macomb in Bloomfield's old Plattsburg headquarters.

Izard had been inducted at the same time as the Commodore into the United States Military Philosophical Society, and he now greeted his naval guest with the cordiality of a fellow lodge member. Producing rum, wine, pipes and cigars, he let an atmosphere of leisureliness take over before he got down to business.

The General had arrived on the Lake May 1st, full of War Department plans for attacking Montreal; today, three months later, none of the plans had jelled. The Commodore asked himself what Izard had in mind now. To pick up as of May 1st and attack? To sit tight and defend? The Commodore took in Izard's broad forehead, his long thin nose, and his large mouth. But mostly he watched Izard's worried eyes. An interesting man, this.

Izard had a reputation, the Commodore had learned in his talks with Alex Macomb, for knowing his own mind. He could be cautious and tenacious; he also could be arbitrary and dictatorial. Because the War Department had constantly moved him from post to post against his own judgment, he doubtless had exaggerated all those qualities for self-protection.

"So far in this war," Izard finally began, "the Secretary of War has seen fit to throw me into a succession of situations that needed a good housecleaning. Halfway through each, he's lifted me out and dropped me into another." His expression bland, he went on: "This assignment, however, looks to have some permanency," he said. "And since you two men share responsibility with me, I'd like to take stock of our mutual situation, if you'll bear with me."

The Commodore felt a quick appreciation. Picking up after Dearborn, Bloomfield, Hampton, and Wilkinson must take considerable doing!

Izard went on:

"Previous commanders, regrettably, let this oldest corps fall into a lamentable state. After a three-day personal examination of troops, following my arrival on this station, I reported to General Armstrong: clothing wretched, arms unfit for use, and proficiency in field maneuvers almost nil. I found an undue proportion of men on the sick list. I found whole battalions composed of year's men, entitled in a few days to discharge from the service. Riflemen had had no pay for considerably more than a year! Several men deserted during my first week on the station.

"In short, I could not produce more than two thousand effectives on this side of the Lake, and these raw, ill-clad, and worse disciplined. General Macomb in Vermont had no more than nine hundred men, with four or five hundred recruits on the way. Yet the War Department expected me to protect the west shore and also to consider approaching and annoying the enemy.

"The Department also expected me, if enlistments warranted, to attack Lacolle and take a position between Isle-aux-Noix and Montreal, compelling the enemy to hazard a battle in defense of his communications."

Sensing that Izard had stopped only for breath, the Commodore glanced at Macomb, whose eyes intently stayed on Izard's lined face during the brief pause. Macomb gave no inkling of his reaction to this recital.

General Izard lighted a cigar and looked across the table toward the Commodore. He said: "I make no observation on your accomplishments on the water, sir, when I add to what I've just said the fact that the War Department hoped that your flotilla would shortly confine the enemy to the Sorel. At last, later than we hoped, you've done just that."

Izard puffed at his cigar, meditatively, for several seconds. Then: "Now my effectives total approximately five thousand five hundred, including Macomb's in Vermont."

He puffed again several times, rolling the cigar between his lips. Finally: "All of which sugars off to this: Can the Navy subdue Isle-aux-Noix and enable the Army to take a position between there and Montreal? If so, reinforcements will come to me from all points, and we can then attack Montreal. It's only forty-seven miles from Chazy."

Izard leaned back, waiting.

The Commodore composed himself with his drink and a second cigar. This scene reminded him of similar meetings with other generals (was it really only four others?), all eager to attack Montreal, all calling on the fleet for support into Canada, and none ever making an effective approach. The Commodore spoke slowly. He said: "I appreciate, perhaps better than you realize, General, the handicaps under which you've found yourself forced to operate on the west side of the Lake." He smiled briefly, to let Izard absorb that the Navy had coped with those predecessors whose messes he had inherited. "I'm anxious, therefore, to give you all possible support and reluctant to say no to any request whatever." He let that, too, sink in, while he wondered what went on behind Macomb's masked eyes. He had never seen Alex so withdrawn, so unapproachable. Did he, like the War Department, consider the Navy inefficient, ineffective?

The Commodore went on: "But the situation as I outlined it to you in the middle of June last, General Izard, remains the same. The enemy has moored its squadron in narrow water close under Ash Island, where the shoalness of the river makes it too hazardous for me to venture the ship. Too, the enemy's shore battery, brig, four sloops, upwards of twenty galleys, and a large scow mounting heavy guns lie across the channel so that I should be obliged to approach their whole line with my vessels in a line ahead, or one vessel after another, and expose them to a raking fire; this on top of the probability of getting *Saratoga* aground. We would gain nothing, but lose a great deal."

The Commodore relighted his cigar, letting Izard study his face. "Furthermore, General," he said, "my control of the Lake becomes questionable the minute the enemy sees fit to sail out and contest it." He could see this came as a rough blow to Izard. "With his frigate, under circumstances favorable to himself, he can meet me with a force that will insure him success."

Before Izard could comment, the Commodore took the offensive with: "I suggest again, therefore, that you place some guns at Point au Roche to protect me in the event I have to retire from a superior force. The narrow water between the Point and Isle la Motte offers a favorable situation for my vessels to act in concert with a shore battery."

Izard bridled. "I've already established a battery of four eighteen-pounders for that purpose," he said, "on Cumberland Head!"

The Commodore knew he now had the ascendancy over Izard as well as the Lake, temporarily at least. He smiled.

"Point au Roche offers better protection," he said, "and would enable us to block the enemy from sailing farther up the Lake."

Izard let that roll off, coming back with: "Your new brig, Commodore, will give you more guns than the British, won't it?"

"Not quite as many as the enemy," the Commodore parried. "And I don't know that Adam Brown can get her ready before the enemy frigate."

In the ensuing comparison of Army intelligence from Canada with Navy reports on the frigate's progress, together with Izard's complaints that his spies seemed as much in the enemy's pay as in his own, "some receiving monthly stipends to no inconsiderable amount," the immediate problem came clear: to block the British fleet as far below Plattsburg and Burlington as possible should it come out in full strength before the brig entered the Lake.

To achieve this, Izard would move troops at once to Chazy where they could support a battery on Point au Roche. The Commodore would put *President* and *Montgomery* to the task of supplying the troops by water.

The meeting ended in a blaze of conviviality, with Izard allowing that the Commodore need not send all the way to New York City for the brig's powder, because the Army had aplenty at Whitehall, which the Navy must consider at its disposal. The Commodore thanked the General profusely, wondering as he did what this cagey soldier really had in his mind. He had acquiesced much too easily to remaining on the defensive. Did he figure he could lure the fleet into early combat despite the Commodore's warning? Did he plan to strike at Montreal without the flotilla's support?

"Now, if we could do something about the cattle-running on both sides of the Lake," Izard threw out by way of farewell, "I'd feel we had the current situation as well in hand as our circumstances permit. I understand the enemy's marines at Isle-aux-Noix have marching orders for Missisquoi Bay, to protect large droves said to be entering Canada just this side of Lake Memphremagog." He handed the Commodore a letter. "Read this. I'm sending it to General Armstrong today."

From the St. Lawrence to the ocean, an open disregard prevails for the laws prohibiting intercourse with the enemy. The road to St. Regis is covered with droves of cattle, and the river with rafts, destined for the enemy. The revenue officers see these things, but acknowledge their inability to put a stop to such outrageous proceedings.

On the eastern side of Lake Champlain the high roads are found insufficient for the supplies of cattle which are pouring into Canada. Like herds of buffaloes they press through the forest, making paths for themselves. Nothing but a cordon of troops from the French hills to Lake Memphremagog could effectively check the evil.

Were it not for these supplies the British forces in Canada would soon be suffering from famine....

Walking Alex Macomb to his gig for the trip back to Burlington, the Commodore tossed out a suggestion.

"Come along with me on the ship tonight, Alex," he said. "I'll deliver you in Burlington tomorrow and go on up to the lines from there." He put his arm around Macomb's husky shoulders. "With Izard and me doing all the talking, I don't feel as if I'd had any time with you today."

Macomb's eyes lighted. "I'd like to join you," he said. "I hear you have dancing girls on all your vessels."

The Commodore laughed. "Not quite!" he said. "But if we're discreet, I think Cookie's chickens might entertain us with a little exhibition of skill." He laughed again. "Cockfight to you, Alex!"

Macomb's face beamed like Aze Bellamy's. "The saints be praised!" he exclaimed, "... as my Irish father used to say to my French mother when he heard good news. Can I wager a loose dollar or two?"

The Commodore's arm directed his guest to *Saratoga*'s gig, waiting beside Macomb's, and said:

"I'm sure we'll find someone glad to take your Army money —me!"

Over a bedtime mug of rum in *Saratoga*'s quarterdeck cabin, Alex Macomb expressed his pleasure with a full evening's entertainment. "I'm glad to see how the other armed service lives, Tom," he said, "with a chef who can supply fine food and excellent cockfights. I should have gone to sea."

The Commodore's hearty laugh filled the cabin. "We have to make life bearable, for ourselves as well as the men," he said. "Cookie's contests do more for our morale than... Sunday services, shall we say?"

Macomb gazed into his glass, thoughtfully. Then:

"You know Burlington's townspeople pretty well, Tom. Maybe you can tell me why your sailors got into so little trouble with them last year while mine keep me immersed in hot water all the time."

The Commodore refilled his guest's mug. "Perhaps," he said, "it's because the Navy gave the town something—jobs for carpenters and mechanics on the vessels, help with civic projects that needed an extra hand or two, things like that."

"There's more to it, Tom."

The Commodore nodded. "Well, if I may speak bluntly," he said, "you and Izard both come by your troubles honestly —through direct inheritance. You should hear my pilot Joe Barron's stories of the way the Army treated civilians before you arrived. And I could tell you a few tales myself, Alex, about officers like your Colonel Clark."

Macomb nodded. "I know," he said. "We antagonize some-body at every turn. Like the University—when I had to take over the building in March to house my troops, at a good high rental of $5,000 a year too, the corporation resolved 'that the regular course of instruction in the University is suspended and the officers whose salaries are annexed be dismissed,' and I had disgruntled students and teachers on my neck for weeks."

"Can you blame them?" asked the Commodore. "Last year, troops interrupted the college exercises, injured the building, and destroyed the fences. Then you come along and put faculty and students out on the street. Remember, they don't take this war very seriously."

"Maybe so," said Macomb. "But I get into the worst pickles. How about that attorney George Robinson claiming my officers planned to burn certain houses in town? Obviously a canard aimed to get back at us for stopping some of the local smuggling." He grimaced. "Then one of our soldiers, drunk as an English earl, sets fire to a house, and I have to provide a guard for all the houses on the so-called black list. By what devious logic they trusted me to guard them I'll never know!"

The Commodore raised his glass. "Shrug those things off, Alex," he said. "Vermonters are a funny race, funnier than the French and the Irish, even. But we have to save them from the British the same as other Americans."

Macomb filled the cabin again with laughter, and raised his glass.

"To the day they join the United States!" he toasted.

Next day the Commodore wrote William Jones:

I have the honor to inform you that the enemy continues under his batteries on the Sorel River, assiduously employed in the preparation of his naval force. It is presumed, however, he will not come out until his new ship is done, which from my last information will be in the beginning of September.

Mr. Brown writes me he has begun to plank the Brig; that he will launch her on the 15th of this month. Stores are arriving and for the present I have directed Lieut. Francis J. Mitchell to attend to her equipment. I have not much faith in his abilities. All my officers are young, but his services in the squadron can be best dispensed with.

Will you be pleased, sir, to give a name for the Brig, or may I call her the *Eagle?*

3

On August 5th, General Izard moved his army to Chazy and sent a company on to Champlain.

Commodore Macdonough transported supplies to both outposts; the fleet then lay near the lines. And while Eleazer Williams, on orders from General Jacob Brown at Niagara, crossed into upper Canada north of Niagara to ferret out details of current troop movements in the West, his rangers let word sift from lower Canada to the Commodore:

At Quebec, "the British continue to land veteran soldiers, sailors and marines, with frames for ships intended for Lake Ontario or Lake Champlain"; at Isle-aux-Noix, "the enemy has every nerve on the stretch in preparing his additional force."

At Vergennes, the American brig entered the water August 11th—only nineteen days from keel-laying; four days ahead of Adam Brown's promise.[1] At Isle-aux-Noix, within twenty-four hours of the brig's launching, the enemy succeeded with the help of a guard in procuring masts for their frigate.

Pressure increased every day. Where would it blow off?

Neck-and-neck with the bad news from Canada, General Izard's gig arrived at *Saratoga*'s landing stage with an aide-de-camp requesting the naval commander's presence at Chazy headquarters for a council of war with Generals Izard and Macomb.

Izard seethed with emotion as he greeted the Commodore before his tent, pitched just above a bend in the Little Chazy

River. Waving his staff out of earshot, he brought his pacing to an abrupt halt with an equally abrupt announcement:

"The War Department has ordered my army to Niagara."

The Commodore's heart almost stopped, then pounded. He felt as though he'd fallen off a cliff. He caught his breath, incredulous. He refused to believe the worst. "Who's coming here for replacement?" he demanded.

Alex Macomb answered. "Nobody," he said. "I stay here with fifteen hundred men."

Fifteen hundred men! The Commodore's jaw tightened. "With the enemy massing in force in front of Montreal at Laprairie and L'Acadie plains, it's an open invitation to invasion!" he declared. "What stupid idiot sent that order?"

Thin-lipped, trembling with rage, Izard found his voice. He said: "Armstrong's excited about the safety of the left division at Fort Erie. I'm to support Jacob Brown there."

"And who," said the Commodore, "fights Prevost when he marches on us from Montreal with six or seven thousand troops?"

"More than eleven thousand, Tom," Macomb amended. "The rangers counted three brigades ... with the British army's most experienced generals and distinguished officers."

The Commodore shook his head, his lips pressed into a straight line.

Izard picked up his violent pacing. "They'll take Champlain and Chazy three days after I leave!" he prophesied.

"You don't think they'll wait for their fleet?" asked the Commodore.

"I wouldn't!" Izard shouted. "I'd swarm over the countryside, live on the cattle provided by fat traitors, and get to New York before New England even knew it was encircled and cut off from the rest of the country!"

The Commodore thought that over. His flotilla could harass and hinder, but not stop, troop movements up the west side of the Lake. For an alert, aggressive British general, moving fast and willing to live on the land instead of depending for his supplies by water, the gamble might pay out.

Macomb shook his head judiciously and said: "General Izard knows the country and has the personal drive it would require to lead an invasion without naval support. But not the British commanders. These," he suggested, "like their creature comforts too well to move with unaccustomed self-denial."

The Commodore searched Macomb's face for signs of levity. He found none. His heart had resumed its normal beat. "You think they'll make a joint land-and-water attack?"

Macomb confirmed what had long seemed obvious. "I do," he said flatly. "They'll come the moment their frigate's rigged for action."

Macomb's words tore William Denning's prediction out of a distant, fuzzy future and smacked it down into the Commodore's immediate, pulsing present. "They'll come the minute the frigate's ready!"

Izard again stopped pacing. Rapt in thought, he looked over the river, his back to his colleagues. When he turned, his face seemed a hundred years old. Slowly he said: "If the War Department insists, Commodore, I'll have to join Brown. But I can stall, and I will stall—if possible—until your brig joins the flotilla." Izard's voice sounded very tired as he continued: "I'll protest to General Armstrong, point out that removing the Champlain army will be tantamount to committing national suicide." He finished with: "Perhaps someone on the staff has a shred of common sense left."

But events proved stronger than General Izard's reasoned appeals to the War Department.

On August 13th and 14th, the American army at Fort Erie repulsed the British but further increased General Armstrong's apprehensions for the western frontier; he ordered General Izard to carry out instructions to take his army to Niagara.

On the 25th, at Isle-aux-Noix, British frigate *Confiance* took the water. It was to mount thirty-seven guns.

On the 27th, the American brig joined the squadron at the lines.

On August 29th, General Izard marched four thousand Plattsburg troops toward Fort Erie, leaving Lake Champlain threatened by eleven thousand veterans of Spain and Waterloo and under the sole protection of General Macomb's fifteen hundred effectives and Commodore Macdonough's fleet.

And as the tramp-tramp of Izard's army trailed off into the West, news reached the Lake from Washington that British troops on the Eastern coast had sacked the capital of the United States and burned the White House.

4

As General Izard predicted, he had hardly turned West before the British advance guard, under General Thomas Makdougall Brisbane, camped on the north side of the Great Chazy River.

Having withdrawn all guns from Cumberland Head and Point au Roche on September 1st to concentrate his meager power, General Macomb suggested that the Commodore bring the flotilla back to Plattsburg to annoy Brisbane should he march on the town by the Dead Creek road.

The same day saw Sir George Prevost's artillery, infantry, light dragoons, and Canadian chasseurs, with miners and sappers, invest Champlain.

In General Mooers' spacious house—now Macomb's headquarters—the Commodore met for a council of war with Alex Macomb. Earlier brushes with Army braid had succeeded only in raising his hackles; this meeting provided a deep sense of dedication. From their intent expressions, he saw at once that Peter Sailly, Eleazer Williams, and General Benjamin Mooers—again well met as on that night the Commodore had arrived fresh on the Lake in the autumn of 1812 —also felt the council's solemn significance.

Courteously making everyone comfortable at a big table laid out with white cloth, candles, decanters, and cigars, Macomb quickly set the tone of the meeting.

"You've come here, gentlemen," he said, "to help me plan how to do the will of the President of the United States." He held up a roughly printed handbill dated Washington, D. C., and read from it: "Whereas the enemy, by a sudden incursion, have succeeded in invading the capital of the nation . . ." He let the similarity of the Lake Champlain situation register, then finished reading: ". . . now, therefore, I, James Madison, President of the United States, do issue this proclamation exhorting all the good people thereof to unite their hearts and hands in giving effect to . . . a manly and universal determination to chastise and expel the invader . . ."

Silence followed. After several seconds, General Mooers reverently said, "Amen."

With earnest authority, General Macomb laid his ideas before the group. And the Commodore felt a sudden surge of affection as, detailing specific plans for deploying fifteen hundred regular troops, the New York State militia, and the Vermont militia, Macomb gave meaning to his words above and beyond their context. His controlled emotion, his firm tone, the sparks from his eyes, his precise phrasings—all conveyed a conviction that, with or without support from anyone, Alexander Macomb intended to knock the props from under the British.

What a man! The Commodore's heart flooded with admiration for this soldier. This man he could work with. Together he and Alex just could do what James Madison asked—chastise and expel the invader, drive the whole British army and impressment-loving navy out of the country forever. William Denning's gentle smile flashed across his mind, and then he found the group silently observing him.

"I just met the British fleet," he revealed with a self-conscious smile, "while Alex took on their army."

Peter Sailly, who so far also had listened without speaking, asked, wryly: "How did you both make out?"

Whether Governor Chittenden would permit Vermont's militia to leave their home state and cross the Lake to fight in New York in case of need, remained the only unanswered question at the meeting's end.

General Macomb expressed his gratitude for the group's contributions . . . this evening and in the future. He made no promises as he said good night; his strong handclasp carried far more assurance.

When the others had gone, Macomb motioned the Commodore to sit down again. "I asked you to stay on, Tom, because I need your moral support," he confessed. Replenishing their rum, he drank quickly. "What do you honestly think? Have we any chance of turning them back, even holding them off?"

For the first time the Commodore realized how much anger, rage, fury had accumulated inside him during two years of frustrative negotiating with purblind Army generals and slow-moving Navy officials; during two years of standing back while the British fleet nipped at his heels like mongrel dogs and then fled at the first sign of retaliation; during two years of repairing, building, rebuilding, building again. He could feel his pent-up emotions still mounting. Yet he knew that he could contain their full pressure until the moment came to blast them loose.

"Alex," he said earnestly, "I've got a grandfather by marriage who believes my Lake squadron can beat the British fleet. I've got a wife, bless her, who's convinced that I could beach the squadron, take a rowboat and a pistol, and single-handed lick the entire British navy. Of course we can turn 'em back! They may be superior in force but, God willing, we can beat 'em!

"Don't misunderstand me," he went on quickly. "David doesn't slay Goliath every day. But here we two stand, on our own soil, backed by patriotic men so eager to expel the invader that they serve for a pittance in the Army and Navy on a rugged frontier like this. And what do we face? A seemingly overwhelming horde, which is just that, in my estimation. Soldiers and sailors puffed up with a victory in Europe, led by well-fed, arrogant officers who, if they're like the others

I've met, don't know enough to suck alum and drool. Three thousand miles from home, ignorant of the terrain, and fighting for what?

"Two things I've learned, Alex: Don't underestimate your opponent; and its corollary, the other fellow can make mistakes, too."

Macomb's face brightened with every word. His almost ever-present smile returned.

"It's good to hear you talk like that, Tom," he said. "Because I don't intend to let Prevost walk over me, big as the British blow him up to be—baronet, general, governor of Canada, and what-all. I have some ideas for making things hard for him. But I need a little time to prepare."

"Will a week do?" asked the Commodore. "Lazare's actually heard British officers say their troops will move only when *Confiance* joins the fleet. They can't get her ready in less than a week, ten days maybe."

Macomb nodded gravely. "That's their first strategic mistake," he said; "a land attack that depends entirely on naval support." After several seconds of judicious thought he added: "I'll go to work, and I'll keep you informed. Meanwhile, stand by in the bay with the fleet, if you will, Tom, in case I suddenly need you to protect the beach road."

Closing his guest's bedroom door an hour later, Macomb looked back at the Commodore, already out of his dress coat. "If we can't pull this off together, Tom," he said by way of good night, "no two men can."

The following day saw the Commodore's first serious run-in with a senior fleet officer, Bob Henley.

Henley came aboard *Saratoga* early to make a detailed report on the brig's status. The Commodore greeted him cordially, waved him informally to a seat, and praised him for the speed with which he had fitted the newly built vessel and brought her to the fleet.

Henley beamed. "She's well constructed, and she handles beautifully," he declared. *"Surprise* is a fine ship."

The Commodore blinked. "Well, *that's* a surprise!"

Henley apparently failed to comprehend.

"The name, I mean," said the Commodore.

"Didn't I tell you?" Henley put in quickly. "I wrote the Navy Office for permission."

"When did you write?"

"Two weeks ago. About the nineteenth."

"Bob," said the Commodore severely, "I wrote Mr. Jones on August second, suggesting the name *Eagle.*"

"I didn't know that!"

"I sent you a copy of my letter."

"I never received it."

The Commodore flexed his jaws, and held his tongue. As a master commandant and commander of the brig, Bob had every right to confer directly with the Navy Secretary. But this smelled slightly of a deliberate attempt to go over his superior's head in a bid for commendation, confirmed by the papers Henley now placed before him; these included a signed letter to William Jones. The letter was headed "U. States Sloop *Surprise* off Plattsburg." The note read:

> I have the honor to enclose a muster roll of the Sloop of War under my command, by which you will perceive she is very deficient in both officers and men.
> In other respects we are in good fighting order.

Boiling mad at this officious conduct—bound to complicate, even jeopardize, current delicate negotiations with Washington for officers and crew for the brig—the Commodore slowly raised his head. Henley had stretched out in his chair, trying to appear at ease. Ann had seen clearly; Bob wanted glory, all right. But he had picked a poor time to go after it; at this moment too much depended on teamwork for personal glorification. The Commodore leveled his eyes at Henley.

"You have my permission to send this letter, if you so desire, Lieutenant," he said evenly. "But you will be pleased to have the name *Eagle* immediately painted on the brig's transom!" He went right on: "You may expect men for your crew almost any day from Lieutenant Thompson in New York, from Commodore Bainbridge in Boston, and from Henry Teue in Newport. Your officers should arrive at any moment. Meanwhile, as I promised, you can have Joseph Smith for your first lieutenant. I'll bring him to you shortly"—he paused for effect—"when I come on board to inspect *Eagle*."

Henley departed silently.

Summoning Joseph Smith, the Commodore told him to pack his trunk, and the youngster's uncontained joy over the assignment compensated in a measure for the Commodore's depression over Bob Henley's defection.

Turning to unfinished fleet business of the past week, the Commodore reread a letter dated August 20th which he'd held off sending the Navy Office in the hope of adding a saving postscript:

I regret having to inform you of an unfortunate accident which took place on the night of the 16th inst. in the State of Vermont. A man was shot by the crew of one of my boats. The circumstances attending and which led to this tragical scene are from my last information as follows:

I had been informed that my guard boats had been in the practice of landing in the night at the house of the deceased, which is a kind of tavern. In order to know an officer who should thus neglect his duty, I sent Lieut. Drury, after the guard boats had gone out, to endeavour to discover what boat was in the habit of landing.

He went to the house of the deceased and as appears, the better to effect his object, wished to pass for an enemy boat, though it appears the disguise did not fully succeed for one said they were Americans, another they were Englishmen. The deceased it appears was of the latter opinion and, entering through a back door, charged furiously on Mr. Drury, asking him to surrender.

Mr. Drury knocked the musket one side. At this instant, seeing his men preparing to fire, it seems he endeavoured to prevent them. But the men, seeing their officer charged upon and another beyond who charged, also with a musket, fired —which took fatal effect.

It is probable the men were doubtful whether they were assailed by friends or foes, although within the United States. Being near the line, it might be supposed they were enemies and concealed in the house for the purpose of taking a guard which might land there.

Mr. Drury has imprudently gone away, supposedly to Washington. His intention is said to be, by his friends in the wardroom, not to avoid a just and impartial trial; it is said by some citizens that he would not get such a trial in the place where the act was committed.

The men concerned in this affair are demanded by the civil authority. They are charged with willful murder, and will be turned over to that authority.

I should have made this affair known to you before, but it was in so confused a state that I deferred it until as clear a statement could be given as in my power.

Calling his clerk in, the Commodore gave Sloane the letter to send off at once and also handed him the August 22nd notes he'd kept on his desk from Captain Peter Fisher, commanding British gunboats lurking off Point au Feu and Windmill Point.

The ship had chased Fisher, who ran for safety and then countered with an offer, sent under a truce, to put his squadron's gunboats against the American's in a chivalric joust. The Commodore's turndown had gone back wrapped in sentiments of high respect:

Taking into account the connection between the land and naval operations at this time on this Lake, however, my government could not forgive an imprudence individually my own.

"What kind of war does that pipesqueak think we're fighting?" he demanded rhetorically. "File these please, Jim, under 'P'—for *pfui!*"

Word from General Macomb advised the Commodore that Sir (Alex underscored the title) George Prevost, finding he could not prevail on the citizens of Champlain to take sides with him against their own government, had impressed all wagons and teams he could lay hands on to carry his troops' baggage and military stores.

And that same September 3rd evening at Plattsburg, the Commodore brought William Jones up to date:

I have the honor to acquaint you with the arrival of the Squadron at this place. As an attack on this place is threatened by a land movement of the enemy, and their fleet evincing no immediate signs of coming out, Brigr. Genl. Macomb and myself considered this movement of our vessels proper and necessary.

The enemy say, when their ship is finished, (which will be in a few days), they will come out, and it is supposed Plattsburg will be attacked by land and water at the same time, and that their army at Champlain is waiting only for their fleet.

5

From Burlington in mid-morning of Sunday, September 4th, Commodore Macdonough's gig brought to *Saratoga* Midshipman Bellamy, Chaplain Fred Watrous of the Army, and a vacationing Yale student named Joseph H. Dulles of Philadelphia, whose letter of introduction from a Burlington friend to the Commodore had elicited an invitation to Sunday dinner with the fleet. Beaming more than usual, if that were possible, Aze went immediately to *Saratoga*'s quarterdeck cabin.

The Commodore's first quick glance brought him to his feet with outstretched hand. "It must be a boy!" he exclaimed, gripping Aze's hand in congratulation. "How is Emily?"

"She's fine, sir," said Aze. "And so is Ann." His voice held a touch each of rejoicing and tenderness. "Do you mind, sir," he asked, shyly, "that we named the baby after Mrs. Macdonough?"

The Commodore turned abruptly away, to look out of the stern cabin windows until he could bring himself under control. When he turned back, he reached for the miniature on his desk. Then: "I hope your Ann turns out as lovely as mine," he said, and gave Aze the delicate painting. "Please take this for your daughter—from Mrs. Macdonough and me, with all our affection."

Before the boy could think up a reason for refusal, the Commodore asked, "May I have the honor of being her godfather?"

Speechless, Aze nodded, and went to spread the news.

The Commodore joined his Philadelphia visitor at noon, sitting with young Dulles on the flagship's quarterdeck with the ship's officers as Chaplain Watrous at the capstan performed divine services for nearly three hundred seamen who filled the gundeck from midships to bow. When Dulles, agog with the novelty of life on board a man-of-war, expressed surprise that the sailors showed such marked attention to the services, the Commodore smiled wryly.

"They behave very well indeed," he agreed. Recalling various punishments meted out before the mast over the past two years, he added: "Not altogether from pious feelings."

Like a benign host, and sure that Eleazer Williams would eventually hear of his good works, he played up to his guest's continuing interest in the Navy's religious activities. He asked the chaplain to deliver the dinner blessing, dutifully bowing his head with Stephen Cassin and other invited officers from *Ticonderoga*. During dinner he gave his much-practiced Sunday conversation piece for visiting celebrities, describing how the Epistle of St. James fitted the sailor's mind, with such quotations as "He that wavereth is like a wave of the sea driven with the wind" and "Behold the ships, though so great, are turned about with a very small helm."

With completion of dessert (had Cookie's wife made the unusually tasty Indian pudding?), the Commodore called for attention before retiring from the table, and said:

"The Commander of the Army has just informed me, gentlemen, that he will signal the advance of the British forces by two guns. You will act accordingly."

Inspecting *Eagle* Monday morning, the Commodore came on Joseph Smith, with palm and needle industriously helping to fit the brig's sails. The Lieutenant looked very tired and very happy.

"We've worked early and late every day since I came on

board," he said, "fitting her rigging, sir. She's tolerably well-fitted out now, but we're short of men to work the guns." He hesitated. "Sir, I have Commander Henley's permission to ask you to let us have some of the flagship's crew."

The Commodore decided quickly. "How many?"

"Sixty."

"You can have forty," said the Commodore. "I'll have to appeal again to General Macomb for soldiers to replace them, but you certainly can use a few trained gunners." He added: "I'll call for volunteers, and you can pick twenty. The other twenty, I'll assign."

He watched with amusement the Lieutenant's effort to hide his awareness that the Commodore would select *Saratoga*'s least desirable men.

"We still won't have enough gunners," Smith managed, while he scanned the Commodore's face to determine if he could push his point. "May I have permission to go on shore to see if I can get some soldiers to help us out?"

The Lieutenant's persistence in going after his brig's needs pleased the Commodore. "I'll give you a note to General Macomb," he said.

"Thank you, sir," replied the Lieutenant. Again he hesitated, then added: "And thank you for naming the brig after our old *Eagle*."

Conferring with Generals Macomb and Mooers that afternoon at the Army installation, the Commodore sat back for the fireworks when Lieutenant Smith arrived with his note. Macomb scanned it quickly.

"General Izard told me, Lieutenant," he fired at the waiting youth, "that the curse of leading the Army on Lake Champlain lay not in enemy bullets but in Navy billets-doux—asking for soldiers to run your boats! Please pay my respects to Commodore Macdonough, the second time today. Request denied."

In the next minute the Commodore swelled with pride at

the resourcefulness of his young officer and, through him, at the spirit activating every officer in the fleet. At attention, neither brash nor intimidated, Joseph Smith spoke up.

"Well, General," he asked, "haven't you a lot of prisoners you'd like to be rid of?" [1]

Macomb's broadening grin threatened to force his ears back, and General Mooers' merry peal of laughter echoed through headquarters.

An hour later, the Commodore saw the Army's prisoners file by, chains knocked off their legs, faces and clothes covered with the red loam of trenches they had been digging. A hard-looking lot. But Smith would scrub them, cut their hair, trim their beards, exchange their rags for pursers' clothing, and make gunners of them if he had to exercise them all night every night. The Commodore watched as the Lieutenant marched intently along behind the detail.

Opposite the window, the Lieutenant caught sight of the Commodore. Straightening, he saluted sharply and, gravely, winked.

The Commodore turned back to the immediate business at hand—defense of Plattsburg whose senior citizens, women and children had packed up and fled for safety at Macomb's urging, leaving their able-bodied menfolk behind to fight with General Mooers and the militia. Though these Plattsburg volunteers included many boys, Mooers had received them with tremendous personal satisfaction.

"They're sons of boys who fought with me in the Revolution," he declared. "They'll do fine!"

Macomb's shrewd and aggressive use of such meager forces increased the Commodore's ever-growing respect for the General's cheerful, energetic stand in the face of the British invasion. Alex's ready assumption that, joined with him, he had brave and patriotic Army, Navy and militia officers, men of intelligence who could learn quickly, gave the Commodore renewed assurance that he had linked his fortunes with those of a generous and big-hearted man, singularly free of envy and jealousy. Alex Macomb had no superciliousness toward irregular troops, militia and volunteers supplied with arms only by themselves, that lesser generals scorned. He both commanded and led.

On an elevated ridge behind the Saranac River, the General had established a strong position to defend Plattsburg. On each side of Fort Moreau, named for one of Napoleon's generals, he had erected another fort, naming each after American northern frontier generals his soldiers revered—Jacob Brown and Winfield Scott. To stimulate officers and men to their utmost, he divided them into detachments for each fort and for two additional blockhouses, and declared in orders that each detachment comprised the garrison of its own fort, bound to defend it to the end; the better they worked to make the defenses effective, the better their protection.

With breastworks well furnished with artillery, his flanks rested on the Lake. Behind him, on the Lake, lay the fleet. Here, when the time came, Macomb would stand.

Before that, as he told General Mooers and the Commodore, he had to train the militia and the volunteers. His methods held the basic elements of his genius—simplicity and function. General Mooers would take his 700 militia with 250 regulars under Major John E. Wool and go north on the Beekmantown road to skirmish with the advancing enemy and to obstruct the road with fallen trees, thus giving his men experience in fighting alongside veterans while they delayed the enemy's advance and provided time to complete Plattsburg's defenses.

To hinder Prevost's second column, advancing along Dead Creek road which circled Plattsburg Bay from the north, Macomb would send troops and count on the fleet to support them with gunfire at the beach.

The General and the Commodore concurred that their hope of turning the British back lay almost entirely in the character of the man leading the invading forces. Sir George

Prevost appeared to have unhesitating confidence that he could march his army anywhere along Lake Champlain. Had he any doubts that he could take Plattsburg, he could have come down the Vermont shore from Canada, forcing the Army and Navy to leave their present positions. He also gave every evidence of an unwillingness to attack without the British fleet; otherwise he could have marched on Plattsburg days earlier.

Apparently Prevost intended to play it very safe. Which gave Macomb time to dig in strongly; it also gave the young and aggressive American commanders time to come up with fresh ways to combat the old and, perhaps, timid British leader.

Eleazer Williams and his scouts made almost hourly reports. To the Commodore they brought news of a new captain, George Downie, coming from Lake Ontario to take over frigate *Confiance* and the British squadron as senior on Champlain to Captain Pring of brig *Linnet*. This in spite of Downie's unfamiliarity with the Lake and strategic conditions.

The rangers also announced that Downie, at this stage dependent for crew on drafts from ships in the St. Lawrence, had grudgingly taken a detachment of soldiers aboard; that *Confiance* still had to be rigged, equipped, her guns mounted, and her powder got into her; and that she would have to be dragged out of the channel where she lay into the Lake, which would take two whole days, though riggers and fitters could work on her under way.

Obviously, Prevost had impatiently moved his troops too soon in his determination to march on New York City before winter caught him in mid-state. Had the Commodore's capture of the masts intended for the frigate decidedly disrupted the general's time schedule? What then might further increase Prevost's impatience, intensify his nervous tension, perhaps disturb, even warp, his judgment?

With word that Vermont volunteers had begun to trickle

into Plattsburg, the Commodore broached to Alex Macomb and Lazare Williams an idea for harassing Prevost at the most appropriate moment.

"Let's give him a dose of the same medicine Brock gave Hull before he surrendered," the Commodore suggested. "You told us, Lazare, how Brock let Hull intercept a faked message that frightened him with news of Indians en route to Brock's support. Why don't we let Prevost capture a letter to General Macomb announcing twenty thousand Vermont and New Hampshire troops racing to *his* support?"

They agreed it might help, at a psychological moment, and Aze Bellamy went forthwith to Waterbury to request Mercy Cobb, as a patriotic woman unknown to the British, to stand by at Betsy Boyd's house in Burlington ready to carry a prepared letter whenever Eleazer Williams deemed the time right for it to fall into Prevost's hands.[2]

6

On Tuesday, September 6th, Macomb's two guns signaled Prevost's advance on Plattsburg.

And while General Mooers, his militia, and Major Wool's infantry slowly fell back along the Beekmantown road to destroy the upper bridge over the Saranac, Commodore Macdonough ordered his gunboats to the head of Cumberland Bay at 10 A.M. to harry the enemy's second column approaching over Dead Creek road.

For two hours, against heavy British artillery fire from screened positions in the woods behind the beach, the galleys laid a galling fire on the shore road. But by noon a gusty wind and menacing seas made accurate fire impossible, and Midshipman Silas Duncan went in the gig with instructions for Lieutenant Robbins in gunboat *Allen* to withdraw his squadron from action.

When the galleys returned from the beach, seamen from *Allen* carried Midshipman Duncan to the ship's cockpit where Dr. Briggs amputated his mangled right arm. *Allen* had also lost one seaman killed and three soldiers injured.

Lieutenant Robbins reported British casualties in the hundreds, and Sailing Master Keteltas in *Burrows,* having blown close inshore under the British guns only to work his galley safely out of jeopardy, confirmed Robbins' report of American damage to the invading British second column.

From Macomb came advices that the lower bridge across the Saranac also had been destroyed, so that, except for a difficult ford west of the demolished Beekmantown road bridge, the British had no way to cross the river. And Macomb's fifteen hundred troops, with Mooers' seven hundred militia, had ensconced themselves safely at the forts south of the Saranac.

Prevost camped on a ridge one mile north of the river, apparently digging himself in to wait for the British fleet.

"His second big mistake," Alex's message optimistically pointed out.

As the Commodore only too well appreciated, Prevost at this moment could take Macomb's paltry defenses within the hour. Too, Prevost still could circle Plattsburg and continue south unmolested. But his British doggedness apparently held him prisoner to a rigid plan. Given a few days, Alex could make Prevost's grimly gripped task more difficult, for Vermont volunteers now poured into Plattsburg.

A ranger reached *Saratoga* with news that Captain Pring in *Linnet*, with *Chubb* and *Finch* and twelve gunboats, had moved up the Lake to Isle la Motte, abreast of the Little Chazy, where on Sunday they had erected a battery of three long eighteen-pounders to cover the landing of supplies for Prevost's troops. There, the Commodore now felt confident from Prevost's halt outside Plattsburg, the British fleet would remain until *Confiance* joined them.

Only then would they move against the American fleet; and Prevost against Macomb.

Like the General, the Commodore took advantage of every minute granted him before coming to grips with the enemy.

Recent recruits from the several rendezvous got intensive training at the vessels' guns. Additional soldiers, sent unasked by General Macomb in frequent batches "to maneuver your squadron and keep the Lake," likewise spent long, hard hours drilling at the galleys' oars; and in the vessels' tops where, as acting marines, they could use their muskets to pick officers and gunners off the British decks.

All told, the American fleet's well-drilled complement included more than a thousand officers and men. A far cry from the lieutenant, the midshipman, the master's mate, and the handful of untrained seamen the Commodore had found on the Lake station two years ago! [1]

What with shifting guns from one vessel to another as the exigencies of building required and circumstances dictated (you never knew what size cannons might arrive from New York or Boston!), the Commodore's armament inventory for each ship did not jibe with earlier reports to the Navy Office. But he took considerable encouragement from the comparative over-all tabulation of guns he now drew up for the two fleets:

United States		British	
Saratoga	26 guns	*Confiance*	37 guns
Eagle	20 "	*Linnet*	16 "
Ticonderoga	17 "	*Chubb*	11 "
President	10 "	*Finch*	11 "
Preble	7 "	Galleys	16 "
Montgomery	6 "		
Galleys	16 "		
Totals	102 guns		91 guns

But immediately his advantage went by the board. For a blustery storm swept the Lake on Wednesday and carried *President,* ferrying a cargo of volunteers from Burlington, ashore twenty miles above Plattsburg. While the Vermont soldiers marched to join Macomb, *President*'s frustrated crew toiled irately to repair the beached sloop.

The comparative armament count now stood: United States ninety-two guns, British ninety-one.

Thursday and Friday saw volunteers from Vermont (including Argalus Cobb and Lawyer Rich from Waterbury) swarm ashore from every boat they could sail or row, escorted by *Montgomery,* herself loaded to the gunwales. Despite Governor Chittenden's refusal to authorize the militia for service outside the state, these volunteers rushed to Plattsburg's defense under General Samuel Strong, the Commodore's old friend and Mayor of Vergennes. They came from central and eastern Vermont as well as from the Lake shore, fathers and sons, Revolution veterans in their old uniforms and boys too young for military service; even all hands from Ann's favorite newspaper in Burlington; and from St. Albans, that hotbed of smuggling—more than two thousand strong, bless their unfathomable Vermont hearts!

At sunset Friday the American soldiers watched the British as they busily erected a battery opposite Fort Brown. And that night, at a council of war with Generals Macomb, Mooers, and Strong, and Peter Sailly, the Commodore gave Plattsburg's defenders the news relayed earlier that day by Eleazer Williams: *Confiance,* almost twice *Saratoga's* tonnage, with the gundeck of a heavy frigate and a furnace for heating shot, had joined the British fleet off Isle la Motte.

As the menace to Plattsburg built up, American fighting blood flowed hotter. To the Commodore it seemed that every minute's delay in the British attack boosted the unvoiced determination of New York's stubborn militia and Vermont's angry volunteers to throw back Prevost's confident hordes. Macomb's regulars, practically a remnant of an army, had come to a full boil. In the person of Captain George McGlossin of the 15th regiment, they appeared before the General at the council of war.

A beardless Scotsman, McGlossin asked Macomb for permission to lead fifty men against Prevost's three hundred building the battery opposite Fort Brown.

Macomb asked, practically: "What for?"

The little Captain, equally practical, said: "To spike the battery's guns."

"You're just up out of sickbed," said Macomb. "What makes you think you can get away with this?"

McGlossin saluted. "Thank you, sir," he said, and vanished.

Before the Commodore returned to his flagship, Captain

McGlossin reported back, wet, mud-stained, red-eyed with fatigue. He had crossed the Saranac halfway between Fort Brown and the upper bridge. From the foot of the battery hill, half of his fifty men had circled to the rear of the battery by a circuitous route while he waited with the other half. Then, said the disheveled Captain:

"I shouted 'Charge, men! Charge front and rear!' And we yelled and rushed forward." The Captain stopped, and chuckled.

"Yea?" said General Macomb.

"Well, sir," said McGlossin, "the British thought we'd overwhelmed them. They fled. And we took the works, and spiked the guns, and came back. That's all, sir. Except we didn't lose a man."

As the Commodore and the Generals smiled at the little Scotsman's bare recital, McGlossin chuckled again, and added: "We think General Prevost must be mortified, sir."

The Commodore guffawed.

Returning to the flagship in Saturday morning's early hours, his gig was all but swamped in the wake of another northwestern that had swept Plattsburg Bay with rain and lightning.

As the scudding clouds that hid the moon occasionally thinned, to filter a pale and ghostly glare down on the tossing American fleet, the Commodore knew that the moment of action had arrived. To the council of war just before it broke up, an Eleazer Williams scout had brought word that Commander Downie of the British fleet had received a series of letters from Prevost, each letter more insulting than its predecessors, all blaming Downie for delaying the attack. Under such pressure, Williams had indicated, Downie might move soon, too soon.

Macomb's satisfaction had equaled the Commodore's.

"As you said, Tom, the other fellow can make mistakes, too!"

7

From Isle la Motte, where the British warships lay, eager and adventurous boys sailed into Plattsburg Bay Saturday morning with reports that riggers and gunners still worked feverishly to get the British frigate ready. And a light southerly head wind made it practically impossible for Captain Downie to bring his fleet up from the island. The Commodore could visualize General Prevost, red-faced, biting his nails over news of this additional delay.

Having met Friday on board the flagship and again reviewed the Commodore's plans to entice over-anxious Downie into attacking inside Plattsburg Bay, the American fleet commanders had lined up their four ships and ten galleys. Waiting to receive the enemy, they went about combat details.[1]

As he inspected each vessel with Executive Officer John Stansbury Saturday morning, the Commodore restudied his battle line. At the line's northern end lay *Eagle*, almost equidistant from the Plattsburg forts and the shore of Cumberland Head which jutted into the Lake in a huge arm bending to form Plattsburg Bay. Second, lay *Saratoga;* third, *Ticonderoga. Preble* brought up the southernmost end of the line, a mile and a half off Crab Island where General Macomb had planted a battery of two twelve-pounders served by Army invalids under Dr. James Mann, Plattsburg Hospital surgeon. *Montgomery* would take her berth astern of *Preble*.

This formation effectively barred any approach to Plattsburg. To break the line, the enemy first would have to bring its attacking vessels, whose shallow drafts and flat bottoms made them slow on the wind, up the Lake with a northerly following wind. Downie then must round the shoals off Cumberland Head and come against the American line close-hauled. Not only would this prove slow going, but almost immediately he would run into light and fitful air in the lee of the Head. Despite these disadvantages, however, Downie would not hold up his attack, the Commodore felt certain, to wait outside the bay for a changing, favorable, wind; not with Prevost breathing fire down his neck!

The Commodore went over *Eagle* carefully with Lieutenants Henley and Smith. Like the three other ships, it lay to its bow anchor; hawsers made fast to the anchor cable came aft to each quarter. With these springs, the sailing masters and their men could sway the brig to one side or the other to better her firing position.

Henley also had dropped a kedge anchor broad off each bow, with hawsers carried to *Eagle*'s quarters. When the present south wind swung into the north and Downie came up the Lake for battle, the brig would swing to the bow anchor with its springs, and her seamen would shift these kedge hawsers to the opposite quarters. Finally, they would carry a stern anchor out. During battle then, with time and good organization—and without setting sail—the sailing master could wind the brig entirely around, to give *Eagle*'s guns great mobility.

The brig already had made preliminary preparations for action. Her crew had cleared decks for passage of ammunition, secured unobstructed areas of fire for all guns, bent topsails, sent down light yards and masts, swiftered in all main and mizzen rigging to diminish danger of fouling gun screws, griped and secured all davit boats and placed sails and awnings around them to check flight of splinters, prepared a spare tiller, thrown overboard all turpentine and varnish and dryers, prepared the surgeon's cockpit, and so on. Left to do: form barricades and shelters with wetted-down hammocks and furled sails and awnings as splinter screens, close below-decks

"Macdonough availed himself of all these....."

SPRINGS

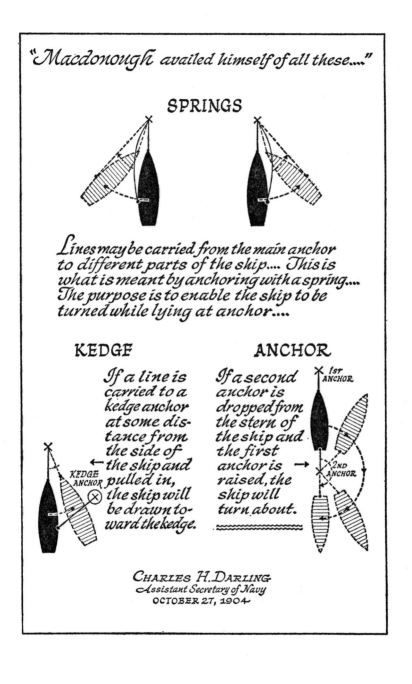

Lines may be carried from the main anchor to different parts of the ship.... This is what is meant by anchoring with a spring.... The purpose is to enable the ship to be turned while lying at anchor....

KEDGE

If a line is carried to a kedge anchor at some distance from the side of the ship and pulled in, the ship will be drawn toward the kedge.

KEDGE ANCHOR

ANCHOR

If a second anchor is dropped from the stern of the ship and the first anchor is raised, the ship will turn about.

1ST ANCHOR

2ND ANCHOR

CHARLES H. DARLING
Assistant Secretary of Navy
OCTOBER 27, 1904

portholes, fill gun tubs and magazine butts and buckets in the tops with fresh water, rig cots and chairs for lowering wounded below, and so on.

"You're in fine shape, Bob," said the Commodore. "I count on you." He then asked, "Who brought that woman aboard—the one we just saw below?"

Henley explained: "Joseph Smith prevailed on a half dozen Army musicians to carry powder and cartridges for us," he said. "They're noncombatants as far as the Army's concerned, but they want to fight. One brought his wife, who insists it's her fight, too. Don't worry, Tom. I'll station her near the magazine, as far from danger as possible."

Lieutenant Cassin on *Ticonderoga,* lying astern of *Saratoga,* made a forthright request for a lieutenant—"John Stansbury preferred." The wrinkles on Cassin's forehead seemed to have set permanently, though his expression in general mirrored the inner ease of a man sure of his ability to cope with job difficulties. "Tom," he said, "you don't need an exec as much as I'll need a good fighter."

The Commodore caught his young executive aide's keenly eager look at the opportunity to join Cassin for fighting duty, and said, "I'll send him over before noon."

On *Preble,* lining up so small with her seven guns behind the brig, the ship, and the schooner, Lieutenant Budd greeted the Commodore with thirty crew members smartly mustered for inspection.

"What we lack in size, Tom, we make up in seamanship," Budd assured the Commodore under his breath. "My sailing master, Rogers Carter, and my bosun, Joe Rose, have a supersaturated solution of salt water in their veins."

Scrutinizing the crew, many of them bearded veterans in striped shirts and hard glazed hats, the Commodore recognized the signs of experience.

Returning to the flagship in the gig, he pointed to *Ticonderoga*'s stern where a dozen fishermen dangled lines overboard, as placid as though they expected the next day to bring them anything but battle, and said to Stansbury: "You might ask Steve Cassin whether he can send me a pike perch or a black bass for tonight's supper. A pickerel if he can. But no suckers."

Stopping the gig as it neared *Saratoga,* he watched with amusement while some of the topboys, obviously to win his attention but giving no sign that they saw him, exuberantly climbed the flagship's ratlines nearly naked. Shouting to each other, they jumped and dived into the cold bay from the ends of the foremast yardarms, to splash awkwardly back to the ship's side and clamber shiveringly up a Jacob's ladder to the deck.

The Commodore felt suddenly old.

On his desk he found waiting for him a letter from Middletown, and he took time to read it thoroughly.

Ann felt wonderful . . . the baby kicked at the most inopportune moments . . . the Doctor expected him to arrive in about six weeks . . . wouldn't Thomas Nathaniel, for his father and his grandfather, suit him as a name? . . . the family kept well . . . Grandfather Denning had paid them a visit and wanted to be remembered . . . and she sent all her love to her dear, dear husband. . . .

The homely family letter warmed him. And he thanked his stars he'd had the good sense to keep from Ann any inkling of the imminence of the British attack.

The recollection of his wife took him forward, alone. In the galley, Cookie's woman sat peeling potatoes. How had Cookie described her? . . . oh, yes—"her head looks like it'd worn out two bodies." But her eyes held much serenity as she looked up at the Commodore.

"I'll send you ashore this evening," he told her.

She shook her head vigorously, so that her yellowed white hair tumbled down over her eyes and timeworn cheeks.

"I'm staying, Captain." She stated it as a long-accepted fact.

A slender Negro woman had come into the galley, wife of

the West Indian gunner Peter Joe, so thin that Joe Barron, in typical Vermontese, had declared she'd "only go twice around a toothpick and halfway back." When had she crossed from Burlington?

"Me, I stay, too!" she declared.

What was her name? Fanny, Freda, Phebe.

He looked at both women, thinking of the musician's wife on *Eagle* and thinking also of Ann. What would he do if Ann were here, demanding to stay on board during the battle?

"My husband says I can help him fight." (So Cookie *had* married her.)

"Me, I stay, too," Phebe repeated.

The Commodore left the galley in the face of their determination to stand at the side of their men.

Watching *Saratoga*'s crew exercise the big guns through the afternoon, the Commodore took tremendous satisfaction in the way Raymond Perry had taught the divisions to handle their long twenty-four-pounders and their thirty-two- and forty-two-pound carronades. Come the moment, he made up his mind, he'd take at least one personal shot at Downie's *Confiance* with his favorite long gun in the starboard quarter-deck battery!

The gun captains' commands, obeyed sharply by loaders, shellmen, handspikemen, tacklemen, spongers, and powder-men, filled the deck. Each gun crew moved fast and sure to the successive "cast loose and provide," "run," "serve vent and sponge," "load," "prime," "point," "ready-fire!" and "secure."

From casting loose of the lanyards which enabled the first loader, aided by the first sponger, to remove the upper half of the port and let down the lower half, each man knew his duty. Handspikemen raised and lowered the gun's breech so that the second gun captain could force the quoin (wedge) between breech and carriage at the proper point of elevation; tacklemen trained the gun laterally; the gun captain touched a quick-match to the powder-filled vent to fire the gun. And by moving from station to station around the gun "with the sun," each man had learned the duties of all others. In an emergency, every gunner could carry out any job.

Exercises completed, the crews secured the loaded guns and closed the ports. The guns would be ready for action in three minutes from the beat of drum calling to quarters.

Dr. Briggs took this moment to notify the Commodore that Lieutenant Raymond Perry, stricken with something the surgeon could not immediately diagnose, exhibited great pain and must join the hospital invalids on Crab Island where Dr. Mann could keep a close watch over him.

Containing his shock at the loss of his excellent first lieutenant, on top of sending Stansbury to *Ticonderoga,* the Commodore called for Lieutenant Peter Gamble.

"Take over at once for Lieutenant Perry as first lieutenant," said the Commodore.

"Yes, sir," said the stocky, solid Gamble. "Thank you, sir." Whatever his inner excitement, he accepted his surprise promotion into Perry's shoes with outward imperturbability.

Another young officer who knew his job!

After supper, of tasty pike, the Commodore took the gig ashore with Lieutenant Gamble as the watchman clanged eight brassy strokes on *Saratoga*'s foremast bell. From the foredeck came shrill crows, and the Commodore knew that Cookie's chickens had sprung into action for the crew's entertainment and relaxation.

"Cookie's new red cockerel already looks like fleet champion," said young Gamble by way of conversation. "He's become very popular. If they had any way to arrange it, sir, I'm sure every man on the ship would bet six months' pay on Oscar to beat the best cocks in the whole British navy."

"Where does this new champion come from?" asked the Commodore.

Gamble looked the other way, to hide his embarrassment.

"Cookie says he . . . er, found Oscar on shore near one of the Army barracks, apparently lost . . . he says, sir."

At Fort Moreau, General Macomb brought the Commodore up to the minute. Prevost had succeeded in setting up eight batteries on the Saranac's opposite shore, for howitzers, mortars, shells, and rockets, one on the beach north of the river's mouth and another on the beach at the head of the bay to keep off the fleet's galleys.

"How can I help you most?" asked the Commodore.

Macomb's reply left no doubt. "Keep *Montgomery* ferrying Vermont volunteers across the Lake," he said. "I need every man of them I can get."

A nice decision indeed! Alex had provided the fleet with upwards of three hundred badly needed hands to row the galleys, to serve as marines on the ships, and even to man some of the guns. But could the Commodore now help Alex get replacements if to do that meant weakening the fleet's fire power by six guns?

An old soldier angrily interrupted the Commodore's cogitation. "I never thought," he said, "that I'd see the disgraceful day when a governor of Vermont would stand on the shores of the Lake discouraging valiant freemen from going to the assistance of their New York brothers. At a time when the enemy threatens a powerful invasion of our frontier towns with the avowed intention of laying them in ruins, he tells us we'll be killed if we cross the Lake."

"Commodore Macdonough, this is Captain David Perry," said Macomb. "He's just arrived with Vermont friends and neighbors to help us."

The wrathful patriarch nodded briefly and went on: "I've lived to see four wars in our country," he said, "and this one's been the hardest to win, what with the enmity toward the general government of politically minded people who don't think we have cause to fight a country that's taken hundreds of our vessels, imprisoned thousands of our citizens, and sent Indians to massacre our defenseless inhabitants.

"I just hope my grandchildren, and their grandchildren—and theirs—never forget there was once a time when party spirit raged to such an extent that it threatened to destroy those liberties that I had some small share in establishing."

"What did you tell Chittenden," the Commodore asked this patriotic counterpart of Grandfather Denning, "when he said you'd be killed if you came to help us?"

The old man drew himself up. "Commodore," he said, "I told him exactly what Pompey told his men in Africa fourteen hundred years ago, after he'd loaded a ship with corn for hungry Rome and his men refused to sail for home in a storm. I said, 'Governor, there's a necessity upon us to sail. There's no necessity upon us to live!' And we came over on your sloop, sir."

When he bade farewell to Peter Sailly and Eleazer Williams late that night, the Commodore replied to Macomb's earlier request: "Get *Montgomery* back to me before Downie arrives," he said, "if you can, Alex."

Returning to the gig, the Commodore and Gamble heard a boy breathlessly telling an Army sentry on the beach: "The officers at my father's house are sure they're going to capture Plattsburg tomorrow. They laid boards on barrels for a table on our front lawn, with a linen cloth and china and glass and silver and wine and rum they'd looted, and had themselves a banquet to celebrate." [2]

The sentry patted the boy's shoulder. "Row on back home, lad," he said, "and tell them British we ain't that easy."

As the gig moved through the moonlight, the wind abruptly shifted from south to north. Boarding *Saratoga,* the Commodore found Sailing Master Brum with all hands easing off the kedge hawsers to shift them to their new positions, hanging in bights under water, when the ship finally swung her bow into the wind.

"This air's what we've waited for, sir," said the knowing Lake skipper. "I think she'll hold steady."

"Then carry the stern anchor out," said the Commodore.

Turning to Gamble, he said: "Signal the other vessels to do the same."

He asked for intelligence from the guard boats.

"They hear the noise of riggers still at work on the frigate," reported the O.D. "But the enemy give every sign of moving up tomorrow morning, sir."

The Commodore nodded his head to his officers. "I think we're ready," he said. "A good night to you all."

His face and his voice registered confidence to his men. But his churning mind, as he went alone to his cabin, would not let sleep come.

Without *Montgomery* to fight with the American fleet next morning, the comparative armaments stood: British ninety-one guns, United States only eighty-six.

$$8$$

Sunday, September 11th, 1814, dawned clear and cloudless over Lake Champlain. Along her quiet shores gulls soared, screaming harsh and loud at the wooded mountains taking on their red and gold autumnal foliage. On just such a day, almost exactly two years ago the Commodore recalled, Lieutenant Thomas Macdonough had first come to the Lake.

Outside Cumberland Head British flagship *Confiance* hove to, having used the night's favoring wind to lead the enemy squadron up from Isle la Motte, her topsails rising new and white over the Head.

To *Saratoga*, a messenger brought news of a gig rowed close to Plattsburg Bay with a British officer who examined the American fleet's disposition and put back to the frigate. That would be Captain Downie.

At 7 A.M. Downie's fleet stood for Plattsburg Bay. Bending to their oars, the Cumberland Head guard boat crew drove toward their own fleet with signals flying.

The American vessels beat to quarters and prepared for action.

On *Saratoga's* quarterdeck at 8 A.M., with his officers in their best uniforms, the Commodore watched the British sail into sight at a distance of six miles. His heart pounded. Around his spyglass, his hand felt moist, clammy. He had waited a long time for this moment.

He controlled his voice. "Midshipman Bellamy," he requested softly, "will you have the kindness to make the agreed signal?"

Original signal officer of the Lake Champlain squadron, Aze proudly sent the Commodore's message flags up to *Saratoga*'s masthead for all the fleet to see:

IMPRESSED SEAMEN CALL ON EVERY MAN TO DO HIS DUTY.

Solemnly then, while the crew looked on from their stations, the Commodore read to his officers the ancient church prayer for those about to engage in battle on the sea. ". . . stir up Thy strength, O Lord, and come and help us, for Thou givest not always the battle to the strong, but canst save by many or by few . . . through Jesus Christ, our Lord."

Lieutenant Gamble reported final preparations completed. The flagship stood ready; splinter screens rigged, pumps in order, and chief caulker provided with hemp plugs, sheet lead, nails, and slings for lowering men overside to close shot holes and pound fresh caulking into *Saratoga*'s hull.

Forty yards inshore from the line of ships stood the squadron's ten gunboats, two off *Eagle*'s larboard bow, two between the brig and *Saratoga*, three between the flagship and *Ticonderoga*, three between the schooner and *Preble*. Kept in position by their sweeps, their guns could fire a continuous barrage of twelve-, eighteen-, and twenty-four-pound balls between the vessels when the enemy came up.

It took the British another hour to round Cumberland Head and move in for battle.

A sloop came first, filled with civilians and, as the Commodore's glass revealed, many women. Spectators, so sure of British victory that they dared enter the bay! The shores, too, as far as he could see were lined with spectators, but Americans all. Keeping well to leeward, the sloop stood down toward Crab Island.

First of the fighting ships around the Head came *Finch* (once American sloop *Growler*), followed by *Confiance, Linnet,* and *Chubb* (Lieutenant Sidney Smith's former *Eagle*).

Hauling up to the wind in a line abreast, formidable, they

lay to for their lateen-rigged galleys to sail up and join them. The Commodore got his first look at *Confiance*.

Eleazer Williams' rangers had described her accurately—enormous, in a class with ocean-going *Constellation*. She carried the gundeck of a heavy frigate, a spacious topgallant forecastle on which she mounted four heavy carronades and a long twenty-four-pounder on a circle, and a poop deck mounting two heavy carronades. *Confiance* could fire a seventeen-gun broadside of 432 pounds; *Saratoga's* broadside metal weighed 414 pounds.

Passing to leeward of their ships, the British gunboats formed a line abreast. At 9 A.M. the quick beat of their drums calling to quarters wafted across the bay, and ships and galleys, close-hauled on the starboard tack, moved en masse against the American squadron.

The Commodore watched warily.

Leading, *Chubb* stood well to windward of *Eagle*, at the head of the American line. *Linnet's* course would bring her, too, on *Eagle's* bow.

Confiance advanced, like a great dog intent on making short work of a small opponent, laying her course to fetch a position ahead of *Saratoga;* far enough ahead to concentrate her fire power on the American, with the American unable perhaps to bring her full broadside to bear.

Finch and the British gunboats stood for *Ticonderoga* and *Preble*.

The enemy strategy came clear. In the van, *Chubb* and *Linnet* aimed to take on *Eagle* while the British flagship set about subduing the American flagship; in the rear, *Finch* and the gunboats sought to reduce *Ticonderoga* and *Preble*.

His heart pounding again, the Commodore patiently waited. The enemy had no sea room to turn his line; nor could they double it, because of the shoal off Crab Island. If they continued to stand in, bows on, he could spring his ships to meet them. If they anchored, they must anchor within reach of his carronades, since he had not left them enough water between

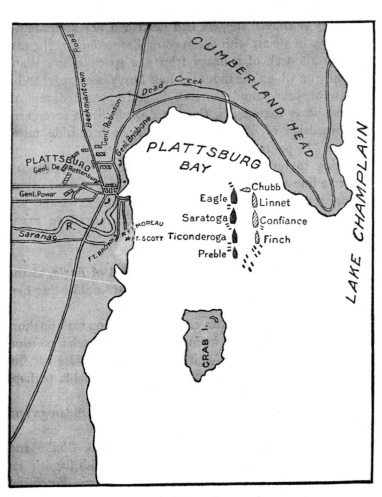

Battle of Lake Champlain

his line and Cumberland Head to stay out of range. Come on, and be damned!

The American sailing masters already had set about springing their vessels to bear broadside on the oncoming squadron, and the Commodore knew that the quiet, before-battle expectation that filled *Saratoga* also filled the other ships as they awaited the flagship's signal to open fire.

While the enemy inched closer, the Commodore continued to contain his impatience. A few minutes more—to bring them within effective range. A few yards more. . . .

Four guns blasted in rapid succession. Fire flashed and black smoke almost enveloped *Eagle*. Bob Henley! Ignoring orders to wait, he had opened fire—short! The Commodore's fingers clenched tight around his glass. He—

Of a sudden *Saratoga's* forecastle resounded with raucous crowing as Cookie's chickens, startled by *Eagle's* booming broadside, flew hysterically out of the galley. Explosive shouts of laughter immediately followed as a single cockerel, perching on the foremast bell and flapping its wings, cried angrily. While the Commodore, officers and seamen stood entranced in spite of themselves, the furious bird flew into the starboard rigging and continued to flap and crow lustily.

"It's Oscar!" Lieutenant Gamble shouted above the uproar. "That's giving 'em what for, Champ!"

Like fog before a gale, tension departed *Saratoga* in laughter and the crew spontaneously cheered the bird's favorable augury.

Eagle's continuing fire now reached *Chubb;* the moment had come.

Bending over his favorite gun, the Commodore turned its breech-sight thumbscrew for the elevation needed to reach *Confiance,* lined it up with the fixed reinforce sight, and touched a match to the vent. As the twenty-four-pounder trumpeted the Commodore's deadly welcome to the enemy, Aze Bellamy had the "close action" flag run up, signaling the American fleet to open fire.

Even before *Saratoga*'s guns blasted their first broadside, a terrific roar swept the flagship's deck. For Captain White Youngs' soldiers, acting as marines in her tops, shouted down that the Commodore's greeting shot, landing near *Confiance*'s outer hawsehole, had torn the length of her deck and carried away her wheel.

At the same moment—9:30 A.M.—rockets, balls, and shells rose over the Saranac River, and Prevost began his attack on Macomb.

9

The Commodore kept in close touch with all parts of his ship, using Aze Bellamy and *Saratoga*'s many midshipmen for messengers. As action developed, he would also dispatch them with instructions to the other vessels. Glass to eye, he swept the bay.

The British advanced steadily and, he forced himself to admit, gallantly, in their attempt to achieve commanding positions. He also appreciated, however, how greatly they had underestimated his gunners' ability to annoy and how grievously they'd overestimated their own power to endure. *Confiance* could take little more punishment from *Saratoga*'s guns; their fire already had cut away the enemy flagship's larboard anchor and spare anchor in the larboard forechains, hanging by the stoppers ready to let go.

The wind lightened as the Commodore held his glass on the frigate to check the havoc of his guns, and he saw *Confiance* turn into the wind a quarter of a mile away and let go a kedge. But in bringing up with her starboard bower, the frigate fouled the kedge, which became useless.

While Downie strained to secure *Confiance,* letting her halyards run and hauling up her courses, *Chubb* and *Linnet* still stood in, farther to windward; until *Linnet* fired a broadside at *Saratoga* from a favorable position forward of *Eagle*'s beam and dropped anchor. *Chubb* kept under way, and *Finch,* with gunboat support, fetched up abreast of *Ticonderoga.*

The handsome manner in which Downie secured *Con-*

fiance, withholding his fire until he had performed his duty, prepared the Commodore in part for the sheet of fire that flashed him warning of the frigate's first broadside.

Directed at *Saratoga* principally from twenty-four-pound, double-shotted British guns leveled to pointblank range and coolly sighted, almost eight hundreds pounds of iron smashed into the American flagship with a blow that seemed to lift her out of the water. *Saratoga* writhed like a stricken whale. Splinters flew over her decks like matchwood. Shrieks and cries rose into the rigging as torn bodies fell beside their guns in pools of blood.

From the quarterdeck, the Commodore made out nearly half his ship's complement lying dead, wounded, stunned. He watched dazed men slowly pick themselves up. Then he counted forty wounded and dead by *Confiance*'s single broadside.

While midshipmen directed the lowering of wounded to the cockpit, the disposal of dead away from the guns, and the remounting where possible of dismounted cannons, the Commodore saw blood pour from the gundeck's scuppers like rain off a roof. And from the bow Midshipman Montgomery brought him word of Peter Gamble, killed without a scratch while sighting a gun, dead from the force of a split quoin driven against his chest.

The Commodore sent George Beale, the purser, to help Lieutenant Vallette with his own and Gamble's gun divisions. And until Downie might try to board *Saratoga,* he sent the acting marines down from the tops—where their muskets could not reach the enemy—to join Captain Youngs and his other soldiers wherever the guns could use them.

The flagship resumed her fire. The battle became a steady carronading.

Twenty minutes from the opening blast, *Eagle* threw a crippling broadside into *Chubb* at the head of the line. The

British sloop drifted down on *Saratoga,* in the line of fire between American ship and British frigate. From *Saratoga's* bow, George Beale put a shot into hapless *Chubb* and she immediately struck her colors.

"Take possession," the Commodore ordered Midshipman Platt.

From *Saratoga's* launch, Plattsburg's native son threw the prize a line. When he crossed the flagship's stern, towing the captured sloop to the mouth of the Saranac, he shouted: "Nearly half her crew killed and wounded, sir." Then: "Captain Downie reported dead on *Confiance."*

In the ensuing hour, the battle raged up and down the line. *Eagle* and *Saratoga* bore the full brunt of every gun *Confiance* and *Linnet* could bring to bear. Encouragingly, *Eagle* sent word that Joseph Smith, wounded early in the action, had returned to duty, as had Lieutenant Spencer.

On *Ticonderoga,* Lieutenant Cassin walked the taffrail in a hail of canister and grapeshot to direct a fire that time and time again beat back the British galleys, some of which reached within a boat's length of the schooner. Finding the schooner's matches useless for firing his division's guns, Midshipman Paulding fired them by flashing his pistol at their vents. Superintending duty with the springs, Lieutenant Stansbury disappeared from the bulwarks forward, cut in two by a round shot.

Making no effort to hide his excitement, Midshipman Monteath returned from the end of the line with news that Lieutenant Budd and his veterans, using springs and two sweeps out of *Preble's* stern port, had kept the sloop broadside to bear on *Finch* and four British galleys—each with more men than *Preble's* entire crew! Boatswain Rose was dead. Aware that he could expect no assistance from the fleet, Budd intended to keep pouring grape into the enemy, get his mainsail on, and go close aboard *Finch.*

Meanwhile the American gunboats had accounted for two enemy galleys sunk. Maintaining their order of battle, these aggressive bantams kept pitching into the frigate.

Black smoke, pouring up from both fleets, clouded the azure sky. Cannon balls—many in deliberate ricochet fire—skipped over the millpond-smooth water between ships, to enter their target near the waterline. Hurtling chain shot tore through rigging, to make decks a shambles. Hot shot from *Confiance*'s furnace set fires on board *Saratoga* and burned her spanker boom over the quarterdeck.

To the Commodore it became increasingly apparent, however, that *Confiance*'s blasts lost power with each roar of the frigate's great guns. Whereas her first and second broadsides had cut to pieces nearly all the hammocks on the American flagship's rail, succeeding fire came higher and higher, cutting the standing rigging farther from the deck. Elevation of *Confiance*'s guns got higher with each broadside—and less effective! Having once leveled them to pointblank range, her gunners no doubt failed properly to replace their loosened quoins at each discharge.

But *Saratoga*'s death toll rose with every broadside. Midships, Cookie sprawled—long, lean, awkward as in life—beside a silenced carronade. His wife, stepping over his body, carried powder to the next active gun. And before the Commodore looked away, a ball entered the gun port where she reached the powder to the loader, drove her across the deck, and left her crumpled form dangling on the larboard rail—head down, dead. His cheek gashed, the boy John Kortz had barely enough clothes left intact to cover his nakedness.

Returning from captured *Chubb,* anchored under the shore forts, Midshipman Platt's launch took an eighteen-pound shot in her middle that sank her and left the officer and his crew struggling in the water among the doughty galleys. But when, waterlogged, he finally made *Saratoga,* Platt brought the good news that General Macomb had repulsed Prevost's every effort to cross the Saranac's fords and bridges.

Macomb still stood firm. So he intended to stand—with his regulars, with Mooers' New York militia, with Strong's Vermont volunteers!

As guns on both sides went out of action, dismounted and disabled by direct hits or flying splinters, the cannonading gradually decreased. Disposing available midshipmen in a desperate effort to remount some of the ship's silenced starboard guns, the Commodore found *Eagle* bearing down on his larboard under topsails, to anchor by the stern between the flagship and the schooner.

Henley again! Leaving *Saratoga* at the head of the line to bear the brunt of *Confiance*'s and *Linnet*'s combined fire!

In the new position, Henley could bring his fresh larboard guns to bear on either *Confiance* or *Linnet*. But by winding the brig he could have done that without leaving his assigned station. Was he trying to fight this battle all by himself, with his own strategy? What a time to throw away the squadron's agreed-on plans and play lone wolf!

Aze Bellamy shouted in the Commodore's ear: "Lieutenant Vallette reports all starboard batteries out of action, sir, with the exception of a single carronade amidships and your long gun."

The Commodore listened as if in shock. Two pieces left on the flagship to fire. One lieutenant left alive to help fight *Saratoga*. Her crew decimated; her decks covered with their blood and mangled bodies.

He saw Aze looking at him strangely. What did the boy perceive in his face? The end? But Aze could not discern that! No thought of defeat had ever held him . . . not before this moment. Why now? Curious, he should finally think of losing. Curious, too, he should remember at this particular time that old saw about men not winning wars—only one man! What do you say now, Grandfather Denning?

He shook himself, blinked his eyes. Had he been hit? His head cleared. He pointed amidships to *Saratoga*'s venerable old sailing master, with Joe Barron splicing a torn rope tackle on the last remaining carronade.

"Tell Mr. Brum to wind the ship at once," he barked at Aze. "Have Mister Vallette prepare the larboard batteries while we get the ship around."

The Commodore bent over the long gun again. As he sighted, the carronade amidships also fired; but its navel bolt broke and the cannon hurtled off its carriage to plunge down the main hatch. In almost the same instant, a round shot from the enemy's frigate struck the spanker boom over the Commodore's head, cut the boom—already weakened by *Confiance*'s hot-shot fire—and hurled the savage spar down on the long twenty-four-pounder. Gun and Commodore smashed to *Saratoga*'s deck together.

10

Holding his breath, Commodore Macdonough struggled in a swirling, submerging vortex. His arms lashed out, to push him up for air. He heard voices. If only he could hold out a few seconds more, two or three seconds, just one, just . . .

Opening his eyes, he looked up. Torn rigging and shattered yardarms cut a ragged pattern across the smoke-fogged sky. Aze Bellamy's agonized face hung over him. A stub of the spanker boom pinned his legs to the deck. The long gun canted at a preposterous angle.

"He's coming to!"

Aze's shout filled the quarterdeck, and many hands finished clawing away the debris and helped the Commodore groggily to his feet.

Brum and the seamen, having clapped on the hawser that led to the starboard quarter, had brought the flagship's stern up over the kedge. But there she hung, with not enough wind to force her bows around.

Taking advantage of *Saratoga*'s silent guns, *Confiance* had attempted also to wind so that her unused starboard guns could come into action. Her fire had temporarily ceased.

But as *Saratoga* rode by her kedge and a line bent to a bight in the stream cable, her stern under *Linnet*'s raking broadside, the British brig kept up a steady and well-directed fire on the American flagship's afterdeck.

Still groggy, swaying unsteadily on his feet, the Commodore surveyed the crisis. In an instant he saw that *Saratoga* lay helpless until Sailing Master Brum could wind her; under *Linnet*'s broadside now; under *Confiance*'s also, as soon as the frigate got around.

"Send the men forward until our guns bear," he ordered. Then he, too, took shelter.

As Sailing Master Brum roused with his men on the line to the stream cable, the minutes mounted. *Linnet*'s devastating round shot poured into the defenseless flagship. And before the Commodore's eyes, a crashing ball catapulted a mast splinter across the deck to rip every stitch of clothing off the laboring Philip Brum—everything but the large blue-and-white kerchief around his neck.

Without a word the stark-naked sailing master yanked a frayed lanyard off the nearest disabled gun and with it tied his handkerchief at his waist, like an apron. Without a word he went back to rousing with his men on the line to the stream cable, and slowly the ship wound until her aftermost gun bore on *Confiance*.

Ordering Vallette to man the single gun and prepare to man the next as it came to bear, and the next until *Saratoga*'s full broadside roared in unison, the Commodore of a sudden saw that *Confiance* failed longer to wind. Hauling on her springs merely forced her ahead. The British frigate could not swing her starboard broadside to bear!

So Commodore Thomas Macdonough came to the moment he'd waited so patiently for! The moment to make up for all the humiliations of two frustrating years! Where was Joe Barron? He would relish this.

"Mr. Barron's in the cockpit," said Aze, "critically injured, sir."

Joe, too!

Then, like a genie's gift, the Commodore's victory vanished. For his flagship would go no farther around; but stood nearly end on to the wind, with only two fresh guns in play. *Linnet* raked her with a deadly fire. He'd fought—and lost!

With his fine plans destroyed, with his dead lying mutilated on the deck, with all but two of his guns out of action, Commodore Macdonough stood alone. No matter how much his men loved him, no matter how loyal, how patriotic, brave, self-sacrificing, in this crisis they could do nothing to help. When he fell, they fell with him.

His mind filled with tumbling pictures, words, remembered faces ... Ann in her wedding gown, Hank de Koven dropping the ring, little Augusta and Charlotte Shaler pertly carrying their flower-girl violets ... Grandfather Denning's "In your hands, son, our whole national future may rest"....

He looked down at his hands, almost black with powder and smoke. In these hands, his hands.... Well, Grandfather Denning, at least we all tried. We did our best. We ...

What tricks did his mind play? And why at a time like this? Beat? Why, they'd just got the enemy where they wanted him! He seized a trumpet from the hands of a midshipman.

"Mr. Brum!" he ordered. "The hawser from the kedge to the larboard quarter ... get it forward under the bows. Then pass it aft to the starboard quarter."

With an exultant shout as he comprehended, the naked sailing master put his men on the hawser. Slowly, powerfully, they brought it under the bows and walked it aft.

Under Brum's skillful guidance the seamen sprang the ship's stern to the westward ... until all her guns lined up to present a fresh and complete broadside to *Confiance* and to *Linnet!*

The Commodore's heart bounded. With every blast of *Saratoga*'s guns and carronades, with every belch of flame and smoke that hurled 414 pounds of deadly Vergennes and Charlestown iron at the British frigate, his heart bounded higher. From his head caulker came reports that the flagship, hulled more than fifty times, remained tight. Bless Noah Brown!

For two hours the battle had waxed and waned. For two hours the advantage had gone from one side to the other. Now the fighting reached its peak.

Saratoga's guns continued to pour metal into the frigate.

Eagle and most of the galleys, still in battle line, kept up their galling fire on *Confiance* and *Linnet.*

But five British gunboats opened an attack on *Ticonderoga,* seeking desperately to close and board. As earlier in the fight, however, the Commodore saw Steve Cassin leap on the schooner's rail to direct her fire against the enemy galleys. Thank God for men like Steve!

At the end of the line, *Preble,* having made a stretch inshore to avoid pursuing British galleys which had poured immense quantities of grape into her, now stood down for *Finch* which, aground off Crab Island, still flew her British colors.

From *Saratoga's* midships the crash of a ball and a shout brought the Commodore's gaze to a still tumbling officer and the shot box on which he had stood. The Commodore's heart sank. But Elie Vallette slowly, deliberately picked himself off the deck, examined his shredded uniform, shrugged his Gargantuan shoulders, and resumed charge of his guns.

John Vance, the Narragansett Indian whose torn canvas shirt and trousers bared much of his coppery skin, showed his beautifully white and even teeth as he called out to Aze Bellamy, near the Commodore: "Lookee," Vance shouted, pointing to a gaping cannon-ball cut in the glazed hat he wore above the single gold ring in his right ear, "how the damned John Bulls have spoiled my hat!"

Then the Indian bent to the deck, picked up John Roberts, the gentle carpenter who took such pride in lifting pork brine with his fingers grasping only the top rim of the barrel, and tenderly carried the limp giant below to have his shattered leg cut off. In the blood-splashed cockpit, the Commodore knew, Surgeon Briggs already had amputated Midshipman Graham's.

Through the battle smoke, the Commodore saw not a mast in either squadron that could stand to make sail on. Lower rigging, nearly all shot away, hung down as if just placed over the mastheads.

With Aze Bellamy beside him, the Commodore watched his flagship's destructive fire reduce the enemy's frigate to utter helplessness. Her masts and yards looked like bunches of broken matches; her sails—so freshly white and new two hours ago—like bundles of old rags. What kept her riddled hull afloat?

Still girdled in part by his neckerchief and ready at a command to spring *Saratoga* to any position, Sailing Master Brum could not contain himself. "I've been on Lake Erie, Commodore," he shouted admiringly, "and as a tactician and a fighter, Perry can't be mentioned in the same breath with you, sir!"

At that moment *Confiance* struck.

The instant her colors came down, Brum went to work—springing the flagship to bear on *Linnet*. And the Commodore, looking quickly around for an officer to go on board surrendered *Confiance,* fastened on Captain Youngs in the ship's waist. Smiling as he recalled Alex Macomb's perennial protests over supplying the Navy with soldiers, he turned to Aze.

"Ask Captain Youngs," he said, "to do me the honor of taking possession of the frigate."

With *Saratoga*'s fire concentrated on the British brig, Aze resumed his place at the Commodore's side. Their powder-blackened faces complemented their begrimed hands and torn uniforms. Aze beamed, unable to conceal the swelling of his heart.

"Sir," he said, "this is a proud day for the United States."

He looked at the Commodore with the concentrated devotion of their two years together on the Lake. "I think this is the proudest day our country ever saw." [2]

Aze's own proud smile remained as a last sixteen-pound ball from the enemy's *Linnet* flew over the flagship's rail. Decapitating the midshipman, the ball drove Aze's severed head into the Commodore's chest, and as the Commodore hurtled across the quarterdeck he heard an anguished cry fill the ship before he crashed, unconscious and covered with blood, into a starboard scupper.

With seamen shouting that their Commander had been killed, George Beale raced to the quarterdeck. Lifting Aze's head from the shaken Commodore's hands, the purser turned away from the tears he saw.

On his feet, Commodore Macdonough grimly watched *Linnet* wilt under *Saratoga*'s withering fire. Fifteen minutes later, he saw her strike. *Finch*—and all the British galleys still afloat—immediately struck, too.

Of sixteen British ensigns that had flown over Plattsburg Bay two hours and a half ago, not one remained aloft. Not a single enemy vessel remained to contest the ascendancy of Lake Champlain.[3]

In his mind the Commodore framed a message to William Jones: "The Almighty has been pleased to grant us a signal victory . . ."

When Midshipman Monteath brought news from General Macomb that Prevost's army had started a precipitous retreat toward Canada, the Commodore still paced back and forth on the flagship's quarterdeck, still gazing at his powder-blackened hands, tinged with red.

"Thank you," he said to the young midshipman as he would have spoken to Aze. He continued to look at his hands as he added: "Our country's thanks to all you boys . . . you men . . . for evicting our enemy . . ." His voice trailed . . . "forever, I hope."

EPILOGUE

While Commodore Macdonough bound up American and British battle wounds, William Jones told the United States Senate Naval Committee:

"To view it [the Commodore's accomplishment] in abstract, it is not surpassed by any naval victory on record. To appreciate its result, it is perhaps one of the most important events in the history of our country."

The Navy Secretary asked the Commodore to accept "the assurance of the high respect and warm approbation of the President of the United States, which I am commanded to present." Approbation took the tangible form of promotion to captain, ranking from September 11th.

Congress thanked Thomas Macdonough, and struck off a gold medal. Vermont deeded him a hundred acres of land on Cumberland Head; New York presented a thousand acres in Cayuga County. The City of New York had his portrait painted, to hang with Macomb's in City Hall; Lansingburgh and Albany gave him the freedom of their cities, silver, and property. His native state, Delaware, presented sword, silver service, and portrait; his adopted state, Connecticut, a pair of gold-mounted pistols.

For his health the Commodore put in for a new assignment, saw the Champlain fleet into winter quarters, received a heart-warming good-by from his officers, and went to New York to command (of all available posts!) a steamboat. Designed by Robert Fulton and built by Adam and Noah Brown, 150-foot *Fulton First* mounted thirty guns and could throw hot water as well as shot. Though this unique assignment made the Commodore the world's first commander of a steam vessel of war, William Denning, with whom the Commodore stayed while in New York, told the family that "he does not seem to like command of the steam frigate." And when *Fulton First* took her trial run the following June, Commodore Macdonough more happily had headed for command of the Portsmouth Navy Yard.

Elected an honorary member of the New York State Society of the Cincinnati and dined from Plattsburg to Washington, the Commodore received his countrymen's grateful appreciation with typical graciousness though, as Ann disclosed, he hated parades. He spent much time in Middletown where sailors from the Champlain fleet came to see him and where, on occasion, he went to Amasa Beach's cooperage shop and sat on the stone horse to "shave a stave." His health continued to fail, as did Ann's, though they had—by 1825—ten children, of whom five died young.

The Commodore's naval duties over the years included fitting out seventy-four-gun *Washington,* helping select a site for fortifications at Plattsburg, conveying the American minister to Russia on frigate *Guerriere,* commanding a line-of-battle ship, seventy-four-gun *Ohio,* and—in the summer of 1824—commanding *Constitution* and the Mediterranean fleet.

On this, his last command, he took his four-year-old son, Rodney, named after Caesar Augustus Rodney. A year earlier, Ann had written an old Navy friend, Abbey Chew, that she must seek all the means provided "for lengthening a life which I have for many months known could not continue long." Word of her death on August 9th, 1825, reached the Commodore in the Mediterranean. Ann had willed him "the locket containing the hair of all my departed children, and the Cornelian."

Ravaged by pulmonary pneumonia, wasted to sixty pounds, the Commodore turned his fleet over to John Rodgers and, on October 14th, left "Old Ironsides" to sail for home with

Rodney and *Constitution*'s surgeon, William Turk. On November 10th, aboard merchant brig *Edwin* six hundred miles off the capes of Delaware, Thomas Macdonough died.

His funeral cortege, marching from New York's Battery to City Hall and St. Paul's chapel, included respectful brass from Navy and Army. A detail of seamen bore the Commodore from the Battery, and back; a steamboat carried him to Middletown.

He lies buried next to Ann, under a single monument which says of her, "the richest gifts of nature and of grace adorned her mind and heart"; and of him, "he was distinguished in the world as the Hero of Lake Champlain."

AUTHOR'S NOTE

When Earl Schenck Miers in 1945 asked me to do a book on Commodore Thomas Macdonough and the building of the Lake Champlain fleet, he sent me out on a detective chase that lasted fifteen years.

Thomas Macdonough had written an "autobiography" in which he starkly outlined twenty-two years of his Navy service but never touched on his private life. What little else I found printed about this laconic sailor merely re-embroidered a few basic naval anecdotes.

The bare facts led, however, to an utterly unanticipated labor of love that became a happy part of fishing, skiing, and motor vacations and carried me to the Commodore's descendants, spread over the United States, and into historical societies, libraries, and museums from Washington to the Canadian border. Bit by bit, like an archeologist's explorations, these expeditions brought to light small facets of Thomas Macdonough's character, and each new, fascinating find impelled me to further digging.

According to the Macdonough family, someone threw a trunkful of the Commodore's personal papers out of the homestead attic just before his grandson Rodney started work on a biography. Because Rodney Macdonough then piously censored the remaining documents the biography, published in 1909, did not add as much as it might to a rounded appreciation of the Commodore's character. (Most of the edition, I learned from the family, foundered in Lake Champlain.) But in Vermont the Commodore's granddaughter, Mrs. Lucy

Macdonough Reade, guided me to his great-nephew Vance Macdonough in Massachusetts, where I read and copied the Commodore's two extant letter-books.

In the Historical Society of Delaware I found his log of frigate *Constellation* for 1802–1803, at the University of Vermont a page from his 1816 account book, in the Naval Academy letters to and from the secretaries of the Navy, and through miscellaneous sources letters from naval compatriots and personal friends. Connecticut and California descendants showed me revealing letters which the Commodore's devoted wife, Ann, wrote to her mother during the years on the Lake, 1812 to 1814. Gradually the personal picture puzzle took shape.

To tell the story of Navy strategy on Champlain, I found it necessary to place it against Army strategy on the northern frontier. This led to studying and weighing the Commodore's relationships with five American generals, a governor, and Eleazer Williams, chief of Army intelligence, as well as with British opponents. Gradually the operational picture also took shape, drawn from the participants' journals, memoirs, and letters, and from contemporary documents, newspapers, and speeches.

Political and local background came piecemeal from contemporary publications and from books—including fiction—and magazines about the period.

Realizing that the Commodore's vanished papers may never reappear to amplify what we now know about his career and private life, I set down an exact timetable of his activities and those of the people he worked with on the Lake, based on the attested facts I had uncovered. The major actions, times, and meetings in this history-biography thus are matters of record. All quoted material, except dialogue, is documentary.

Imagination has had to provide:

1. A few minor incidents, falling between and filling out the recorded framework of events, including the scenes of

the Commodore's domestic life which have their basis in his and Ann's family letters;

2. Most of the dialogue, which represents the speakers, I believe, as closely as a fifteen-year association with them permits at a distance of a century and a half;

3. Three characters, the Argalus Cobbs and Jacob Dibble, invented to personify documented local background.

All other characters are historical, with the following elucidation about two of them:

The youth called here Aze Bellamy combines the unnamed "country lad" who Lieutenant Macdonough tells us accompanied him from Portland to Burlington and his "favorite gunner," about both of whom we know nothing more. Aze serves to visualize naval procedural details and the outlook of midshipmen in the Champlain fleet, all of which are matters of record, and to do miscellaneous chores for the Commodore.

Mrs. Macdonough's grandfather, William Denning—appointed from New York to the Continental Congress in 1778, patriot, friend of Washington, Lafayette, and Hamilton—takes on an appropriate role of elder statesman in this book; he voices, and writes of, the period's high thinking and keeps the Commodore's sights raised—which Grandfather Denning most likely did.

The following notes about particular passages are intended to throw additional light on people and events touched on or alluded to. They will prove more illuminating if read after finishing the narrative—or before starting.

CHARLES G. MULLER

Greenwich, Connecticut
1960

NOTES

PART ONE: THE LAKE

1

1. After Lieutenant Macdonough brought *Gulliver* back to Boston from Calcutta, he wrote Paul Hamilton on August 25, 1811, "to acquaint you with my arrival in this country and that I have performed the India voyage agreeable to the permission you gave me." That followed protocol.

But in the next paragraph he put the Secretary on the spot, flatly announcing that he had taken charge of another vessel for his Boston merchants. No by-your-leave.

Four days later Secretary Hamilton responded briefly: "Under existing circumstances I cannot consistently with my duty to the public grant the furlough you have asked."

Giving the Secretary time to reconsider, the Lieutenant a month later wrote: "Could you now consistently place me on furlough with permission to leave the United States, I should much prefer it to leaving the Navy entirely. Could you not, Sir, I assure you I am with much reluctance compelled to beg you to accept of my resignation."

After three weeks on tenterhooks, the Lieutenant on October 15 wrote again: ". . . I suppose it necessary to be notified of the acceptance of my resignation, or of my being placed on furlough and to have your permission to leave the United States."

On the same day that this second threat-of-resignation letter sped out of Middletown, Hamilton's answer to the previous ultimatum left Washington. The Secretary had, considering "the high character you have sustained in the service," decided to grant the furlough. He pointed out, however, that "you were certainly wrong in making any private engagements, which required your leaving the United States without my previous permission & of this you cannot, from your feeling as an officer, but be sensible on reflection. Your having done so has induced me to hesitate upon the proper answer to be given your proposition to resign, if you could not have a furlough. As this however is the first instance of your having to any degree acted exceptionally—since you have belonged to the Navy—I have thought fit to overlook it ..."

When the Lieutenant's second ultimatum arrived after the Secretary had made this magnanimous capitulation to the first, Paul Hamilton, still burning, endorsed the second letter with a thumping: "Resignation to be accepted."

But the letter lies in the records with Hamilton's irate endorsement crossed out. Who changed his mind?

3

1. Even to a blacksmith, a fight with Lieutenant Macdonough—who had trained on pirates—must have felt like a very real assault. Lawyer Van Hook's following letter to the Lieutenant paints a titillating picture:

New York September 4, 1812
No. 36 Broad Street

Dear Sir

Within the last few days I have had several conversations with *Tucker* the lawyer of your man the Blacksmith on the subject of a compromise of his claim for Damages against you. From all that I can learn the man is extremely stubborn and difficult to satisfy. If I could see him myself I think I could do something more with him but they take good care to keep him in the Back Ground, and I cannot learn his name or where he resides. In answer to my proposals his lawyer mentions that he will not consent to take less than $300 and his Costs say some $25 to $40 dollars more. I stated to him that the statute of limitations would soon release you from all Responsibility to him he ought of Course to Consult his interest and take less. His attorney says in answer to that that an Indictment for this assault has been found against you in Kings County, Long Island and against that the Law does not Run. Of this last Circumstance I was not apprized until he mentioned it. I think I mentioned to you the last time I saw you that our Statute of Limitations barred actions of this kind after *three* years. I find by looking at our law that I was mistaken and that it was *four* Years instead of three. This affair happened if I mistake not in the fall or winter of 1808 if I am Correct in the time four Years have not yet elapsed. Our court have decided that if the suit is not brought within the time prescribed by law after the party was at large in the State and not *secreted* that then it is barred. You best know how long after this affair happened you came to town or went *out of the Yard* on Long Island as from that time the Law will Commence running under all the Circumstances of the Case it will be for Yourself to determine on the Course you had best adopt.

If there will be no occasion for your coming to this City until the next Spring I think you will after that time have nothing to apprehend from the *Event* of a suit tho' I have no doubt he will have you arrested if it should only be to alarm you.

> I am Dr Sir
> Your hble St
> Wm. Van Hook

T. J. Macdonough Esq.

Did the Lieutenant pay? All we know for sure is that he found himself very busy the next spring—and summer and fall—and had no occasion to go to New York.

4

1. The *Syren* incident has taken many forms in the telling since 1806. Laconic Thomas Macdonough put it this way in his autobiography:

"When I was first lieutenant of the *Syren* brig an occurrence took place in the harbour of Gibraltar which excited a good deal of feeling both on the side of the English and ourselves. A British man-of-war's boat boarded an American merchantman which lay near the *Syren* and took out, or impressed, one of her men. I went alongside the British boat in one of ours and demanded him, which demand was refused. I then took hold of the man and took him in my boat and brought him on board the *Syren*. He was an American and of course we kept him." Of course! An assistant Navy secretary tells how.

In an address before the Vermont Historical Society in 1914, Charles H. Darling said: "The captain of the [British] frigate went on board the *Siren* in a great passion and demanded of Macdonough [Captain Smith was on shore] how he dared take a man from one of his majesty's boats. He then threatened to bring his frigate alongside the *Siren* and retake the man by force. Macdonough replied that he supposed the frigate could sink the *Siren,* but so long as she could swim he would keep the man."

The *Analectic Magazine and Naval Chronicle* of March 1816 ended the scene like this:

"The English captain said to Macdonough, 'you are a very young, and very indiscreet, young man; suppose I had been in the boat, what would you have done?' 'I would have taken the man, or lost my life.' 'What, sir, would you attempt to stop me if I were now to attempt to impress men from that brig?' 'I would, and to convince yourself I would, you have only to make the attempt.'

"On this, the Englishman went on board his ship, and shortly afterwards was seen bearing her in a direction for the American merchant brig. Macdonough ordered his boat manned and armed, got into her himself, and was in readiness for pursuit. The Englishman took a circuit around the American brig, and returned again to the frigate. When Captain Smith came on board, he justified the conduct of Macdonough and declared his intention to protect the American seaman."

5

1. The Lieutenant fails to mention this episode, but Assistant Navy Secretary Darling told the Vermont Historical Society:

"It is related that while the squadron was at Syracuse the officers and men were often set upon by ruffians and that on one occasion Decatur and Midshipman Macdonough, while passing down one of the streets of the city at night, were attacked by three men. Drawing their swords, they defended themselves so successfully that the men were driven off, and Macdonough pursued one of them to the top of a house, from which the man jumped to the ground and perished from the fall."

The *Analectic Magazine and Naval Chronicle* of March 1816 gives this more colorful version while leaving Decatur out:

"Robberies and assassinations are the nightly amusements of Syracusans [Sicily], and our officers in their evening rambles, were frequently assailed by soldiers or fellows armed with knives or daggers. Their favorite mode of fighting is to blow out the candles, and in that situation their knives and daggers are the most dangerous of all weapons. On some occasion, which occurred in Syracuse, Macdonough was attacked by three of these desperados; with his back against a door, he had the good fortune to wound two, and the other took to his heels. He was followed by the lieutenant, who pushed him so hard that he climbed up to the roof of the barracks, whither Macdonough followed him still, and finding no other means of escape, he jumped off with the loss of his life."

A following item in the magazine amends the foregoing in this wise:

"The occasion we are told was: While the American fleet lay at Messina, Macdonough was detained one night on shore till all the ships' boats had returned to the fleet. He then hired a boat to take him on board; but finding three instead of two men (the usual complement) going in it, he suspected them of some evil design and refused to go. Whereupon they drew their poniards and attacked him in the manner related."

2. How strongly Lieutenant Macdonough felt about British impressment of American seamen showed when he stood up against the British frigate captain at Gibraltar. These feelings came, beyond doubt, from great depth. That they sprang from personal impressment can be questioned. Darling, in his Vermont address, said they did:

"On the evening before the brig [*Gulliver*] was to leave Liverpool, Macdonough, who had been on shore, was returning to the wharf to proceed to his ship, when he was accosted by a man who asked if he belonged to any ship in the harbor. On his replying that he belonged to the brig *Gulliver*, he was seized by several men and taken to a British frigate, enrolled on the purser's list, given a hammock and ordered forward, no attention being paid to his assertion that he was not only an American but an officer in the Navy.

"Lying in his hammock he made plans for his escape, and when the corporal of the guard had entered and gone to sleep in an adjoining hammock, Macdonough dressed himself in the corporal's uniform and walked boldly on deck. Saluting the officer of the deck, he asked permission to examine the second cutter alongside, in which he said he suspected there was rum concealed. Not being recognized, permission was readily given, but as Macdonough passed the forward hatch he saw the real corporal's head coming up. With a blow of his fist he sent the corporal to the bottom of the ladder and quickly swung himself into the cutter and severed the rope. The strong current soon carried the boat off and in spite of pursuit Macdonough reached the shore and joined his own ship.

"At this time he is reported to have said: 'If I live, I'll make England remember the day she impressed an American sailor.' "

Rodney Macdonough reported that family tradition cherished this incident, but he found no source for it. He pointed out that "if such a thing actually happened it would have been Macdonough's duty, as an officer, to report it to Washington, and it is not likely that our government or any government, however supine, would have hesitated to demand an instant and ample apology for the national insult."

Personally, I like the Navy Secretary's story—no matter whether he found it outside department files.

6

1. Records show that Eleazer (also called Lazar, Lazare, Lazarre, Lazo) Williams volunteered for the war from Bakersfield, Vermont. He held pension certificate No. 30391.

This fabulous character combined variety and audacity in the roles of adventurer, do-gooder, and (this is moot) charlatan. (W. W. Wight wrote that he "wore a tinsel star on his left breast and styled himself Count de Lorraine" at Dartmouth College where, the records show, he went for one week in 1807.) Excerpts from his Journal during 1812–1814 show that his secret corps of rangers and scouts spread out in every direction on the northern frontier and collected from Canada's Indians important information about movements of British forces. He received commendation "for zeal, bravery, fidelity."

He later moved in the direction of Wisconsin as teacher, preacher, and translator of religious documents into Indian.

Still later, he astounded both sides of the Atlantic by claiming to be France's last, and lost, dauphin. This kept *Putnam's Magazine* and sundry clergymen raging for years. The controversy he incited merely dwindled; it didn't die out. And Professor Erl A. Bates of Cornell, whose help I sought in running down Lazare's journals, has this latest word to say:

"My chief interest in Eleazer now is his vaccination scar which I think I have definitely tied with that of the Marie clan. Eleazer grows in my research as a member of the Household and perhaps was in the line of succession or a blind settled in America to throw the searchers away from the real 'Dauphine.' The 'e' on the end is found in Tallyrand and letters in the North country."

With or without an 'e,' Williams had color!

7

1. As a local sailor, Joseph Barron, Jr., provided the Lake Champlain fleet with much of its navigational know-how. His letters to "Sister Sarey" and Uncle Abel provided me with invaluable detail and verification of vessels, armament, and battle actions.

Pilot on steamboat *Vermont* (second steamboat in the world in regular commercial operation) before his unhappy experiences with the Army, Joe Barron worked loyally for Lieutenant Macdonough's naval flotilla until struck and mortally wounded at the very close of the fleet's critical engagement. Of this capable and patriotic Vermonter, a schoolmate said at Barron's graveside:

"A warmer-hearted or a braver man never trod the deck of a ship."

PART TWO: THE SHIPS

4

1. Stages had treated the Lieutenant as roughly as horses, as evidenced in a letter that includes enlightening observations to William Van Dusen on the task of enlisting men for *Wasp* while she waited to put to sea.

New York, March 11, 1807

Dear Van,

Pardon me my good fellow for not writing you sooner but I assure you I have been so busy shipping men for the ship and so many damn things in the way that I have no time. I did not get your letter till a few days ago when I arrived at Washington. I stayed there about a week, then opened a rendezvous at Baltimore where I have been until three days ago. I came on here to ship the remainder of the crew (one hundred men) and expect to be at least a month in shipping them owing to the low wages. In the meantime you must write me often for the ship is ready for sea and will sail immediately the above men are procured.

You had better be on the look out. Hooper and his wife have parted in a squall. That is they have separated but I cannot give you information respecting the cause of their dispute. I got upset a short time ago in the damn stage, and was near breaking my leg, arm, back, and fracturing my skull; a damn hard fall and a narrow escape of broken bones.

I would make this longer but the damn sailors are making such a noise together with the Drum and Fife and they confuse me or would the Devil himself who has a larger rendezvous open than I have.

2. Ann Macdonough's father, Nathaniel Shaler, comprised a unique mixture of qualities. In June of 1771, John Adams visited Middletown, stayed at the house of Nathaniel's mother, and wrote in his diary:

Landlady has an only son, Nat. Shaler, and she is very fond and very proud of him. He lives with a merchant; is now twenty-five or twenty-six and contents himself still to keep that merchant's books without any inclination to set up for himself; has a great proficiency in music, plays upon the flute, fife, harpsichord, spinet, etc.; associated with the young and the gay, and is a very fine Conn. young gentleman.

Nathaniel Shaler also played the violin, and the organ at Middletown's Christ Church. Fond of books, he took pleasure in reading aloud to his family (including their Negro boy-of-all-work Lewis). He liked nature; had brought the two large tulip trees in front of the house from the woods, and planted them himself. He'd chosen these because they blossomed on King George's birthday!

An avowed Tory, he must have given William Denning a hard time in deciding whether daughter Lucretia Ann would be happy as Nathaniel's second wife. Despite his political sentiments, this genial, cultivated man had the esteem of his townsmen and, more important, his family, including William Denning. He had taken no active part in the Revolution; his loyalties had, apparently, been of the mind.

3. This route reversed the northerly thrust that General Philip John Schuyler suggested to General Washington in 1777 after two British officers, prisoners from Burgoyne's army, stopped at Schuyler's quarters in Saratoga on their way back to Canada on parole.

They talked about the surrender, and blamed the Canadian Governor,

Sir Guy Carleton. One of the officers, attached to General Burgoyne, accused Carleton of retaining too many troops in Canada; the other insisted that Carleton hadn't kept enough to protect the country. General Schuyler drew them on, pouring wine, and the pair went from claims to proofs, while Schuyler listened and learned the exact distribution of all forces remaining in Canada.

He sent off a dispatch to Washington with a well-conceived plan for attacking Canada. He proposed a rapid winter advance, with sledges to transport provisions, stores, and even disabled soldiers. He showed the feasibility of collecting, in a month's time, between the Connecticut and Hudson rivers, fifteen hundred sledges, two thousand horses, and two thousand oxen. As the Army marched, they could kill oxen for food.

In the War of 1812 the British might well have worked Schuyler's plan in the opposite direction, with a sweep down the eastern border of Lake Champlain. At the beginning of the conflict they did not seem anxious, however, to irritate New England by threats from the north, and continued for some time to reach west.

6

1. America's shipbuilders, "predominantly intelligent and observant artists," in the early 1800's used tradition, rule-of-thumb, and a well-developed sense of proportion as guides in the arts of fashioning half-models and putting timbers together. Heads of firms, these master carpenters owned their yards, designed vessels, fashioned half-models, chose timbers, and supervised construction.

Henry Eckford, called the best mechanic of his age, and Adam and Noah Brown turned their skills in 1812 to building America's lake fleets. They did incredible jobs from the felling of timbers in adjacent forests to launching of warships—"thus dimly shining through the halo that encircles the fame of Perry and Macdonough. . . ."

8

1. York then; Toronto now.

10

1. Yeo apparently liked to sound off. Having had word that David Porter had mistreated a British subject serving under him (likely British propaganda of the period, since many British naval officers considered American seamen as British subjects forced to fight against his majesty), Sir James had this letter published in an American newspaper:

A passenger of the brig *Lyon*, from Havana to N.Y., captured by the brig *Southampton*, Sir Yeo, commander, is requested by Sir

James Yeo to present his compliments to Captain Porter, commander of the frigate *Essex*. Would be glad to have a tete-a-tete anywhere between the Capes of Delaware and the Havanna, when he would have the pleasure to break his own sword over his damned head and put him down forward in irons.

Porter replied, but the meeting never took place. Later, Yeo cruised Lake Ontario for months without bringing on a major engagement.

11

1. Whatever the Commodore felt about Sidney Smith's debacle, the Court of Inquiry finally held at Sackett's Harbor, on board U.S. Brig *Jones,* April 4, 1815, reported:

The Court are unanimously of opinion that the general conduct of Lieutenant Sidney Smith on Lake Champlain was correct and meritorious. The Court are further of opinion that the sloops *Growler* and *Eagle* were lost in consequence of their being taken too far below the lines in a narrow channel where there was not room for them to work and where they were exposed to musketry from the shore. The Court, however, taking into consideration the practicability of a successful attack by the enemy on the sloops while lying at anchor at Champlain and badly manned, the assurance of Captain Herrick that his company would be withdrawn the next day, and being satisfied by the testimony that Lieutenant Smith was deceived by his pilot, are of opinion that the sloops *Growler* and *Eagle,* when attacked by a superior force, were gallantly defended and that they were not surrendered until all further resistance had become vain.

Melancthon T. Woolsey,
President
Samuel Livermore,
Judge Advocate

Approved,
  B. W. Crowninshield

PART THREE: THE MAN

2

1. Besides helping Peter Sailly and his customs men, the Champlain fleet also caused the Treasury Department's representative occasional headaches. Sailors, like civilians, wanted English-made merchandise and picked up what they thought of as London luxuries wherever they came on them—fine cloths mostly—to send home to eager wives. To Commodore Macdonough, Sailly wrote:

Custom House, District of Champlain
December 1, 1813.

Sir

The following facts have taken place—Mr. John Banker returned from a Cruise Saturday and left Chazy that morning with British Goods, taken previously from an American Citizen in a *very* peaceable manner . . . and was himself on board of your vessel that night.

On Monday following you had the goodness to inform me that the Said John Banker had a Commission for Privateering and we both agreed that it was a Scheme for Smuggling.

One of your officers arrived yesterday at Cumberland Head from the Northward with a parcel of British Goods. I had, then, the honor to inform you of it instantly. That officer has returned to the fleet this Day and put the goods thus brought on board the Sloop *President*.

I thought it my duty as Collector of the Customs to call upon you this afternoon in relation to these transactions. I mentioned that merchandise imported, no matter by whom or in what manner from Canada under the present Laws and State of War, were in all cases to be reported to the Collector of the Customs and be disposed of according to the nature of the Capture as the law directs. I offered to convince you of the correctness of that course, if you would call at my office, by communicating to you the laws, the letters of Mr. Gallatin on a similar subject, and of the present Acting Secretary of the Treasury.

You condescended to tell me that you would inquire whether the Goods brought in by Mr. Banker were on Board of your vessel or not, and that you was not yet acquainted with the capture made by your officer.

As I ought not to lose a moment in informing the head officers of Government of transactions, which if suffered to pass unnoticed, strike at the root of our Laws and of all regulations, I have thought it fair to inform you, Sir, of that which is prescribed to me by duty —and that I shall also send to the acting Secretary of the Treasury a Copy of this my letter to you. In the mean while permit me to protest in my official capacity of Collector of the Customs, against the restoration of these Goods to any person whatever claiming the Same on this side of the boundary-line as it would be equal to smuggling the same.

I am   Respectfully
Your obt. servt.
Peter Sailly

P.S. I just received by Col. Durand your letter stating that Mr. Banker has been with his Goods amongst your vessels & people. Mr. J. Banker having thus literally smuggled his cargo, in not entering it at the Customhouse and paying or securing the duties due to the Un. States, on the Captured Goods, has forfeited his vessel & his bond, if ever he gave any, which I doubt.

Being destitute of the means to apprehend an Armed Privateer, permit me, sir, to call upon you for the application of the force under your command for the purpose of taking Said Privateer and Cargo and to bring the same to me.

I have no doubt that the necessity of the case will be considered as sufficient apology for this new request, and your attachment and respect for the Laws of your Country will be a strong inducement to comply with it.

I have no objection to assume the whole responsibility of that step.

I shall transmit your letter of this evening with a copy of this Postscription to the Treasury Department.

Peter Sailly

3

1. Dated Plattsburg January 5, 1814, this letter—from a John Smith—says he has word the British fleet is building.

PART FOUR: THE AXES

1

1. John Wesley Jarvis painted the Macdonough portrait which today hangs in the Council Room of New York's City Hall.

2. To the Navy Secretary, in the latter part of December, 1813, Lieutenant Macdonough had remarked on President Madison's failure to mention Lake Champlain in a recent message to Congress:

I hope, sir, it will be considered that I have fulfilled the duties required of me on this lake and that I have merited the trust and confidence reposed in me by my government.

Since the completion of a force adequate to the meeting of our enemy he has never appeared except in predatory excursions at the most favorable times for him. I can assure you, sir, that we have always been prepared to repel or defeat him. We have frequently sought him and he has as frequently avoided us. The flotilla under my command has, I am very conscious, always manifested a perfect willingness to see the enemy on fair terms.

Should you deem this letter improper, I beg you will consider it as emanating from feelings not at ease because it may be considered that I have not done that which is in my power to do.

To which William Jones replied:

... the President entertains the highest confidence in your capacity, zeal and patriotism, and is perfectly satisfied with your services.

2

1. Secretary Darling told the Vermont Historical Society that Daniel Wright, in an 1835 letter, wrote that he was called into the service of the United States in March of 1814 to aid in forwarding timber to the shipyard at Vergennes to build three large vessels and several gunboats. Fifty men were sent to his house to be boarded while cutting timber. He labored with them, with a team of his own. The order to procure and forward the timber was executed in five and a half days by one hundred and ten men.

3

1. Ann touched on two problems in a letter to her mother March 24, 1814, from Vergennes: the aftereffects of losing her first baby and the approaching loss of lodgings:

> I enjoy excellent health, though unable to bear fatigue, nor do I believe my constitution will ever recover from the shock it has sustained—but I should be ungrateful to complain where occasional weakness is the only thing I have to contend with.
>
> I have told you the people here seemed very *clever;* you will also think they are very *queer.* The lady who charitably took us to board, has concluded she can keep us no longer; accordingly we depart bag and baggage on Tuesday. Like the shilling who said he went through so many hands, our "next owner" is Col. Fisher. The females of the family are pleasant, but how long they will be content to keep us is uncertain. There is an universal dread of Officers among the enlightened inhabitants of V————. They are so *domestic* that they have not as yet invited us to drink tea with them, but say they intend to. However the mud is so much worse than ever it was in Hartford, that it is almost an impossibility to get out of the house.

PART FIVE: THE BATTLE

1

1. He did. His grandson, Harold Wilson, Jr., reports the Commodore as having said: "Now, Doctor, let us each swear we will never part with this watch, keep it as long as we live, and transmit it to our descendants as an heirloom."

3

1. "The time in which Perry built his ships has often been mentioned in praise and wonder," said Navy Secretary Darling, "but Mac-

donough's ships were not only of larger tonnage but were built and completed in a shorter time."

5

1. Admiral Smith, at eighty-five, reminisced to Admiral A. S. Barker in 1875: "These prisoners ... were all at work with ball and chain, digging trenches in a kind of red loam. They were sent for, and came in with their faces and clothes—what few clothes they had—covered with red dirt—a hard-looking set. I told them I had come to take them to the *Eagle* to fight.

"The prisoners were delighted at the prospect; so I had their irons knocked off and marched them down to the landing. Although I had a good sized boat, it took two trips to get them aboard the *Eagle*. I think there were about forty of them."

2. Lossing attributed the hoax to Williams ... a trick similar to the one played on Hull by the British. Colonel Fassett of Vermont had been over to Plattsburg from Burlington the Friday before the battle. He assured Macomb of the Vermont militia's support despite Governor Chittenden, and Williams suggested to Macomb that a letter from Fassett, declaring that a heavy body of militia was about to cross the Lake, be allowed to fall into Prevost's hands. Williams went to Burlington, got a letter saying that Chittenden was marching with ten thousand men for St. Albans; that five thousand more were marching from St. Lawrence County; that four thousand were in motion from Washington County. The letter was placed in the hands of a shrewd Irish woman on Cumberland Head, who took it to Prevost at the proper time.

6

1. Too, the Commodore's 1814 flotilla loomed more impressive than his "poor forlorn-looking squadron" of 1812. Darling said: "Macdonough's flagship and the British flagship were each somewhat smaller than the *Constitution*, but they were larger than the *Peacock, Wasp, Hornet, Intrepid, Boxer, Enterprise, Bonhomme Richard*, and all other famous ships of the Navy up to that time, save the *Constitution*, the *President*, and their class."

7

1. "... Macdonough placed his fleet knowing that the British would not dare pass up the Lake leaving him to harass their rear," Darling explained. "He thereby compelled the British to tack around Cumberland Head and attack his fleet, bows on, thus exposing themselves to a raking fire from his broadsides. By so doing, Macdonough accomplished

what rarely occurs in a sea fight, namely, chose his own position and forced the enemy to attack him to the enemy's greatest disadvantage. In short he forced the enemy to attack him where he chose and as he chose."

2. Helen Mariette Lawrence Marshall gave the following eve-of-battle report as it came down through the Lawrence family via Grandfather William, who built the first dock at Chazy Landing, and her father Putnam:

"Soldiers rolled up casks and barrels, stood them on end and laid boards across to make a table. Some of the casks contained wine, Jamaica rum, and other liquors which in those days were by many considered to be good to drink. Over the boards they spread fine linen table cloths, and set the table with China, glass, and silver and made quite a banquet. [Grandfather an invited guest—father watched.] The affair was quite a celebration in anticipation of the capture of Plattsburgh and the American fleet. Plattsburgh would make quite a nice breakfast for them, they said."

Grandfather called the turn: told them they'd be back in three days!

8

1. To C. A. Rodney, May 2, 1815, the Commodore wrote from Washington:

As you desire, I will tell what signals I made on the 11th Sept. last when the enemy hove in sight at the distance of six miles. I made the signal 'Impressed seamen call on every man to do his duty'—and just as the first gun was fired from my ship I made the signal 'close action.'

9

1. According to G. H. Richards, in "Memoir of Alexander Macomb," "Macomb planned, if Macdonough lost the battle, to use the Quartermaster's bateaux at Plattsburg to retake the fleet and also to capture the enemy's! He reasoned that, if the Americans practiced their usual precision of fire, however the decision of battle might turn, the hostile squadron would be greatly crippled and, after the action, would be in such a state of confusion, fatigue, intoxication, negligence, and general debility as to become an easy conquest. He therefore ordered the bateaux to be arranged under the banks of the Lake and prepared to receive 600–800 men, with which he would embark and board the fleets. The actual situation of the squadron at the close of the engagement confirmed the feasibility of the project."

10

1. Aboard *Confiance,* Youngs found that Captain Downie had died early in the action when a ball from *Saratoga* hit the twenty-four-pounder behind which he stood, knocking the cannon completely off its carriage. No part of Downie's skin was broken; his watch, flattened, stopped with its hands marking the moment of his death. The cannon that hit and killed him stands today outside Macdonough Hall at Annapolis.

2. According to *Niles' Weekly Register,* Lieutenant Colonel John Murray, former Plattsburg raider, after the British defeat said: "This is a proud day for America—the proudest day she ever saw."

3. Mahan, Cooper, Roosevelt, and Paine summed up Macdonough's accomplishments on Lake Champlain; Darling summed up their views in these words:

> Perry's gallant conduct in battle, the transfer of his flag from the *Lawrence* to the *Niagara* after the former was disabled, his famous dispatch to General Harrison, "We have met the enemy and they are ours," have made his name famous. But Perry's force exceeded the British in ships, men, tonnage, and metal, while the British force on Lake Champlain exceeded Macdonough's in the same particulars. In fact, Macdonough alone among all the American commanders is distinguished in having commanded the only smaller fleet that ever defeated a larger one.
>
> This comparison with the battle of Lake Erie is not made for the purpose of detracting anything from the glory of that battle, for which all honor is due, but because the battles of Lake Champlain and Lake Erie perhaps more closely resemble each other than any others in American history. Great as was the battle of Lake Erie, the battle of Lake Champlain was greater.
>
> Nor does history furnish many examples of greater severity, for the American loss numbered 104 killed and 116 wounded, and the British 168 killed and 220 wounded ... When the battle ceased, hardly a mast was standing in either fleet and an old sailor who had been with Nelson at Trafalgar declared that that was "but a flea bite to this."

And it was the last naval battle fought between English-speaking nations.

BIBLIOGRAPHY

GENERAL

Adams, Henry, *History of the United States of America*, New York, 1889. *The War of 1812*, Washington, 1944.

Aldrich, L. C., *History of Franklin and Grand Isle Counties*, Syracuse, 1891.

Alison, Archibald, *History of Europe from 1789-1815*, New York, 1844-1846.

American Guide Series, *New Hampshire*, Washington, 1938.

American State Papers, *Documents of Congress of the United States. March 3, 1789–March 5, 1825*. Washington, 1834.

Anderson, Frank Maloy, "A Forgotten Phase of the New England Opposition to the War of 1812," *Proceedings of the Mississippi Valley Historical Association*, (1912-1913) IAA, 176.

Angle, Paul M., *The American Reader*, New York, 1958.

"A True Republican," *Jefferson Against Madison's War*, Boston, 1812.

Babcock, Kendrick C., *The Rise of American Nationality*, New York, 1906.

Barnes, James, *A Loyal Traitor*, New York, 1897. *The Unpardonable War*, New York, 1904.

Beard, Charles A., *Rise of American Civilization*, New York, 1927.

Bowen, Catherine Drinker, *John Adams and the American Revolution*, Boston, 1950.

Bowers, Claude G., *Jefferson in Power*, Boston, 1936.

Brant, Irving, "Timid President? Futile War?" *American Heritage*, October 1959.

Bullus, Oscar, *Memorial to the Congress of the United States*, New York, 1856.

Burdick, Eugene, "The United States Navy," *Holiday* Magazine, October 1958.

Catherwood, Mary H., *Lazarre*, Indianapolis, 1901.

Centinel, The (Burlington), All news items available from December 17, 1812 through August 26, 1814; (*Northern Sentinel* starting 1814).

The Champlain Transportation Company, *The Steamboats of Lake Champlain 1809 to 1930*, Albany, 1930.

Channing, Edward, *A History of the United States*, New York, 1905.

Chase, Francis, *Sketches from the Early History of New Hampshire,* Claremont (N.H.), 1856.

Chastellux, Marquis François Jean de, *Travels in North America in the years 1780, 1781 and 1782,* London, 1782.

Churchill, Winston, *A History of the English-Speaking Peoples,* New York, 1956-1958.

Commager, Henry Steele, *Growth of the American Republic,* New York, 1956.

Cooper, James Fenimore, *The Lake Gun,* New York, 1832; *Ned Myers; or a Life Before the Mast,* Philadelphia, 1843; *The Pilot,* New York, 1852; *The Red Rover,* London, 1836; *The Two Admirals,* New York, 1873; *The Water Witch,* Philadelphia, 1843.

Dallas, A. J., *An Exposition of the Causes of the Late War with Great Britain,* Philadelphia, 1815.

Dean, J., *An Alphabetical Atlas, or, Gazeteer of Vermont,* Montpelier (Vt.), 1808.

Dean, Leon W., *Guns Over Champlain,* New York, 1946.

Dwight, Timothy, *Travels in New England and New York,* New Haven, 1821-1822.

Evans, E. E., *The Story of Louis XVII of France,* London, 1893.

Fassett, James H., *Colonial Life in New Hampshire,* Boston, 1896.

Fevret de Saint-Memin, C.B.J., *Collections of Portraits,* New York, 1862.

George, Noah J., *A Pocket Geographical and Statistical Gazeteer of the State of Vermont,* Haverhill (N.H.), 1823.

General Address to Freemen of New Hampshire (Title page gives no author), n.p. 1816.

Gleason, Benjamin, Oration delivered (July 5, 1813) before the Republican Citizens of Charlestown, Mass., on the 37th anniversary of national independence, in Wilbur Library.

Hamilton, Alexander, Jay, John, Madison, James, *The Federalist,* New York, 1937.

Hamilton, Edith, *The Roman Way,* New York, 1932.

Hanson, J. H., *The Lost Prince,* New York, 1854.

Hawes, Lucy W., *Buffalo Fifty Years Ago,* Buffalo, 1886.

Haywood, Charles Fry, *No Ship May Sail,* Lynn (Mass.), 1940.

Hemenway, Abby Maria, *Vermont Historical Gazeteer,* Ludlow (Vt.), 1860-1863.

Hill, Ralph Nading, "Shelburne Shipyard," *Vermont Life,* (1953) vol. VIII, no. 1.

Hurd, Duane Hamilton, *History of Clinton and Franklin Counties,* Philadelphia, 1880.

Ingham, Adella (compiler), "In the Days of the Monkton Iron Co. of Vergennes—1807-1830," A paper in the Vergennes (Vt.) Library.

Ingraham, J. H., *Arthur Denwood,* New York, c. 1870.

Jennings, Isaac, *Jennings' Family Present; or Instruction for the Preservation of the teeth and gums,* Natchez (Miss.), 1831.

Kendall, Edward Augustus, *Travels Through the Northern Parts of the United States,* New York, 1809.

Kennedy, Archibald, *Observations on the Importance of the Northern Colonies Under Proper Regulations,* New York, 1750.

Koier, Louise, "The House That John Built," *Vermont Life,* Spring 1958.

Life, Editors of, "The Sturdy Age of Homespun," *Life,* July 18, 1955.

Martin, Deborah Beaumont, *Eleazer Williams 1821-1921,* Green Bay (Wis.?), 1921 (?).

Massachusetts Historical Society, ed., "Historic Adams Papers: A First View," *Life,* July 2, 1956.

McClellan, Elisabeth, *Historic Dress in America 1800-1870,* Philadelphia, 1910.

McMaster, John Bach, *A History of the People of the United States from the Revolution to the Civil War,* New York, 1885-1913.

Metropolitan Museum of Art, *The American Wing: A Picture Book,* New York, 1952.

Mooers, Benjamin, *Memorial of Heirs of Benjamin Mooers,* n.p. 1851.

Mudgett, H. P., *The Seas Stand Watch,* New York, 1944.

Napier, Henry Edward, *New England Blockaded in 1814,* Salem (Mass.), 1939.

Nicholson, Thomas, *An Affecting Narrative of the Captivity and Sufferings of Thomas Nicholson,* Boston, 1818.

Pike, Robert E., "The Dreaded Scout," *Vermont Life,* Spring 1959.

Plummer, Edward Clarence, *Reminiscences of a Yarmouth Schoolboy,* Portland (Me.), 1926.

Rann, William S., *History of Chittenden County,* Syracuse, 1886.

Redway, J. W., *Making of the Empire State,* New York, 1904.

Roberts, Kenneth, *Captain Caution,* Garden City (N.Y.), 1934.

Robertson, C. F., "The Last of the Bourbon Story," *Putnam's Magazine,* July 1868.

Robinson, Rowland E., *Out of Bondage,* Boston, 1905; *Vermont: A Study of Independence,* Boston, 1892.

Royce, Caroline Halstead, *Bessboro: A History of Westport, Essex County, N.Y.,* Elizabethtown (N.Y.), 1904.

Saveth, Edward Norman, *Understanding the American Past,* Boston, 1954.

Smith, Bradford, *Why We Behave Like Americans,* New York, 1957.

Smith, John D., *History of Addison County; City of Vergennes,* No imprint, in Wilbur Library.

Spofford, Jeremiah, *A Gazeteer of Massachusetts,* Newburyport (Mass.), 1828.

Stevenson, B. E., *Poems of American History,* Boston, 1922.

Street, James, "The American Revolution," *Holiday* Magazine, July 1954.

Taylor, Fitch W., *The Broad Pennant,* New York, 1848.

Taylor, Robert, *Diary of Robert Taylor,* New York, 1844.

Thomas, R., *The Glory of America*, New York, 1834.

Thompson, Zadock, *A Gazeteer of the State of Vermont*, Montpelier (Vt.), 1824; *History of the State of Vermont from Its Earliest Settlement to the Close of the Year 1832*, Burlington (Vt.), 1833.

Tourtellot, Arthur Bernon, *William Diamond's Drum*, Garden City, 1959.

Tucker, Glenn, *Poltroons and Patriots,* Indianapolis, 1954.

Tuttle, Mrs. George Fuller, *Three Centuries in the Champlain Valley*, Plattsburg (N.Y.), 1909.

Tyler, Royall, *The Algerian Captive*, Walpole (N.H.), 1797.

U.S. Senate, *Report of the Naval Committee Expressive of the Gallant Conduct of Cap. Macdonough*, Washington, 1814.

Van De Water, F. F., *Lake Champlain and Lake George*, Indianapolis, 1946.

Van Dusen, Albert E., "Middletown," *Rockfall Corporation of Middletown and Middlesex County Historical Society publication,* (1950).

Villiers, Alan, "We're Coming Over on the *Mayflower*," *National Geographic Magazine,* May 1957.

Vinton, Francis, *Louis XVII and Eleazer Williams*, New York, 1868.

Walker, Jesse, *Tales of the Niagara Frontier*, Buffalo, 1845.

Wallace, Willard M., "Middletown, 1650-1950," *Rockfall Corporation of Middletown and Middlesex County Historical Society publication,* (1950).

Ward, John William, *Andrew Jackson: Symbol for an Age*, New York, 1955.

Waterhouse, Benjamin, *A Journal*, Boston, 1816.

Wight, William Ward, *Eleazer Williams: His Forerunners and Himself*, Milwaukee, 1896.

Wilbur, James Benjamin, *Ira Allen, Founder of Vermont, 1751-1814*, Boston, 1928.

Wilbur, La Fayette, *Early History of Vermont*, Jericho (Vt.), 1899.

Wisconsin Historical Society, "Eleazer Williams," *Lyman C. Draper Collection of Journals*, (1876) vol. VII, 355.

Woodward, W. E., *The Way Our People Lived*, New York, 1944.

NAVAL AND MILITARY

Abbot, Willis John, *Blue Jackets of 1812,* New York, 1887; *Naval History of the United States,* New York, 1896.

"Accounts of the Battle of Plattsburgh," *Vermont Antiquarian,* (Sept. 1902) vol. 1, 75-93.

Adams, Israel, *Captain Israel Adams: A Personal Narrative,* Utica (N.Y.), 1847.

Albert, Marvin H., *Broadsides and Boarders,* New York, 1957.

Alden, C. S. (and) Earle, Ralph, *Makers of Naval Tradition,* Boston, 1925.

Alden, F. Arlington, "Vergennes and the Battle of Plattsburg," Typescript in Vergennes Library.

Bailey, Isaac, *American Naval Biography*, Providence, 1815.

Barker, A. S., "Battle of Plattsburgh: The Heroism of One Woman," *Plattsburgh Press*, March 12, 1914.

Barnes, James, *Commodore Bainbridge*, New York, 1897; *Naval Actions of the War of 1812*, New York, 1896; *Yankee Ships and Yankee Sailors*, New York, 1913.

Bassett-Lowke, Wenman, *Ships and Men*, London, 1949.

Beirne, Francis F., *The War of 1812*, New York, 1949.

Binney, Amos, *Documents Relative to the Investigation of Navy Agent*, Boston, 1822.

Bowen, Abel, *The Naval Monument—1816*, Boston, 1840.

Brady, C. T., *American Fights and Fighters*, New York, 1900; *For the Freedom of the Sea*, New York, 1899.

Brainerd, John, "Private Letters of a Hero of the Naval Battle of Plattsburgh," *Plattsburgh Press*, October 16, 1905.

Brand, Silas H., "Naval Battle of Plattsburgh," *Plattsburgh Press*, April 17, 1914.

Brannan, John (ed.), *Official Letters of the Military and Naval Officers of the United States*, Washington, 1823.

Brown, Arthur W., *Leaves from Lives Trained on Old Ironsides*, Providence, 1931.

Brown, Samuel R., *Authentic History of the Second War*, Auburn (N.Y.), 1815; *Views on Lake Erie*, Troy (N.Y.), 1814.

Burney, William, *Dictionary of the Marine*, London, 1830.

Chapelle, Howard I., *History of the American Sailing Navy*, New York, 1949.

Charnock, John, *An History of Marine Architecture*, London, 1800-1802.

Chatterton, Edward K., *Ships and Ways of Other Days*, London, 1913; *The Ship Under Sail*, London, 1926.

Christie, Robert, *The Military and Naval Operations, in the Canadas*, Quebec, 1818.

Clark, Byron N., *List of Pensioners of the War of 1812*, Burlington (Vt.), 1904.

Clark, George R., *A Short History of the United States Navy*, Philadelphia, 1911.

Coffin, Charles, *The Lives and Services of Maj. Gen. John Thomas, et al.*, New York, 1845.

Company of Military Collectors and Historians, *Military Uniforms in America*, Washington, 1949.

Congreve, William, *Concise Account of the Origin and Progress of the Rocket System*, Dublin, 1817.

Cooke, Edward W., *65 Plates of Shipping and Craft*, London, 1829.

Cooper, James Fenimore, *Cruise of the Somers*, New York, 1844; *History of the Navy of the United States*, Philadelphia, 1839; *Lives of Dis-*

tinguished American Naval Figures, Philadelphia, 1846; *Old Ironsides,* New York, 1853.

Cozzens, Frederick S., *Old Naval Prints,* New York, 1894.

Culver, Henry B., *Book of Old Ships,* London, 1936; *Contemporary Scale Models,* New York, 1926.

Dahlgren, J. A. B., *System of Boat Armament in the United States Navy,* Philadelphia, 1852.

Darling, Charles H., Address delivered (Oct. 27, 1904) before the Vermont Historical Society, in Wilbur Library.

Daughters of 1812, "Fort Cassin in History," *Burlington Daily Free Press,* May 18, 1908.

Dobbins, William W., *The Battle of Lake Erie,* Erie (Pa.), 1929; "The Dobbins Papers; Early Days on the Lakes," *Buffalo Historical Society Publications,* (1905) vol. 8, 283-379.

Dunshee, Kenneth H. (ed.), "Save Our Ship," *News from Home,* (1954) vol. XV, no. 1.

Duyckinck, Evert A., *National Portrait Gallery of Eminent Americans,* New York, 1862.

Elgar, Francis, *Ships, Old and New,* (Sette of odd vols., No. 33), London, 1896.

Ellis, Albert G., "New York Indians," *State Historical Society of Wisconsin Collections,* (1856) vol. 2, 415-449; "Recollections of Rev. Eleazer Williams," *State Historical Society of Wisconsin Collections,* (1879) vol. 8, 322-352.

Euler, Leonhard, *A Complete Theory of the Construction and Properties of Vessels,* London, 1776.

Fairbanks, Charles, *The Old Soldier's History,* Haverhill (Mass.), 1861.

Fassett, Frederick (ed.), *The Shipbuilding Business in the U.S.A.,* New York, 1948.

Fish, Frank L., "Macdonough Took the Ship," *Addison County Newspaper List,* March 19, 1914.

Folsom, William R., *Vermonters in Battle,* Montpelier (Vt.), 1953.

Forester, C. S., *The Age of Fighting Sail,* Garden City (N.Y.), 1956; *Commodore Hornblower,* Boston, 1945; *Lieutenant Hornblower,* Boston, 1952.

Frost, John, *Pictorial History of the American Navy,* New York, 1850.

Gilman, Emma C., "Hero of Battleship 'Saratoga'—Macdonough of Connecticut," *Connecticut Magazine,* (1907) vol. 11, no. 4, 553-559.

Goldsborough, C. W., *Original and Correct List of the United States Navy,* Washington, 1800; *The United States Naval Chronicle,* Washington, 1824.

Guernsey, R. S., *New York City and Vicinity During the War of 1812-1815; A Military, Civic and Financial Local History of that Period,* New York, vol. 1, 1889; vol. 2, 1895.

Hannay, James, *How Canada Was Held for the Empire,* London, 1905.

Heck, J. G. (ed.), Spencer F. Baird, *Iconographic Encyclopedia,* New York, 1851.

Heitman, Francis B., *Historical and Dictionary Register of the U.S. Army from 1789 to 1903,* Washington, 1903.

Henderson, William J., *Strange Stories of 1812,* New York, 1907.

Henry, John, *Documents from Henry, the British Spy,* Boston, 1812.

Hill, Frederick Stanhope, *Romance of the American Navy,* New York, 1910; *Twenty-Six Historic Ships,* New York, 1905.

Hill, Ralph Nading, "Gateway Struggle," *Vermont Life,* (1959) vol. XIII, no. 4.

Holden, James Austin, "The Battle of Plattsburgh," Address (Dec. 9, 1913) delivered before the Lake Champlain Association of New York City.

Hobbs, Edward W., *Sailing Ships at a Glance,* London, 1925.

Hutchinson, William, *A Treatise on Practical Seamanship,* Liverpool, 1777.

Irving, Lukin H., *Officers of the British Forces in Canada during the War of 1812-1815,* Toronto, 1908.

Izard, George, *Official Correspondence with the Department of War,* Philadelphia, 1816.

James, William, *Naval Occurrences,* Whitehall (Eng.), 1817.

Jenkins, John S., *Generals of the Last War with Great Britain,* Auburn (N.Y.), 1849.

Johnson, Allen (ed.), *Dictionary of American Biography,* New York, 1937.

Johnson, Herbert T. (ed.), *Roster of Soldiers in the War of 1812,* St. Albans (Vt.), 1933.

Johnson, Rossiter, *History of the War of 1812-1815,* New York, 1822.

Lewis, Charles Lee, *Famous American Naval Officers,* Boston, 1924.

Lossing, Benson J., *Eminent Americans,* New York, 1855; *Our Country,* New York, 1876-1878; *Pictorial Field Book of the War of 1812,* New York, 1875.

Lovette, Leland P., *Naval Customs, Traditions and Usage,* Annapolis, 1939.

Lucas, Charles P., *Canadian War of 1812,* Oxford (Eng.), 1906.

Macdonough Commission of Vermont, *Souvenir Program of Macdonough Centennial at Vergennes and Fort Cassin,* Montpelier, 1914.

Macdonough, Rodney, *Life of Commodore Thomas Macdonough,* Boston, 1909; *Macdonough-Hackstaff Ancestry,* Boston, 1901; "A Paper on Commodore Thomas Macdonough," *Papers of the Historical Society of Delaware,* (1897) vol. XIII; "Address," *Papers of the Historical Society of Delaware,* (1908) vol. XVIII.

Macdonough, Thomas, *Account Book for 1816,* in Wilbur Library.

Maclay, Edgar Stanton, *A Youthful Man-o'-Warsman,* New York, 1910.

Mahan, Alfred Thayer, "Commodore Macdonough at Plattsburgh," *North American Review,* (1914) vol. 200, 203-221; *Sea Power in Its Relations to the War of 1812,* London, 1905.

Mann, James, *Medical Sketches of the Campaigns of 1812, 13, 14,* Dedham (Mass.), 1816.

Marshall, Helen M., *An Echo of the Battle of Plattsburgh*, Champlain (N.Y.), 1929.

McDowell, William, *The Shape of Ships*, London, 1950.

McKeon, Loretto M., "Commodore Thomas Macdonough," A paper (1942) at Trinity College, Middletown, Conn.

Mercier, Henry James, *Life in a Man-of-War*, Philadelphia, 1841.

Meredith, Roy, *The American Wars: A Pictorial History from Quebec to Korea, 1775-1953*, Cleveland, 1955.

Monroe, John A., "Biographical Sketch of Captain Thomas Macdonough," *Analectic Magazine and Naval Chronicle*, (March 1816) vol. VII, no. 39, 201-215.

Morison, Samuel Eliot, *John Paul Jones: A Sailor's Biography*, Boston, 1959.

Morrison, John Harrison, *History of New York Shipyards*, New York, 1909.

Murphy, John M., *American Ships and Shipbuilders*, New York, 1860.

New York Public Library, *List of Works in New York Public Library on Naval Art*, VX ib 1907.

New York Public Library, *'President' Steam and Sail Scrapbook*.

New York Public Library, *Scrapbook of Military and Naval Uniforms 1700-1800*.

New York Public Library, *United States Navy 1811 Folder*.

(No author) *Annual Register for 1814*, London, 1815.

(No author) *Art of Making Masts, Yards, etc.*, London, 1816.

(No author) "Garrison Orders at Burlington—July 13-Aug. 4, 1813," *Moorsfield Antiquarian*, (Aug. 1937) vol. 1, no. 2, 79; "Maine Troops on Lake Champlain," *Moorsfield Antiquarian*, (May 1938) vol. 2, no. 2.

(No author) *Mariner's Mirror*, v. 10, Jan., p. 53, London, 1924.

(No author) *Naval Chronicle*, London, 1799-1818.

(No author) *Niles' Weekly Register 1811-1849*, Baltimore, Vols. 2-9.

(No author) *Shipwright's Vademecum*, London, 1805.

Noble, Henry Herman, "The Battle at Cassin," *Burlington Daily Free Press*, July 2, 1908; "Gorgeous Military Uniforms," (*Albany*) *Argus*, March 16, 1902.

Norie & Wilson, *Varieties of Sailing Vessels*, London, 188?.

Paine, Ralph D., *Colonial Ships and Sailors*, New York, 1926; *The Fight for a Free Sea*, New Haven, 1921.

Palmer, Peter Sailly, *History of Lake Champlain*, Plattsburg, 1853.

Parker, Foxhall A., *Fleets of the World*, New York, 1876; *The Naval Howitzer Afloat*, New York, 1866; *The Naval Howitzer Ashore*, New York, 1865.

Penley, Joseph, *Scenes and Incidents in the War of 1812*, Norway (Me.), 1853.

Pennewill, James, "Address," *Papers of the Historical Society of Delaware*, (1908) vol. XVIII.

Penny, Joshua, *Life and Adventures of Joshua Penny*, Brooklyn, 1815.

Perry, David, *Recollections of an Old Soldier: the Life of Captain David Perry,* Windsor (Vt.), 1822.

Peterson, Charles J., *The American Navy,* Philadelphia, 1856.

Phelps, Benajah, "The Battle of Lake Champlain," *Outlook Magazine,* (Nov. 2, 1901).

Plattsburgh Centenary Commission, *The Battle of Plattsburgh: What Historians Say About It,* Albany, 1914.

Pratt, Fletcher, *Preble's Boys; Commodore Preble and the Birth of American Sea Power,* New York, 1950.

Preble, George Henry, *History of the Flag of the U.S.A., and of the Naval Signals, etc.,* Boston, 1880.

Quaiffe, Milo M., "General Alexander Macomb," *Burton Historical Collection Leaflet,* (1931) vol. 10, 1-16.

Quartermaster General, *Uniforms of the Army of the United States, illlustrated from 1774-1907,* New York, 1885-1907. Plates by H. A. Ogden.

Richards, George H., *Memoir of Alexander Macomb,* New York, 1833.

Riddell, William Renwick, *A Canadian's View of the Battle of Plattsburgh,* New York?, 1915.

Roberts, James, *The Narrative of James Roberts,* Chicago, 1858. (Heartman's Historical Series—No. 71)

Rogers, S. R. H., *The Sailing Ship,* New York, 1950.

Roosevelt, Theodore, *The Naval War of 1812,* New York, 1882.

Roscoe, Theodore and Fred Freeman, *Picture History of the United States Navy,* New York, 1956.

Russell, W. Clark, *The Ship; Her Story,* London, 1899.

Sawyer, Edmund Ogden, *Our Sea Saga,* San Francisco, 1929.

Seawell, M. Elliot, *Midshipman Paulding,* New York, 1891; *Twelve Naval Captains,* New York, 1897.

Severance, Mrs. Frank H., "An Episode in U.S. History," *The Vermonter,* July 1937.

Smith, Michael, *A Complete History of the late American War with Great Britain,* Lexington (Ky.), 1816.

Soley, James Russell, *The Boys of 1812 and Other Naval Heroes,* Boston, 1887.

Spears, J. R., *A History of the United States Navy,* New York, 1908.

Stahl, John M., *The Battle of Plattsburg; A Study in and of the War of 1812,* Illinois, 1918.

Steinitz, Francis, *The Ship; Its Origin and Progress,* London, 1849.

Strickland, Franklin N., "Macdonough Digs the Dugway," *The Vermonter,* (August 1939).

Stubbs, Samuel, *A Compendious Account of the Late War,* New York, 1915.

Thompson, John Lewis, *Historical Sketches of the Late War between United States and Great Britain,* Philadelphia, 1816.

Thorpe, F. N., "The Building of the Fleet," *The Pennsylvania Magazine of History and Biography,* (1913) vol. 37, 257.

Tomlinson, E. T., *The War of 1812,* New York, 1906.

University of the State of New York, *The Centenary of the Battle of Plattsburgh,* Albany, 1914.

U.S. Library of Congress, *Early American Ships and Shipping: A bibliographical list,* Washington, 1928.

U.S. Navigation Bureau, *Exercises of Great Guns in Broadside,* Washington, 1867.

U.S. Navigation Bureau, *General Instructions,* Washington, 1896.

U.S. Navigation Bureau, *The Making of a Man-o'-Warsman,* New York, 1906.

U.S. Navy Department, *The Deck and Boat Book of the U.S. Navy,* Washington, 1914.

U.S. Navy Department, *Naval Regulations, issued by command of the President of the United States,* Washington, 1809.

U.S. Navy Department, *Rules, Regulations and Instructions for the Naval Service of the United States,* Washington, 1818.

U.S. Navy Department, *Signals for Use of the United States Navy,* Washington, 1813.

U.S. Navy Department, *Uniform Dress of Officers of the Navy of the United States,* Washington, 1814.

Vandergrift, Lewis C., "Memoir of Commodore Thomas Macdonough," *Papers of the Historical Society of Delaware,* (1895) vol. XII.

Williamson, W. M., "Shipyards of New York," A paper (1954) in the Marine Museum of the City of New York.

Wilmer, James Jones, "A Narrative Respecting the Conduct of the British—1813," (?), 1813.

Wilson, Thomas, *The Biography of the Principal American Military and Naval Heroes,* New York, 1817.

Wilson, William Henry, "Two Incidents," From War Record, by his daughters, Bessie and Mary. Furnished by Harold Wilson, Jr., Clermont, N.Y., his grandson.

Woodworth, S. & Co., "News of the War of 1812," *The War: Being a Faithful Record* (Weekly publication, New York, starting June 27, 1812).

Wyatt, Thomas, *Memoirs of Generals, Commodores and Other Commanders,* Philadelphia, 1848.

LIBRARIES, MUSEUMS, SOCIETIES CONSULTED

Atlantic Mutual Insurance Co. Library, New York, N.Y.

Baker Library, Dartmouth College, Hanover, N.H.

Bennington Museum, Bennington, Vt.

The Libraries: Columbia University in the City of New York, New York, N.Y.

The Library of Congress, Washington, D.C.

Cornell Indian Boards, Cornell University, Ithaca, N.Y.

Detroit Public Library, Detroit, Mich.

Fletcher Library, Burlington, Vt.
Franklin County Civil Service Commission, Malone, N.Y.
Frick Art Reference Library, New York, N.Y.
Goodspeed's Bookshop, Boston, Mass.
Hamilton Grange, New York, N.Y.
Hartford Public Library, Hartford, Conn.
Historical Society of Delaware, Wilmington, Del.
Mrs. Henry Hubbard's House, Middletown, Conn.
Marine Historical Association, Inc., Mystic, Conn.
Marine Library, New York, N.Y.
Marine Museum of the City of New York, New York, N.Y.
Marine Museum: Seamen's Church Institute of New York, New York, N.Y.
Marine Society of New York, New York, N.Y.
Massachusetts Institute of Technology Libraries, Cambridge, Mass.
Middlesex County Historical Society, Middletown, Conn.
Missouri Historical Society, St. Louis, Mo.
Pierpont Morgan Library, New York, N.Y.
Museum of the New York City Hall, New York, N.Y.
National Archives and Records Service, Washington, D.C.
New York Historical Society, New York, N.Y.
New York Public Library, New York, N.Y.
New York State Historical Association, Ticonderoga, N.Y.
The New York State Library, Albany, N.Y.
Olin Library, Wesleyan University, Middletown, Conn.
Franklin D. Roosevelt Library, Hyde Park, N.Y.
Russell Library, Middletown, Conn.
Shelburne Museum, Shelburne, Vt.
State of Delaware Public Archives Commission, Dover, Del.
State (Wisconsin) Historical Society, Madison, Wis.
Charles E. Tuttle Co.: Old and Rare Books, Rutland, Vt.
United States Naval Academy Library, Annapolis, Md.
United States Naval Academy Museum, Annapolis, Md.
University of the State of New York: Division of Archives and History, Albany, N.Y.
Wilbur Library, Burlington, Vt.
Vergennes Library, Vergennes, Vt.

DOCUMENTS, LETTERS

Delaware Archives, Letters to and from Commodore Macdonough, Plattsburgh locale, Sept. 3-20, 1814; Resolutions passed by Delaware Senate and House of Representatives, 1815.

Samuel R. Dabney Collection, Letters of Lucy Ann Macdonough to Mrs. Thomas Chew—1822-1823; Lucy Ann Macdonough's will (no date).

The Historical Society of Delaware, Log Book of *Constellation*, kept by Midshipman Macdonough, 1802-1803; Letter of Micah McDonough to brother Patrick about Indian Wars campaign, 10 November 1791; Letters to C. A. Rodney and Lydia Roberts, 1815-1822.

Vance Macdonough Collection, Accounts, receipts, letters in connection with personal and naval business 1812-1814.

Hall Park McCullough Collection, Resolutions and deeds from Vermont, New York, New York City, Lansingburgh to and from Commodore Macdonough; Letters to Commodore Bainbridge, Commodore Preble, David Phipps, Lydia Roberts, 1803-1824.

Museum of the City of New York Library, Letters of Clement C. Moore to his mother, from Washington—May and June 1812.

The National Archives, Letters from Thomas Macdonough to William Jones—July-Sept. 1814—Record Group No. 45; Occurrences and Remarks on Board the U.S. Sloop of War Eagle, Robert Henley, Esq. Commander on Lake Champlain, Sept. 11-29, 1814—Record Group No. 24.

Lucy Macdonough Reade Collection, Miscellaneous manuscripts, pamphlets and letters, 1812-1814.

Thomas M. Russell, Jr., Collection, Typescript description of Lucy Ann Macdonough, extract of her will, and letters from 1813 to 1819, by L.H.R.D.; Typescript history of William Denning, by L.H.R.D.

U.S. Naval Academy Library, Letters to Officers, Ships of War: 1811-1814; Master Commandant's Letters—1814, vol. 1-2.

U.S. Naval Academy Museum, Letter from Crew of Frigate *Essex* to Capt. Macdonough—6 Sept. 1809; Letter from Officers of Champlain fleet to Com. Macdonough—11 Nov. 1814.

ACKNOWLEDGMENTS

Thanks go to many men and women for their individual contributions to the background and technical accuracy of this account of Commodore Macdonough on Lake Champlain. They include, besides those elsewhere mentioned:

Macdonough descendants: Samuel R. Dabney of Los Olivos, California; Rodney McDonough of North Caldwell, New Jersey; Rose Shaler McDonough of Mansfield Center, Connecticut; Thomas M. Russell, Jr., of Middletown.

Librarians: Grace W. Bacon of the Olin Library of Wesleyan University in Middletown; Professor Louis H. Bolander, Professor Vernon D. Tate, and Patrick F. Clausey of the United States Naval Academy; C. E. Dornbusch of the New York Public Library; Gladys Flint of the Wilbur Library at the University of Vermont; Bess Lewis of the New York State Historical Association; Mrs. H. Clay Reed of the Historical Society of Delaware; Elizabeth Skinner of the Middlesex County Historical Society in Connecticut; and Hall Park McCullough of North Bennington, Vermont, who made available his private Macdonough collection.

Special technical help: Professor Bristow Adams of Cornell University; Joseph Bruzek and George Keester of the United States Naval Academy; W. M. Williamson of the Marine Museum of the City of New York; Professor Vernon D. Tate, Librarian of the United States Naval Academy for factual checking of the proofs.

Manuscript assistance: Mr. Mort for an inexhaustible supply of ball-point pens; Clara Chanin for patient typing.

And to Marian G. Muller for laborious copying of manuscripts and letters, and for infinite encouragement.

INDEX